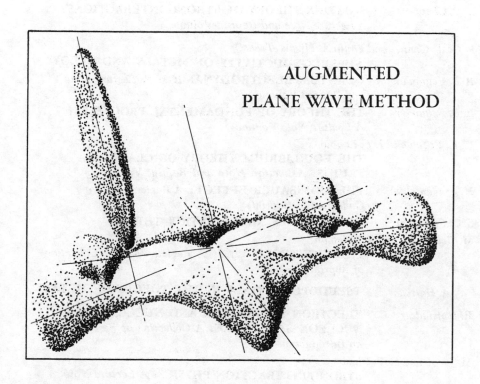

AUGMENTED PLANE WAVE METHOD

Frontiers in Physics

DAVID PINES, Editor

AUGMENTED
PLANE WAVE METHOD

A Guide
to Performing
Electronic Structure Calculations

T. L. Loucks

Iowa State University

W. A. Benjamin, Inc.   *New York, Amsterdam*

1967

AUGMENTED PLANE WAVE METHOD

A Guide to Performing Electronic Structure Calculations

Library of Congress Catalog Card Number 67-15550
Manufactured in the United States of America

Final copy ready for camera was received from the author
on November 4, 1966; this volume was published on
January 27, 1967

W. A. Benjamin, Inc.
New York, New York 10016

EDITOR'S FOREWORD

The problem of communicating in a coherent fashion the recent developments in the most exciting and active fields of physics seems particularly pressing today. The enormous growth in the number of physicists has tended to make the familiar channels of communication considerably less effective. It has become increasingly difficult for experts in a given field to keep up with the current literature; the novice can only be confused. What is needed is both a consistent account of a field and the presentation of a definite "point of view" concerning it. Formal monographs cannot meet such a need in a rapidly developing field, and, perhaps more important, the review article seems to have fallen into disfavor. Indeed, it would seem that the people most actively engaged in developing a given field are the people least likely to write at length about it.

"Frontiers in Physics" has been conceived in an effort to improve the situation in several ways. First, to take advantage of the fact that the leading physicists today frequently give a series of lectures, a graduate seminar, or a graduate course in their special fields of interest.

Such lectures serve to summarize the present status of a rapidly developing field and may well constitute the only coherent account available at the time. Often, notes on lectures exist (prepared by the lecturer himself, by graduate students, or by postdoctoral fellows) and have been distributed in mimeographed form on a limited basis. One of the principal purposes of the "Frontiers in Physics" series is to make such notes available to a wider audience of physicists.

It should be emphasized that lecture notes are necessarily rough and informal, both in style and content, and those in the series will prove no exception. This is as it should be. The point of the series is to offer new, rapid, more informal, and, it is hoped, more effective ways for physicists to teach one another. The point is lost if only elegant notes qualify.

A second way to improve communication in very active fields of physics is by the publication of collections of reprints of recent articles. Such collections are themselves useful to people working in the field. The value of the reprints would, however, seem much enhanced if the collection would be accompanied by an introduction of moderate length, which would serve to tie the collection together and, necessarily, constitute a brief survey of the present status of the field. Again, it is appropriate that such an introduction be informal, in keeping with the active character of the field.

A third possibility for the series might be called an informal monograph, to connote the fact that it represents an intermediate step between lecture notes and formal monographs. It would offer the author an opportunity to present his views of a field that has developed to the point at which a summation might prove extraordinarily fruitful, but for which a formal monograph might not be feasible or desirable.

Fourth, there are the contemporary classics--papers or lectures which constitute a particularly valuable approach to the teaching and learning of physics today. Here one thinks of fields that lie at the heart of much of present-day research, but whose essentials are by now well understood, such as quantum electrodynamics or magnetic resonance. In such fields some of the best pedagogical material is not readily available, either because it consists of papers long out of print or lectures that have never been published.

"Frontiers in Physics" is designed to be flexible in editorial format. Authors are encouraged to use as many of the foregoing approaches as seem desirable for the project at hand. The publishing format for the series is in keeping with its intentions. In most cases, both paperbound and clothbound editions of each book are available.

Finally, suggestions from interested readers as to format, contributors, and contributions will be most welcome.

PREFACE

The whole point of these notes is to explain how to perform APW calculations. They are written for anyone with a modest background in quantum mechanics and the most elementary aspects of the theory of Bloch electrons in an ideal crystal. They represent an expanded version of lectures originally given to a graduate seminar at Iowa State University in the summer of 1965.

In the first chapter, after briefly introducing the subject, I have reviewed existing calculations and compared the APW method with other methods which are in general use today. The second chapter is devoted to a very detailed development of the theoretical background. The third chapter deals with the practical aspects, the things which are not particularly elegant or exotic, but which are required in order to get the job done. I have compiled all the things that one usually tells students who are preparing to do an APW calculation for the first time. The fourth chapter is devoted entirely to the relativistic generalization of the APW method.

In the appendices I have included listings of our computer programs. This was done somewhat reluctantly because I am a notoriously unsophisticated programmer. I seem to get the job done, but my programs do not represent man's greatest accomplishments in the field of computer programming. If you can make them faster, shorter, etc., please be my guest (and send me a copy). In this respect, my original programs have already been substantially improved by the combined efforts of Mr. Tom Reglein, Mr. Torben Brun and Dr. Stewart Keeton. I am not mentioning their names in an attempt to transfer any guilt if the programs contain some "bugs", but rather to indicate that I am not the sole author and have been greatly assisted by these men.

I should also mention Mr. Tom Clark who, along with Dr. Keeton, assisted in the proof reading of the manuscript. Their suggestions were appreciated and, in most instances, have been incorporated into the text.

CONTENTS

Reprints

1 INTRODUCTION LITERATURE SURVEY AND CRITIQUE OF THE APW METHOD

INTRODUCTION

During the last few years there has been a large increase in the
number of calculations based on the augmented plane wave (APW)
method. Although the method was originally formulated in 1937, it did
not come into general use until around 1960. During the six year
period from 1960 through 1965 there were approximately 20 APW calculations reported in the literature, almost half of these during the
last year. By midyear 1966 more APW calculations had been reported
than for the entire preceding year and the number of preprints in cir-
culation indicated that this accelerated pace would continue.

The rapid growth in the number of APW calculations is due to
several factors. Most important is the availability of large, high-
speed computers. The extensive calculations required in the APW
method are not practical without these. Prior to 1960 they were available at only a few research facilities, but by 1966 many universities
and research laboratories had adequate computing facilities for performing APW calculations. Another factor influencing the increase in
APW calculations has been the shift of interest from the simple metals

(those described by the nearly free-electron (NFE) model) to the transition elements. This is partially due to improved procedures for growing the ultra-high-purity crystals required in experiments relating to electronic structure. Much of the first experimental data of this type which became available could be interpreted in terms of the NFE model, and consequently considerable theoretical effort was devoted to making these calculations both practical and meaningful. In recent years methods for purifying some of the transition elements have been perfected, thus making these elements available for electronic structure studies. The theoretical methods developed primarily for the NFE metals could not be extended to the transition elements; the APW method, however, proved to be applicable for both simple and transition metals.

The number of APW calculations has also increased because the procedure has become fairly routine for many applications. This is not to say that the formalism is particularly simple or that the calculations are not complicated. The point is that once the computer programs have been prepared, very little must be done to modify them from one application to the next. The input parameters for an element having one of the standard crystal structures can easily be determined in a short time. Even the input parameters for one of the less familiar crystal structures can be determined with very little effort.

The factors cited above as being responsible for the rapid increase in APW calculations will continue to be effective for several years. The speed and capacities of computers will continue to increase, and these machines will be made available to more researchers. In addition, more experimental data on transition elements (also compounds and certain alloys) will become available, thus inviting electronic structure calculations to aid in their interpretation. The fact that the APW method can be easily converted from one application to the next will make it increasingly useful in this respect.

In the past, APW calculations have been performed primarily by specialists. This was necessary because initially the method itself had to be studied. At the present time, however, it is possible in many applications for the novice to use existing programs and, with a little advice, to perform useful calculations. It is my opinion that in the future an increasing number of the APW calculations will be performed in this manner. All that is necessary is a set of computer programs and information on how to prepare the input data, and one of the purposes of this volume is to provide both of these.

Experience has shown, however, that one can get only limited use from a computer program that is not fully understood. The varied needs of research programs require a high degree of flexibility, and this necessitates modifications of an unpredictable nature. Therefore, in these notes we have not only presented APW computer programs (both relativistic and nonrelativistic) but have also attempted to fully explain the method itself and the numerical techniques involved. Thus, although the programs are necessarily specialized in some respects, it should be possible for the reader to make any modifications required for his own research needs. The variety of applications already available in the literature should be helpful in this respect.

In the following sections we include a brief history of the APW method, a survey of recent applications, and a comparison with the other methods commonly used in energy band calculations. Chapter 2

is devoted to a complete derivation of the APW matrix elements, based
on a variational expression which permits the use of discontinuous
functions. The numerical techniques for calculating these matrix elements and evaluating the secular determinant are discussed in Chapter
3. The relativistic generalization of the APW method is explained in
Chapter 4. The computer programs are listed in the Appendixes, and
all the input and output variables are defined with reference to equations presented in the text whenever appropriate. This is followed by
a collection of reprints which includes the original papers on the subject and most of the recent applications.

LITERATURE SURVEY

The APW method was originated in 1937 by J. C. Slater [47]. Of
course, at that time there were no high speed computers available.
The first calculation had to be carried out using a desk calculator, and
this was done by M. Chodorow [6] for metallic copper in 1939. At that
time he concluded that the method was too cumbersome, except for
certain states of high symmetry. This apparently discouraged further
calculations for a period of time, and then the Second World War inter-
vened. About thirteen years passed between Chodorow's first calculation and the appearance of two more applications in the Czechoslo-
vakian Journal of Physics (Trlifaj [59], Antoncik [2]). At about the
same time Slater [49] presented some theoretical modifications in an
attempt to simplify the original scheme. Further modifications were
suggested by Saffren and Slater [44], and this approach was used by
Howarth [18] in a calculation for copper. There was then a second interval of time during which no APW calculations were published. However, a related paper dealing with variational expressions for the

energy and the use of discontinuous functions was published by Leigh [23].

During this period of apparent inactivity a joint effort by members of the Solid State and Molecular Theory Group under the direction of Professor Slater at M. I. T. reexamined the two forms of the APW method and decided the original 1937 form of this method was the most suitable to be programmed for a computer. Many details of this work can be found in the Quarterly Progress Reports of this group and in a review article by Slater [50]. The first results to come out of this effort were the extensive calculations for iron by J. H. Wood [61, 62]. These and similar calculations for copper by G. A. Burdick [3, 4] showed that the APW method was practical with modern computers and yielded useful results. Thus, although the APW method was originated in 1937, it did not become practical until some twenty three years later. Once adequate computing facilities became available, however, a series of important results was published.

Johnson, Conklin, and Pratt [7, 19] reported results for PbTe, including relativistic effects for the first time; Terrell [58] performed APW calculations for Be. Mattheiss [34], in a calculation for solid argon, established a simple procedure for determining the muffin-tin potential and this procedure has been used in most applications of the APW method. Another important contribution by Mattheiss was an article on the iron transition series (Mattheiss [35]). He calculated the energy bands along one symmetry direction for most of the elements in this series. Also, in collaboration with Watson, he included spin-orbit coupling in a pertubation calculation for tungsten (Mattheiss and Watson [38]) estimating the splittings of certain degenerate levels.

The results of a more complete APW calculation of the Fermi surface for tungsten appeared the following year (Mattheiss [37]).

The first APW calculation for a rare earth metal was reported for gadolinium by Dimmock and Freeman [10]. Further results on the Fermi surface, magnetic ordering and electrical properties of rare earth metals were reported in 1966 (Freeman, Dimmock and Watson [12]).

The first application of the APW method to compounds was reported in 1965 for TiC, TiN and TiO (Ern and Switendick [11]). Soon after this Mattheiss [36] presented results for V_3X compounds, and Scop [46] published the band structure of AgCl and AgBr.

The same year a relativistic generalization of the APW method was developed by Loucks and first applied to W and Pb [26, 27, 29, 30]. He also reported nonrelativistic APW calculations for the Fermi surface of Cr, Mo and W [28].

At this time two relevant articles on ℓ-dependent pseudopotentials were published (Lloyd [25], Ziman [66]). Further discussion of this has been given by Slater [51, 52].

Williams, Loucks and Mackintosh [60] reported the results of APW calculations for the rare earth metal holmium and for yttrium. These results included an example of the use of APW wave functions in calculating the angular distribution of photons from positron annihilation in a crystal (Loucks [31]). Switendick [57] published an article on the self-consistent energy band calculation for Cr. Freeman, Furdyna and Dimmock [13] calculated the band structure and Fermi surface for Pd metal. Snow, Waber and Switendick [54] studied the effect of assumed electronic configuration on the energy band structure of Ni.

Further results using the relativistic APW method were presented by Keeton and Loucks [21] for the Th, Ac and Lu. The energy bands and Fermi surface of Ga were calculated by Wood [63]. An application to the compound cuprous oxide was given by Dahl and Switendick [8].

At the time of writing there were several applications of the APW method which had appeared only as preprints and it is possible that they will not have been published before this volume goes to press. They include relativistic APW calculations of the Fermi surfaces for Hg, Th, Gd, Dy and Er by Keeton and Loucks, for Pt by Mackintosh, and for Re by Mattheiss. Further results for Be have been completed by Terrell; Snow and Waber have determined the effect of self-consistency on the density of states for metallic copper. Kmetko and Waber have performed nonrelativistic calculations of the band structure for plutonium and its monocarbide. Fermi surface and positron annihilation results similar to those for yttrium have been calculated for Zr by Loucks. The energy bands in diamond are to be published in the Physical Review by Keown.

Other recent developments can be found in the Quarterly Progress Reports of the Solid State and Molecular Theory Group (SSMTG) at M. I. T. One of the issues to be published in the near future will contain a complete history of the SSMTG written by Professor Slater. There are also several pertinent theses written at M. I. T. which we have not referenced (see Slater [50]). Finally, Professor Slater has started a new research group at the University of Florida in Gainesville, and further developments in the APW method can be expected from this project.

CRITIQUE OF THE APW METHOD

There have been a large number of APW calculations performed during the last few years, and these have had an important effect on our understanding of the electronic structure of crystals. The APW method can be expected to give meaningful results in a wide variety of applications, but it is not the best method to use for all crystals. It is important to know the applications for which the APW method is most suited, and in this respect there are certain general guide lines that can be established. These will necessarily be based on my own experience, however, and as such will be as much opinion as fact. It has been easy in these notes to be reasonably objective in describing the APW method and its application. As with women, however, it is far easier to give descriptions than to give useful advice on how to choose one.

Descriptions of the other methods commonly used in energy band calculations can be found in several tests (Jones [20]; Ziman [65]; Callaway [5]; Slater [51]; Harrison [14]). These include the tight-binding method, the cellular method, the orthogonalized plane wave (OPW) method, the pseudopotential method and the Green's function method. The most practical applications of the tight-binding method have been for core states and the more localized itinerant electrons such as those identified with the d bands in the transition elements. The pseudopotential method, on the other hand, has been most practical for calculating NFE energy bands. These include applications to the alkali metals, the alkali-earth metals, Al, C, Si, and most of the metals, semi-metals and semi-conductors with completely filled d shells. The pseudopotential methods in common use (see Harrison

[14]) are based on the OPW method. Pseudopotential methods based

on the APW and related methods have been considered (Lloyd [25];

Ziman [66]), but these have not yet led to simplifications in either the

formalism or the practical aspects of the calculations. OPW-based

pseudopotential methods are relatively easy to apply and are prefer-

able to the APW method in those applications for which they are ap-

propriate. This is not to say that the APW method is inappropriate for

NFE crystals. This is certainly not the case. One of the advantages

of the APW method is that it is applicable for a wide variety of ma-

terials.[†] But, if one is entering into an energy band calculation with

no prior background, it would probably be easier to understand the

formalism and the practical aspects of an OPW-based pseudopotential

method.

The APW method was originally developed to overcome difficul-

ties inherent in the cellular method. In the latter it is difficult to

satisfy the periodic boundary condition for all points on the boundary

of the unit cell. In the APW method these boundary conditions are

identically satisfied. This is also true, of course, for the OPW and

Green's function methods.

The OPW method has one main advantage over the APW and

Green's function methods: there is no implicit dependence of the ma-

trix elements on the characteristic energy in the secular determinant.

It therefore involves only the usual eigenvalue-eigenvector problem for

nonorthogonal basis functions. The diagonalization procedure yields

all the eigenvalues and eigenvectors simultaneously and it is not

---

[†]Terrell has shown that the APW method gives nearly the same results as the OPW method for the NFE metal Be (Terrell [58]).

necessary to examine the secular determinant as a function of energy
in order to find the zeros. The calculations therefore require much
less computer time than for the other two methods. The applications
of the OPW method, however, have been limited primarily to NFE
crystals. This is because the method requires the electrons in the
crystal to be separated into two categories: core electrons and itinerant electrons. In the most practical form of the method all the atomic
functions which do not overlap on neighboring lattice sites are included
in the core. The OPW basis function is constructed by orthogonalizing plane waves to these core states. For crystals containing no d
electrons (or completely filled d shells) it is easy to separate the core
and itinerant electrons. The inner atomic states are well separated in
energy from the outer ones and there is very little overlap between
these functions on neighboring lattice sites.[†] The resulting OPW has
nodal character in the core region but is essentially a plane wave in
the outer part of the unit cell. This basis function is very suitable for
describing the corresponding itinerant electrons which derive from
atomic s and p states and tend to be almost uniformly distributed in the
region outside the core.

In crystals containing transition elements the electrons are not
as easily separated into core and itinerant electrons. The electrons in

---

[†] The noble metals are exceptions to this rule. Although the d bands
are completely filled, they still have energies in the same range as
the outer s electron, and there is overlap between these functions on
neighboring lattice sites. The d bands are relatively narrow compared to other transition elements in the same series. They cut the
NFE bands due to the outer s electron about halfway between the bottom of the band and the Fermi energy. States near the Fermi energy
are frequently described by the NFE model, but this description is
not adequate for the d bands. There is some evidence that a similar
situation exists in solid mercury.

partially filled d shells do not fall naturally into either category. The
energies of these states are comparable with those of the outer s and p
states, and there is considerable overlap between these functions.
Hence, they cannot easily be included with the core states. On the
other hand, these electrons do not tend to be uniformly distributed outside the core but retain more of their original atomic character. The
OPW, however, is essentially a plane wave outside the core and therefore not good for describing this type of function. The APW method
does not require this separation of the electrons in a crystal into core
and itinerant electrons. One of the main advantages of this method has
been its applicability to both NFE crystals and to those containing
transition elements.

    Another disadvantage with the OPW method is that it is more
difficult to apply to crystals containing heavy elements since these
have more core states. Thus, orthogonalizing a plane wave to these
states requires more effort for the heavy elements. Furthermore, in
one of the most practical forms of the OPW method, it is assumed that
the core states are eigenfunctions of the crystal Hamiltonian. This is
different from the usual atomic Hartree-Fock Hamiltonian, and hence
it is necessary to calculate the core eigenfunctions based on the crystal potential. In the APW method all that is required is the total electronic charge density based on atomic self-consistent-field calculations
which are readily available (Liberman, Waber and Cromer [24]). The
procedure is independent of the number of states in the core, and
hence the method is as easy to apply to Th as to Li.

    The same comments can be made concerning the construction of
the crystal potential. In the OPW method the crystal potential is

written as a summation of atomic-like potentials centered on the lattice sites. In most applications it has been customary to include many
individual contributions to this atomic-like potential, some of these
requiring considerable thought and effort to calculate. In comparison,
the most commonly used procedure for constructing the muffin-tin potential is relatively simple (Mattheiss [34]). It can be programmed so
that only a few easily determined input parameters are required for
each application; this adds to the over-all flexibility of the APW and
related methods.

The APW method is based on the so-called muffin-tin model of
the crystal potential. The unit cell is divided into two regions by non-
overlapping spheres centered on each lattice site. Inside the spheres
the potential is assumed to be spherically symmetric, and outside it is
constant. In most metals the region outside the spheres is a relatively small fraction of the unit cell volume, and the muffin-tin approximation is very good. However, in the Group IV diamond-lattice
semiconductors, for instance, there is directional bonding and the
muffin-tin model is not as good. In this type of application the OPW
crystal potential written as a sum of atomic-like potentials is more
appropriate. Of course, departures from the muffin-tin potential can
be included by perturbation calculations, and this would not be an un-
reasonable thing to do. But it would seem more natural to use the
OPW method or the pseudopotential method in these applications as
long as the results are satisfactory.

The Green's function method is also based on the muffin-tin
model of the crystal potential, and the formalism is very similar to
that of the APW method [52]. It has been shown [3] that the two

methods give identical results if the same muffin-tin potential is used.
Both methods involve a summation over atomic orbitals (labeled by
quantum numbers ℓ and m) inside the spherical regions and a summation over reciprocal lattice vectors. In the usual form of the APW
method the coefficients in the atomic orbital expansion are specified,
and those in the reciprocal lattice vector expansion are determined
variationally. Hence, the size of the secular determinant is equal to
the number of reciprocal lattice vectors included in the expansion; this
ranges from 20-40 in most applications. Each of the matrix elements
involves a summation over the atomic orbital quantum number ℓ. In
principle this summation is over all non-negative integers, but in
practice it is seldom necessary to include more than 12 terms.

The situation is just reversed in the usual form of the Green's
function method. The reciprocal lattice expansion is carried out for-
mally and the atomic orbital expansion coefficients are determined
variationally. The size of the secular determinant is equal to $(\ell + 1)^2$
where ℓ is the maximum value included in the atomic orbital expansion
($\ell = 2$ or 3 is usually adequate). The matrix elements involve a summation over reciprocal lattice vectors which is relatively easy to
evaluate but is a function of the characteristic energy and the wave
vector of the electronic state.

The main advantage of the Green's function method is that the
secular determinant is generally smaller than in the APW method and
therefore requires less computer time to evaluate. In the Green's
function method it is usually adequate to include atomic orbitals with
s, p, d and f symmetry. This leads to a 16 x 16 secular determinant
which can easily be evaluated on the computer. In the APW method it

is sometimes necessary to include as many as 40 reciprocal lattice vectors. The evaluation of a 40 x 40 secular determinant requires appreciably more computer time than a 16 x 16. However, the matrix elements in the Green's function method are considerably involved, and this tends to offset any advantage gained by the smaller secular determinant. For special applications, however, the procedure involved in calculating these matrix elements can be simplified. The reciprocal lattice expansion involved in each matrix element depends on the energy, the crystal structure, and the wave vector of the electronic state. It does not, however, depend on the muffin-tin potential. Thus, if several calculations are to be made for a particular state and a given crystal structure, it is possible to tabulate the energy dependence of these terms once and for all. The method is then well suited for studying the effects due to changes in the potential. For research projects which involve several different crystal structures and a large number of different wave vectors, however, the APW method is more convenient.

Another factor in the choice between the APW and Green's function methods is the form of the wave function. In many applications it is necessary to have each of the variational expansion coefficients identified with a reciprocal lattice vector (see for instance [31]). The APW method is more convenient in such cases. On the other hand, if it is desirable to identify the expansion coefficients with the atomic quantum numbers ℓ and m, then the Green's function method is appropriate.[†]

———————

[†]See footnote on next page.

Three of the methods discussed in this section have been generalized to the relativistic case: the OPW method (Soven [56]), the
APW method (Loucks [29]), and the Green's function method (Onodera,
Okazaki and Inui [40]).   Relativistic effects become important in metals
for atomic numbers greater than about 55 (cesium).   For semiconductors and semimetals these effects can be important for atomic numbers
greater than about 32.   Of course, there are many applications, even
for these heavier metals, in which high accuracy in the energies is not
required and relativistic effects do not need to be included.   However,
all the applications to date have indicated that relativistic calculations
are a necessity for atomic numbers greater than about 71.

[†] Ziman [66] has reformulated the Green's function method into a form
similar to the APW method, i.e., the secular equations are based on
a reciprocal lattice vector expansion. Lloyd [25] and Slater [52] have
also discussed this subject. It would seem possible to reformulate the
APW method into a form similar to the Green's function method, i.e.
with the secular equations based on an atomic orbital expansion. If
this were the case, both methods would be available in either representation. The important factors in choosing between the two methods
would be the convergence rates and the relative simplicity of the matrix elements.

2 THEORETICAL DISCUSSION OF THE APW METHOD

Except for an occasion encounter with the surface, the itinerant electrons in a perfect single crystal have a fairly boring experience. The electronic potential energy is quite repetitious. This periodicity can be expressed by

$$V(\vec{r} + \vec{\ell}) = V(\vec{r}) \tag{2-1}$$

where

$$\vec{\ell} = \ell_1 \vec{a}_1 + \ell_2 \vec{a}_2 + \ell_3 \vec{a}_3 \tag{2-2}$$

The vector $\vec{\ell}$ specifies the positions of each of the unit cells in the crystal. It is formed by adding integral multiples of the basic transla-tion vectors $\vec{a}_i$ as shown in Fig. 2-1 for a two dimensional lattice. In the example shown, there are two atoms in the unit cell, and their relative positions are specified by the vector $\vec{\tau}$.

In the APW method we are concerned with finding solutions of the Schrödinger equation based on an approximate model of the actual

16

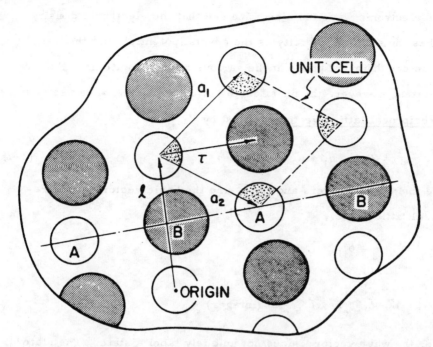

Figure 2-1.   Unit cell of a two-dimensional crystal showing basic
              translation vectors $\vec{a}_1$ and $\vec{a}_2$ and the vector $\vec{\tau}$ which
              specifies the relative positions of the two different atoms.

electronic potential V(r). However, there are some very general results which are valid for any periodic potential. These have been discussed by many authors; a very enjoyable account may be found in the
first chapter of the recent text by J. M. Ziman [65]. We only need to
review the key points.

In the hydrogen atom we label orbital states with the three
quantum numbers, n, ℓ and m_ℓ. In a crystal the states are also labeled by three numbers, the components of the wave vector $\vec{k}$. This
arises from the periodicity of the potential, which imposes the Bloch
condition

$$\psi_{\vec{k}}(\vec{r} + \vec{\ell}) = e^{i\vec{k}\cdot\vec{\ell}}\,\psi_{\vec{k}}(\vec{r}) \qquad (2\text{-}3)$$

on the electronic wave function. We see that the electronic density $|\psi|^2$ has the same periodicity as the crystal potential, but the wave function has different phase at the various atomic positions. For certain states, however, the phase factor is unity. If the wave vector $\vec{k}$ is a reciprocal lattice vector, defined by

$$\vec{g} = 2\pi(n_1 \vec{b}_1 + n_2 \vec{b}_2 + n_3 \vec{b}_3) \qquad (2\text{-}4)$$

where the n_i are integers and the $\vec{b}_i$ are the basic vectors of the reciprocal lattice, i.e.,

$$\vec{a}_i \cdot \vec{b}_j = \delta_{ij} \qquad (2\text{-}5)$$

then

$$e^{i\vec{k}\cdot\vec{\ell}} = e^{i\vec{g}\cdot\vec{\ell}} = e^{i2\pi(\text{integer})} = 1 \qquad (2\text{-}6)$$

Hence, the wave vector $\vec{k}$ does not uniquely label a state. The state with $\vec{k}' = \vec{k} + \vec{g}$ satisfies the Bloch condition as if it had the wave vector $\vec{k}$. This really is a convenience for us. It is not necessary to consider all possible wave vectors in order to fully describe the electronic structure of a crystal. We shall only discuss those wave vectors contained inside the smallest region bounded by the planes which perpendicularly bisect the reciprocal lattice vectors given in (2-4). This region of reciprocal space is called the Brillouin zone. Of course, in order to represent all the different states which happen to have the same wave vector inside the Brillouin zone, a complete set must include all of the wave vectors $\vec{k} + \vec{g}$, in addition to $\vec{k}$.

MUFFIN-TIN MODEL OF THE CRYSTAL POTENTIAL

The APW method is based on the muffin-tin approximation to the actual crystal potential V(r): inside spheres centered at each atomic site, the potential is assumed to be spherically symmetric, and out-

side these spheres the potential is taken to be constant. This is shown

schematically in Fig. 2-2. The radius of the spherical region around

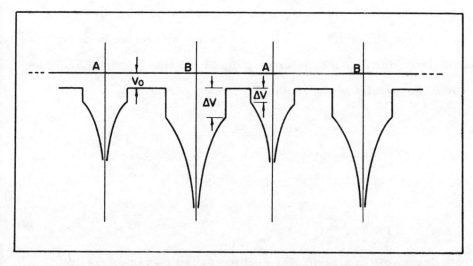

Figure 2-2.   The muffin-tin potential corresponding to the line ABAB
              in Fig. 2-1. The quantities ΔV determine the relative
              depth of the spherically symmetric potentials inside each
              sphere with respect to the constant value V_o outside.

a particular atomic site is arbitrary, except that the spheres should

not overlap. The APW method gives quite accurate solutions to the

Schrödinger equation for this approximate potential. Whether or not

these solutions agree with experimental results depends entirely on

how appropriate the model is for a particular crystal. Fortunately, the

model is very flexible, and hence the APW method can be applied to a

large variety of materials. It is the responsibility of the user, how-

ever, to construct the model so that it represents the best possible

approximation for a particular application. If the model very closely

approximates the actual potential, then the APW method can be ex-

pected to give meaningful results. Even in cases where the muffin-tin

model is a rather crude approximation, the solutions based on it can
serve as a starting point. Aspects of the crystal potential which cannot
be included in this model, such as nonspherical symmetry inside the
spheres, can frequently be included in a perturbation sense. Sometimes the actual perturbation calculations can be avoided by using experimental information to determine the small changes which must be
made in the results based on the muffin-tin approximation.

APW FUNCTION

The APW method is based on a variation function ϕ which is the
sum of a number of linearly independent functions χ^1, χ^2, ..., χ^M.

$$\phi = \sum_{i=1}^{M} c_i \chi^i \tag{2-7}$$

The index specifies a particular reciprocal lattice vector (recip)

$$\chi^i = \chi(\vec{k} + \vec{g}_i) \tag{2-8}$$

The APW method is characterized by the muffin-tin potential and the
particular form of the functions χ^i in (2-7). After considering the form
of these functions as used in the APW method, we will discuss the
procedure for determining the expansion parameters c_i.

Inside a particular sphere the muffin-tin potential is spherically
symmetric, and the solutions of the Schrödinger equation are of the
form

$$\psi_{\ell m}(\vec{\rho}) = Y_{\ell m}(\hat{\rho}) R_\ell(\rho) \tag{2-9}$$

The $Y_{\ell m}(\hat{\rho})$ are spherical harmonics; these are discussed in most
quantum mechanics texts (Powell and Crasemann [42]). The vector $\vec{\rho}$
has its origin at the center of the sphere, and $\hat{\rho}$ indicates the angular

part of $\vec{\rho}$. The radial function $R_\ell(\rho)$ satisfies

$$-\frac{1}{\rho^2} \frac{d}{d\rho} \left(\rho^2 \frac{dR}{d\rho} \right) + \left[\frac{\ell(\ell+1)}{\rho^2} + V_\nu(\rho) \right] R = E'R \qquad (2-10)$$

$V_\nu(\rho)$ is the spherically symmetric potential inside the νth sphere. The only boundary condition which must be imposed at this stage is that the radial solutions be regular at the origin. Without specifying the boundary condition at the surface of the sphere, the energy E' in (2-10) can take on any value.

Each of the functions $\psi_{\ell m}(\rho)$ in (2-9) is a solution of the Schrödinger equation for the potential $V_\nu(\rho)$. The APW function inside the νth sphere is taken to be a linear combination of these,

$$\chi(\rho) = \sum_{\ell=o}^{\infty} \sum_{m=-\ell}^{+\ell} A_{\ell m} Y_{\ell m}(\hat{\rho}) R_\ell(\rho) \qquad (2-11)$$

The coefficients $A_{\ell m}$ are not yet specified. The number of ℓ values to be included in the summation is arbitrary at this point, but we shall certainly want to include all the lower values ($\ell = 0, 1, 2, 3$) in order to represent any s, p, d, or f character in the crystal wave functions.

In the region outside the spheres the muffin-tin potential is constant (V_o) as shown in Fig. 2-2. Although the electronic structure is dependent on the depth of the spherically symmetric potential with respect to this constant (ΔV), the entire potential can be shifted so that the constant is zero. For convenience, let us agree to always construct the muffin-tin with $V_o = 0$.

A solution of the Schrödinger equation valid in the zero potential region is

$$\chi(\vec{k}, \vec{r}) = e^{i\vec{k} \cdot \vec{r}} \qquad (2-12)$$

This satisfies the Bloch condition (2-3), as can be readily shown:

$$\chi(\vec{k}, \vec{r} + \vec{\ell}) = e^{i\vec{k} \cdot (\vec{r} + \vec{\ell})} = e^{i\vec{k} \cdot \vec{\ell}} \chi(\vec{k}, \vec{r}) \qquad (2-13)$$

Thus it is an acceptable wave function for the Schrödinger equation based on a periodic potential. To summarize, we have decided to use the linear combination of atomic orbitals (2-11) as the form of the APW function inside a particular sphere. These orbitals should adequately represent the nodal character of the crystal wave function in these regions. In the zero potential region the plane wave solution (2-12) is to be used. We have chosen the most appropriate form in each of the regions. Also we have satisfied the boundary condition imposed by the periodicity of the potential. However, the different forms do not match up at the sphere boundaries. The APW function is discontinuous over these surfaces.

We could proceed quite generally at this point, leaving the APW function discontinuous in both slope and value. However, in the form of the APW method most generally used [47] the discontinuity in the value of the APW function at the sphere boundaries is eliminated; the discontinuity in the slope remains. This is accomplished by specifying in a particular way the arbitrary expansion coefficients $A_{\ell m}$ in (2-11).

Consider the form of the plane wave solution in the vicinity of the νth sphere. We see in Fig. 2-3 that the radius vector $\vec{r}$ can be written $\vec{r} = \vec{r}_\nu + \vec{\rho}$ where $\vec{\rho}$ is centered on the νth sphere, located at $\vec{r}_\nu$. Thus

$$\chi(\vec{k}, \vec{r}) = e^{i\vec{k} \cdot \vec{r}} = e^{i\vec{k} \cdot (\vec{r}_\nu + \vec{\rho})} = e^{i\vec{k} \cdot \vec{r}_\nu} e^{i\vec{k} \cdot \vec{\rho}} \qquad (2-14)$$

The second factor in this equation can be expanded in spherical harmonics. It is a standard result derived in most quantum mechanics

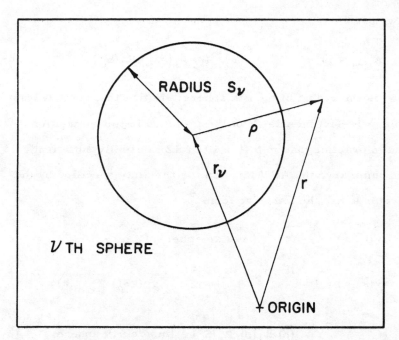

RADIUS S_ν

ρ

r_ν

r

ν TH SPHERE

+ ORIGIN

Figure 2-3.   In the vicinity of the νth sphere the position vector $\vec{r}$
relative to an arbitrary origin can be expressed as
$\vec{r} = \vec{r}_\nu + \vec{\rho}$ where $\vec{\rho}$ is centered at the position of the
νth sphere.

texts (Powell and Craseman [42]) that

$$e^{i\vec{k} \cdot \vec{\rho}} = 4\pi \sum_{\ell=0}^{\infty} \sum_{m=-\ell}^{\ell} i^\ell \, \mathcal{J}_\ell (k\rho) \, Y^*_{\ell m}(\hat{k}) \, Y_{\ell m}(\hat{\rho}) \qquad (2\text{-}15)$$

where $\mathcal{J}_\ell (x)$ is a spherical Bessel function of order ℓ. As before, the
unit vectors $\hat{k}$ and $\hat{\rho}$ indicate the angular parts of $\vec{k}$ and $\vec{\rho}$, respectively.
Thus (2-14) becomes

$$e^{i\vec{k} \cdot \vec{r}} = 4\pi \, e^{i\vec{k} \cdot \vec{r}_\nu} \sum_{\ell=0}^{\infty} \sum_{m=-\ell}^{+\ell} i^\ell \mathcal{J}_\ell (k\rho)$$

$$Y^*_{\ell m}(\hat{k}) \, Y_{\ell m}(\hat{\rho}) \qquad (2\text{-}16)$$

Evaluating this at the surface of the νth sphere and equating to $\chi(\vec{\rho})$ in

(2-11) we get

$$A_{\ell m} = 4\pi \; e^{i\vec{k} \cdot \vec{r}_\nu} \; i^\ell \; Y^*_{\ell m}(\hat{k}) \; \mathcal{J}_\ell(kS_\nu)/R_\ell(S_\nu) \tag{2-17}$$

where S_ν is the radius of the νth sphere. Notice that now, at least in principle, we must include all of the ℓ values in the summation. We will find in practice that up to $\ell = 10$ or 12 is usually sufficient.

In summary, the APW function for the state specified by the wave vector $\vec{k}$ has the following form:

$$\chi(\vec{k}, \vec{r}) = e^{i\vec{k} \cdot \vec{r}} \qquad \text{(outside spheres)} \tag{2-18}$$

$$\chi(\vec{k}, \vec{r}) = 4\pi \; e^{i\vec{k} \cdot \vec{r}_\nu} \sum_{\ell=o}^{\infty} \sum_{m=-\ell}^{+\ell} i^\ell \; \mathcal{J}_\ell(kS_\nu) \; Y^*_{\ell m}(\hat{k})$$

$$Y_{\ell m}(\hat{\rho}) \; R_\ell(\rho)/R_\ell(S_\nu) \qquad \text{(inside νth sphere)} \tag{2-19}$$

These different forms match up at the sphere boundaries, but there is a discontinuity in the slope. It should be emphasized, however, that the discontinuity in slope is in the individual APW functions $\chi^i = \chi(\vec{k} + \vec{g}_i)$. The crystal wave function (2-7) determined variationally as a linear combination of APW's is continuous, a perfectly acceptable, well-behaved wave function.

VARIATIONAL EXPRESSION FOR THE ENERGY

We want to form a linear combination of APW's, each corresponding to a different recip as indicated in (2-7). The expansion coefficients are to be determined variationally. This requires a variational expression for the energy which is valid for functions which have a discontinuity in slope on the spherical surfaces. Schlosser and Marcus [45] have presented variational expressions valid for trial wave functions which are discontinuous on an arbitrary surface in the unit cell. We shall consider the special case where this surface consists of spheres as shown in Fig. 2-4 (see also Leigh [23]).

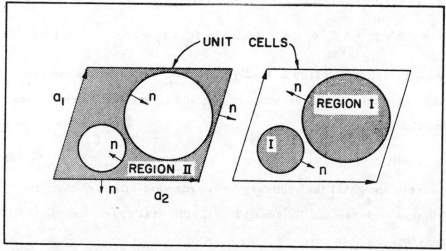

Figure 2-4. The outward normals for the regions inside and outside the muffin-tin spheres.

$$E \int_{I+II} \phi^* \phi d\Omega = \int_{I+II} \phi^* H \phi \, d\Omega + \frac{1}{2} \int_{surfaces} (\phi_{II} - \phi_I) \left(\frac{\partial}{\partial \rho} \phi_{II}^* + \frac{\partial}{\partial \rho} \phi_I^* \right)$$

$$- (\phi_{II} + \phi_I)^* \left(\frac{\partial}{\partial \rho} \phi_{II} - \frac{\partial}{\partial \rho} \phi_I \right) \Big] dS \qquad (2\text{-}20)$$

where

$$H = -\nabla^2 + \text{muffin-tin} \qquad (2\text{-}21)$$

The volume integrations in (2-20) are over the unit cell, and in the surface integral $\partial/\partial\rho$ is in the direction of the outward normal for region I as shown in Fig. 2-4. The variation function ϕ is a linear

combination of APW's with the form (2-19) in region I, and (2-18) in
region II. In (2-20) these different forms are also indicated in the
surface integral, which extends over each of the spheres. We shall
see that there is no contribution from the unit cell boundary because
the APW functions satisfy the Bloch condition.

To see that (2-20) is the proper variational expression, we write

$$E = E_t + \delta E, \quad \phi_I = \phi_t + \delta \phi_I, \quad \text{and} \quad \phi_{II} = \phi_t + \delta \phi_{II} \tag{2-22}$$

E is the variational energy in (2-20); ϕ_I and ϕ_{II} are the variation functions in region I and II, respectively. ϕ_t and E_t are the true solutions
of the Hamiltonian (2-21),

$$H \phi_t = E_t \phi_t \tag{2-23}$$

We want to show that the arbitrary first order variations of the trial
function in regions I and II, result in δE, the first order variation of
the energy, equal to zero.

Substituting (2-22) into the left hand side of (2-20) and retaining
only first order terms, we get

$$\text{LHS} = E_t \int_{I+II} \phi_t^* \phi_t \, d\Omega + \delta E \int_{I+II} \phi_t^* \phi_t \, d\Omega$$

$$+ E_t \left\{ \int_I (\delta \phi_I^* \phi_t + \phi_t^* \delta \phi_I) \, d\Omega \right.$$

$$\left. + \int_{II} (\delta \phi_{II}^* \phi_t + \phi_t^* \delta \phi_{II}) \, d\Omega \right\} \tag{2-24}$$

Similarly, with the use of (2-23), the right-hand side of (2-20) becomes

$$\text{RHS} = E_t \left\{ \int_{I+II} \phi_t^* \phi_t \, d\Omega + \int_I \delta\phi_I^* \phi_t \, d\Omega + \int_{II} \delta\phi_{II}^* \phi_t \, d\Omega \right\}$$

$$+ \int_I \phi_t^* H \, \delta\phi_I \, d\Omega + \int_{II} \phi_t^* H \, \delta\phi_{II} \, d\Omega$$

$$- \int_{\text{spheres}} \left\{ \phi_t^* \frac{\partial}{\partial\rho} (\delta\phi_{II} - \delta\phi_I) - (\delta\phi_{II} - \delta\phi_I) \frac{\partial}{\partial\rho} \phi_t^* \right\} dS \quad (2\text{-}25)$$

There is no contribution to the surface integrals in (2-25) from the cell boundary because both ϕ_t and $\delta\phi_{II}$ satisfy the Bloch condition (2-3). Every point on the cell boundary has a conjugate point separated from it by a basic lattice vector, as shown in Fig. 2-5. According to the

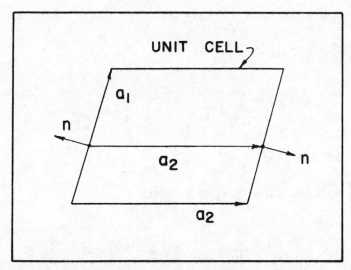

Figure 2-5. Contributions to the surface integration over the unit cell boundary cancel because the outward normals of conjugate points (those separated by a basic translation vector) are in opposite directions.

Bloch condition, the wave function at two conjugate points differs only by a phase factor. Hence contributions to the surface integrals in

(2-25) from conjugate points on the cell boundary cancel because the outward normals are in opposite directions.

Consider the first term involving the Hamiltonian in (2-25). Because $\delta \phi_I$ is only continuous over a finite region we cannot operate H to the left. However, by writing

$$\int_I \phi_t^* H \, \delta \phi_I \, d\Omega = \int_I \phi_t^* (-\nabla^2 + V(r)) \, \delta \phi_I \, d\Omega \qquad (2-26)$$

we can use Green's theorem [16] in the form

$$\int_I \phi_t^* (-\nabla^2) \, \delta \phi_I \, d\Omega = \int_I \delta \phi_I (-\nabla^2) \, \phi_t^* \, d\Omega$$

$$- \int_S (\phi_t^* \frac{\partial}{\partial \rho} \delta \phi_I - \delta \phi_I \frac{\partial}{\partial \rho} \phi_t^*) dS \qquad (2-27)$$

and the reality of $V(r)$ and E_t to get

$$\int_I \phi_t^* H \, \delta \phi_I \, d\Omega = E_t \int_I \phi_t^* \, \delta \phi_I \, d\Omega$$

$$- \int_S (\phi_t^* \frac{\partial}{\partial \rho} \delta \phi_I - \delta \phi_I \frac{\partial}{\partial \rho} \phi_t^*) \, dS \qquad (2-28)$$

Similarly, for region II we get

$$\int_{II} \phi_t^* H \, \delta \phi_{II} \, d\Omega = E_t \int_{II} \phi_t^* \, \delta \phi_{II} \, d\Omega$$

$$+ \int_S (\phi_t^* \frac{\partial}{\partial \rho} \delta \phi_{II} - \delta \phi_{II} \frac{\partial}{\partial \rho} \phi_t^*) \, dS \qquad (2-29)$$

The surface integrals in (2-28) and (2-29) have opposite signs because of the convention that $\partial / \partial \rho$ should have the sense indicated for region I in Fig. 2-4. Substituting (2-28) and (2-29) into (2-25) we find

$$\delta E \int_{I+II} \phi_t^* \phi_t \, d\Omega = 0 \tag{2-30}$$

and since the normalization integral is non zero we have shown that (2-20) is a variational expression for the energy. Although we shall not examine the proof, it can also be shown [45] that (2-20) has the useful property that E is real for any trial wave function.

Because of the surface terms in (2-20), it is not necessary for the trial function to have the same form in regions I and II. As in the construction of the APW functions, it is possible to choose the most suitable form in each of the regions without concern for continuity across the sphere boundaries. Of course, as was pointed out in the discussion which precedes (2-17), at the surface of the spheres the APW function has the same value in both regions. Hence, the form of (2-20) which we shall use is

$$E \int_{I+II} \phi^* \phi d\Omega = \int_{I+II} \phi^* H \phi d\Omega$$

$$- \tfrac{1}{2} \int_{spheres} (\phi_{II}^* + \phi_I^*)(\frac{\partial}{\partial \rho} \phi_{II} - \frac{\partial}{\partial \rho} \phi_I) \, dS \tag{2-31}$$

where the remaining surface term takes account of the discontinuity in slope.

APW MATRIX ELEMENTS

We can use the variational expression (2-31) to determine the best expansion parameters c_i in (2-7) by minimizing the energy with respect to each coefficient,

$$\frac{\partial E}{\partial c_i} = 0 , \qquad i = 1, 2, \ldots, M \tag{2-32}$$

Substituting (2-7) into (2-31) yields

$$E \sum_{i,j}^{M} c_i^* c_j \int_{I+II} (\chi^i)^* \chi^j \, d\Omega = \sum_{i,j}^{M} c_i^* c_j \int_{I+II} (\chi^i)^* H \chi^j \, d\Omega$$

$$- \tfrac{1}{2} \sum_{i,j}^{M} c_i^* c_j \int (\chi_{II}^i + \chi_I^i)^* (\tfrac{\partial}{\partial\rho} \chi_{II}^i - \tfrac{\partial}{\partial\rho} \chi_I^i) \, dS \qquad (2\text{-}33)$$

where, from (2-19)

$$\chi_I^i = \chi(\vec{k}_i, \vec{r}) \qquad (2\text{-}34)$$

inside the ν th sphere and, from (2-18),

$$\chi_{II}^i = e^{i\vec{k}_i \cdot \vec{r}} \qquad (2\text{-}35)$$

If we define

$$H^{ij} = \int_{I+II} (\chi^i)^* H \chi^j \, d\Omega \qquad (2\text{-}36)$$

$$\Delta^{ij} = \int_{I+II} (\chi^i)^* \chi^j \, d\Omega \qquad (2\text{-}37)$$

$$S^{ij} = - \tfrac{1}{2} \int_S (\chi_{II}^i + \chi_I^i)^* (\tfrac{\partial}{\partial\rho} \chi_{II}^j - \tfrac{\partial}{\partial\rho} \chi_I^j) \, dS \qquad (2\text{-}38)$$

then (2-33) can be written

$$\sum_{i,j}^{M} (H^{ij} + S^{ij} - E \Delta^{ij}) c_i^* c_j = 0 \qquad (2\text{-}39)$$

In this form the minimization procedure for determining the c_i is the same as for continuous functions. The effective Hamiltonian matrix element is now $H^{ij} + S^{ij}$, the surface term S^{ij} representing the contribution to the kinetic energy due to the discontinuity in slope of the

APW function. We quote the familiar result [41] that the c_i are given by solutions of

$$\sum_{j}^{M} (H^{ij} + S^{ij} - E \Delta^{ij}) c_j = 0, \qquad (2-40)$$

where i = 1, 2, ..., M and E can take on only those values for which the secular determinant is zero, i.e.,

$$DET \ |H^{ij} + S^{ij} - E \Delta^{ij}| = 0 \qquad (2-41)$$

Let us now find the explicit expressions for the matrix elements in (2-40) and (2-41) as defined in (2-36), (2-37) and (2-38). It is convenient to consider the terms in the following combinations:

$$H_I^{ij} - E \Delta_I^{ij} \qquad (2-42)$$

$$H_{II}^{ij} - E \Delta_{II}^{ij} \qquad (2-43)$$

$$S^{ij} \qquad (2-44)$$

In (2-42) the integral extends throughout each of the spherical regions. Inside the ν th sphere the Hamiltonian consists of the kinetic energy operator and the spherically symmetric potential $V_\nu(r)$. This potential was in fact used in the construction of the APW function itself for this region; in (2-19) the function $R_\ell(\rho)$ is a solution of the radial Schrödinger equation (2-10). Thus

$$H_I^{ij} - E \Delta_I^{ij} = (E' - E) \Delta_I^{ij} \qquad (2-45)$$

where E' is arbitrary. In order to make this term zero and thus simplify the APW matrix elements, it was originally proposed [47] that the energy E' be taken to be the same as the characteristic energy which satisfies (2-41). This has the disadvantage that the APW functions themselves now depend implicitly on the characteristic energy, and the resulting diagonalization procedure is less convenient to carry out than the usual eigenvalue-eigenvector routine. However, in addition to simplifying the form of the matrix elements, this approach has the virtue that inside the sphere the resulting APW's are exact solutions of the muffin-tin potential corresponding to the crystal energy eigenstates. The portion of the crystal wave function outside the spheres must be found variationally, but for itinerant electrons the plane wave expansion is quite appropriate for this region and is usually highly convergent. It is this aspect of the method, namely the suitability of the APW function as a basis function for representing the actual crystal wave function, that accounts for its success in a wide variety of applications. The APW function itself adjusts to a particular potential and forms a very suitable trial function. The loss of convenience in the diagonalization procedure is adequately compensated for by this inherent advantage of the APW method.

The volume integration in (2-43) is over that portion of the unit cell outside of the spheres. An easy way to evaluate this is to extend the plane wave (2-35) throughout the entire unit cell and subtract the contribution which results from the region inside the spheres. Thus

$$H_{II}{}^{ij} - E \, \Delta_{II}{}^{ij} = (H_{II}{}^{ij} - E \, \Delta_{II}{}^{ij})_{\text{cell}}$$

$$- (H_{II}{}^{ij} - E \, \Delta_{II}{}^{ij})_{\text{spheres}} \tag{2-46}$$

The first term is simply

$$\int_{\text{cell}} e^{-i\vec{k}_i \cdot \vec{r}} \, (-\nabla^2 - E) \, e^{i\vec{k}_j \cdot \vec{r}} \, d\Omega = \Omega_o \, (k_j{}^2 - E) \, \delta_{ij} \tag{2-47}$$

where Ω_o is the volume of the unit cell. We can evaluate the second term in (2-46) for the νth sphere and then sum over all the spheres in the unit cell. Using the coordinates indicated in Fig. 2-3, we have

$$(H_{II}{}^{ij} - E\,\Delta_{II}{}^{ij})_\nu = (k_j{}^2 - E) \int_\nu e^{i\vec{k}_{ij}\cdot\vec{r}}\,d\Omega$$

$$= (k_j{}^2 - E)\,e^{i\vec{k}_{ij}\cdot\vec{r}_\nu} \int_\nu e^{i\vec{k}_{ij}\cdot\vec{\rho}}\,d\Omega \qquad (2\text{-}48)$$

where

$$\vec{k}_{ij} = \vec{k}_j - \vec{k}_i = \vec{g}_i - \vec{g}_i \qquad (2\text{-}49)$$

The origin for $\vec{r}_\nu$ is arbitrary. For one sphere in the unit cell we can take $\vec{r}_\nu = 0$; for two spheres, the midpoint between their centers has certain advantages to be discussed later. By specifying the z axis of the spherical coordinate $\vec{\rho}$ along $\vec{k}_{ij}$, the integral over the νth sphere in (2-48) becomes

$$2\pi \int_0^{S_\nu} \rho^2 d\rho \int_0^\pi \sin\theta\,d\theta\,e^{ik_{ij}\,\rho\cos\theta}$$

$$= 4\pi\,S_\nu{}^2\,\mathcal{J}_1(k_{ij}\,S_\nu)/k_{ij} \qquad (2\text{-}50)$$

where S_ν is the sphere radius and $\mathcal{J}_1(x)$ is the spherical Bessel function of order one,

$$\mathcal{J}_1(x) = (\sin x - x\cos x)/x^2 \qquad (2\text{-}51)$$

Summarizing to this point, we have for (2-42) and (2-43)

$$(H^{ij} - E\,\Delta^{ij})_{I+II} = (k_j{}^2 - E)\Big[\Omega_\circ\,\delta_{ij}$$

$$- 4\pi\,\sum_\nu S_\nu{}^2\,e^{i\vec{k}_{ij}\cdot\vec{r}_\nu}\,\mathcal{J}_1(k_{ij}S_\nu)/k_{ij}\Big] \qquad (2\text{-}52)$$

The surface term (2-44) is defined by (2-38). Again we will consider the contribution from the surface of the ν th sphere and then sum over all the spheres in the unit cell. In (2-38) we shall use χ_I as given in (2-19), and the plane wave χ_{II} in its expanded form (2-16). Then

$$\chi_{II}^{\ i} + \chi_I^{\ i} = 2\chi_{II}^{\ i}$$

$$= 8\pi e^{i\vec{k}_i \cdot \vec{r}_\nu} \sum_{\ell=0}^{\infty} \sum_{m=-\ell}^{+\ell} i^\ell \mathcal{J}_\ell(k_i S_\nu)$$

$$Y_{\ell m}^*(\hat{k}_i)\, Y_{\ell m}(\hat{\rho}) \qquad\qquad (2\text{-}53)$$

and

$$\frac{\partial}{\partial \rho}(\chi_{II}^{\ j} - \chi_I^{\ j}) = 4\pi e^{i\vec{k}_j \cdot \vec{r}_\nu} \sum_{\ell=0}^{\infty} \sum_{m=-\ell}^{+\ell} i^\ell \mathcal{J}_\ell(k_j S_\nu)\, Y_{\ell m}^*(\hat{k}_j)\, Y_{\ell m}(\hat{\rho})$$

$$\left(\frac{k_j \mathcal{J}_\ell'(k_j \rho)}{\mathcal{J}_\ell(k_j S_\nu)} - \frac{R_\ell'(\rho)}{R_\ell(S_\nu)} \right) \qquad\qquad (2\text{-}54)$$

The prime on $\mathcal{J}_\ell$ in (2-54) indicates the derivative with respect to $k_j \rho$; $R_\ell'(\rho)$ is the derivative of $R_\ell(\rho)$ with respect to ρ. Substituting (2-53) and (2-54) into the surface integral (2-38) with $\rho = S_\nu$ and

$$dS = S_\nu^{\ 2} \sin\theta\; d\theta\, d\phi = S_\nu^{\ 2} d\hat{\rho} \qquad\qquad (2\text{-}55)$$

we get

$$S_\nu^{\ ij} = -4\pi S_\nu^{\ 2} e^{i\vec{k}_{ij} \cdot \vec{r}_\nu} \sum_{\ell=0}^{\infty} (2\ell+1) P_\ell(\hat{k}_i \cdot \hat{k}_j) \mathcal{J}_\ell(k_i S_\nu) \mathcal{J}_\ell(k_j S_\nu)$$

$$\left(\frac{k_j\, \mathcal{J}_\ell'(k_j S_\nu)}{\mathcal{J}_\ell(k_j S_\nu)} - \frac{R_\ell'(S_\nu)}{R_\ell(S_\nu)} \right) \qquad\qquad (2\text{-}56)$$

In arriving at this result we used the orthonormality condition for the
spherical harmonics,

$$\int Y_{\ell m}^{*}(\hat{\rho}) \, Y_{\ell' m'}(\hat{\rho}) \, d\hat{\rho} = \delta_{\ell \ell'} \delta_{mm'} \tag{2-57}$$

and the addition theorem [42]

$$\sum_{m=-\ell}^{+\ell} Y_{\ell m}^{*}(\hat{k}_i) \, Y_{\ell m}(\hat{k}_j) = \frac{2\ell + 1}{4\pi} \, P_{\ell}(\hat{k}_i \cdot \hat{k}_j) \tag{2-58}$$

where the P_{ℓ} are Legendre polynomials. There is a contribution of
the form (2-56) from each of the spheres in the unit cell. Together
with the result of (2-52), we have for the APW matrix elements

$$M^{ij} \equiv H^{ij} + S^{ij} - E \Delta^{ij} = \Omega_{o} \, (k_j^{2} - E) \, \delta_{ij}$$

$$- 4\pi \sum_{\nu} S_{\nu}^{2} \, e^{i\vec{k}_{ij} \cdot \vec{r}_{\nu}} G_{\nu}^{ij} \tag{2-59}$$

where

$$G_{\nu}^{ij} = (k_j^{2} - E) \, \mathcal{J}_1(k_{ij} S_{\nu})/k_{ij}$$

$$- \sum_{\ell=o}^{\infty} (2\ell+1) P_{\ell}(k_i \cdot k_j) \mathcal{J}_{\ell}(k_i S_{\nu}) \mathcal{J}_{\ell}(k_j S_{\nu})$$

$$\left[\frac{R_{\ell}'(S_{\nu})}{R_{\ell}(S_{\nu})} - \frac{k_j \mathcal{J}_{\ell}'(k_j S_{\nu})}{\mathcal{J}_{\ell}(k_j S_{\nu})} \right] \tag{2-60}$$

There is an alternate form of G_{ν}^{ij} which is generally used for
computational purposes. It follows immediately from

$$(k_j^{2} - \vec{k}_i \cdot \vec{k}_j) \frac{\mathcal{J}_1(k_{ij} S_{\nu})}{k_j \, k_{ij}}$$

$$= - \sum_{\ell=o}^{\infty} (2\ell+1) \, P_{\ell}(\hat{k}_i \cdot \hat{k}_j) \, \mathcal{J}_{\ell}(k_i S_{\nu}) \, \mathcal{J}_{\ell}'(k_j S_{\nu}) \tag{2-61}$$

which we shall prove. In Fig. 2-6 we have indicated the relationship

between $\vec{k}_{ij}$, $\vec{k}_i$ and $\vec{k}_j$. If (as indicated in this figure) we replace these

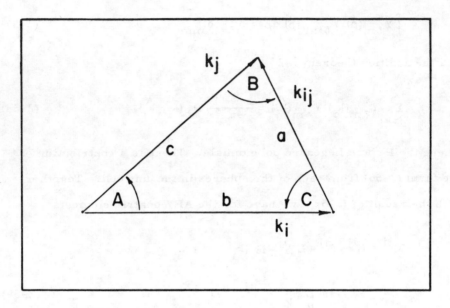

Figure 2-6. The relationship between the vectors $\vec{k}_i$, $\vec{k}_j$ and $\vec{k}_{ij}$ with
standard notation for the sides and angles of a triangle
introduced for simplification.

variables by the more familiar notation usually associated with the

sides and angles of a triangle, the proof of (2-51) is much easier to

follow. In this notation (2-61) can be written as

$$- \cos B \; \mathcal{J}_1(aS) = \sum_{\ell=0}^{\infty} (2\ell+1) P_\ell(\cos A) \; \mathcal{J}_\ell(bS) \; \mathcal{J}_\ell'(cS) \qquad (2\text{-}62)$$

since

$$ac \cos B = \vec{k}_{ij} \cdot \vec{k}_j = (\vec{k}_j - \vec{k}_i) \cdot \vec{k}_j = k_j^2 - \vec{k}_i \cdot \vec{k}_j \qquad (2\text{-}63)$$

The proof of (2-62) follows immediately from the following expansion

[1]:

$$\frac{\sin aS}{aS} = \sum_{\ell=o}^{\infty} (2\ell+1)P_{\ell}(\cos A) \, \mathcal{J}_{\ell}(bS) \, \mathcal{J}_{\ell}(cS) \tag{2-64}$$

Differentiating the right-hand side with respect to cS_{ν} obviously yields
the result in (2-62). That the left-hand side also agrees follows from

$$a = \sqrt{b^2 + c^2 - 2bc \cos A} \tag{2-65}$$

and

$$\frac{\partial}{\partial c} = \left(\frac{c - b \cos A}{a}\right) \frac{\partial}{\partial a} = \cos B \frac{\partial}{\partial a} \tag{2-66}$$

Hence

$$\frac{\partial}{\partial(cS)} \frac{\sin aS}{aS} = \frac{\cos B}{S} \frac{\partial}{\partial a} \frac{\sin aS}{aS} = -\cos B \, \mathcal{J}_1(aS) \tag{2-67}$$

and (2-61) is verified. Substituting into (2-60) yields

$$G_{\nu}^{ij} = (\vec{k}_i \cdot \vec{k}_j - E) \, \mathcal{J}_1(k_{ij}S_{\nu})/k_{ij}$$

$$- \sum_{\ell=o}^{\infty} (2\ell+1)P_{\ell}(k_i \cdot k_j)$$

$$\mathcal{J}_{\ell}(k_i S_{\nu}) \, \mathcal{J}_{\ell}(k_j S_{\nu}) \, R'_{\ell}(S_{\nu})/R_{\ell}(S_{\nu}) \tag{2-68}$$

which, along with (2-59) is the more familiar form of the APW matrix
elements originally proposed by Slater [47].

3 PRACTICAL ASPECTS OF THE APW METHOD

CRYSTAL STRUCTURE AND RECIPROCAL LATTICE

The initial stage in an APW calculation is to determine the following:

(1) $\vec{k}$, the wave vector specifying the state for which the energy eigenvalues and/or wave functions are to be calculated;

(2) Ω_o, the unit cell volume;

(3) $\vec{r}_\nu$, the position of the ν th APW sphere in the unit cell;

(4) S_ν, the radius of the ν th APW sphere;

(5) $\vec{g}_i$, the reciprocal lattice vectors to be included in the basis set;

(6) $V_\nu(\rho)$, the potential inside the ν th APW sphere.

All of these can be determined from crystal structure data, with the exception of the potentials which require, in addition, information on the atomic electronic states.

As an example, let us consider the hexagonal close-packed (HCP) crystal structure. The unit cell and reciprocal lattice for this structure have been described by several authors. In general, most information of this type can be found in the following references: [64], [51], [39], [20] and [53]. For the HCP structure the basic translation vectors are

$$\vec{a}_1 = c \, \hat{e}_z$$

$$\vec{a}_2 = a \, \hat{e}_x \qquad\qquad\qquad (3-1)$$

$$\vec{a}_3 = -\tfrac{1}{2} a \, \hat{e}_x + \frac{\sqrt{3}}{2} a \, \hat{e}_y$$

where $\hat{e}_x$ is a unit vector in the x direction, etc., and a and c are the lattice constants. The unit cell is shown in Fig. 3-1. The volume is given by

$$\Omega_\circ = \vec{a}_1 \cdot (\vec{a}_2 \times \vec{a}_3) \qquad\qquad\qquad (3-2)$$

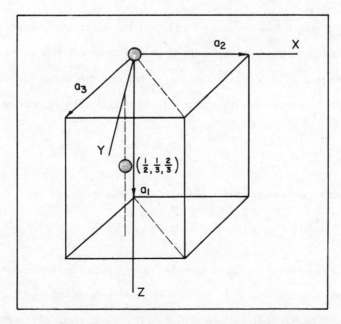

Figure 3-1. Unit cell for hexagonal close-packed crystal structure.

which for the HCP structure is $\frac{\sqrt{3}}{2} a^2 c$. We see that for this structure there are two atoms in the unit cell. They are, of course, both the same atomic species for an element but for a compound they would be different.

In Fig. 3-1 the two atoms are at the positions

$$\vec{\tau}_1 = 0 \, \vec{a}_1 + 0 \, \vec{a}_2 + 0 \, \vec{a}_3$$

$$\vec{\tau}_2 = \tfrac{1}{2} \vec{a}_1 + \tfrac{1}{3} \vec{a}_2 + \tfrac{2}{3} \vec{a}_3 \tag{3-3}$$

The origin of coordinates, however, is arbitrary and could also be chosen at the midpoint between these two atoms. The positions of the two atoms would then be given by

$$\vec{r}_1 = - \tfrac{1}{2} \vec{\tau}_2$$

$$\vec{r}_2 = + \tfrac{1}{2} \vec{\tau}_2 \tag{3-4}$$

This choice of orgin has the advantage that the matrix elements (2-59) do not have an imaginary component if both atoms are the same. Since the sphere radius S_ν and the potential $V_\nu (\rho)$ are the same for both atoms, the summation over the atoms in the unit cell in (2-59) reduces to

$$\sum_\nu e^{i\vec{k}_{ij} \cdot \vec{r}_\nu} \tag{3-5}$$

the so-called structure factor. Using (3-4) this reduces to

$$\sum_{\nu=1}^{2} e^{i\vec{k}_{ij} \cdot \vec{r}_\nu} = 2 \cos \left(\vec{k}_{ij} \cdot \vec{\tau}_2 / 2 \right) \tag{3-6}$$

for two identical atoms in the unit cell. For compounds the individual contributions to the summation in (2-59) must be considered for each different atom in the unit cell, and the resulting matrix elements would be complex.

The choice of the sphere radius S_ν is somewhat arbitrary. However, it is usually chosen as large as possible. This minimizes the region in which the potential is approximated by a constant and reduces the portion of the crystal wave function which must be expanded in plane waves. The former improves the muffin-tin approximation to the crystal potential, while the latter improves the convergence of the APW method by requiring fewer recips in the expansion. Hence, unless special considerations warrant a different choice, the sphere radius is usually equal to half of the nearest neighbor distance. This is illustrated in Fig. 3-2. For the HCP structure we have

$$S = \tfrac{1}{2}\left|\vec{\tau}_2\right| = \tfrac{1}{2}\, a\sqrt{\tfrac{1}{3} + \tfrac{1}{4}\left(\tfrac{c}{a}\right)^2} \;,\qquad \tfrac{c}{a} \le \sqrt{8/3}$$

$$S = \tfrac{1}{2}\, a\,, \qquad \tfrac{c}{a} \ge \sqrt{8/3}\,.$$

$$(3\text{-}7)$$

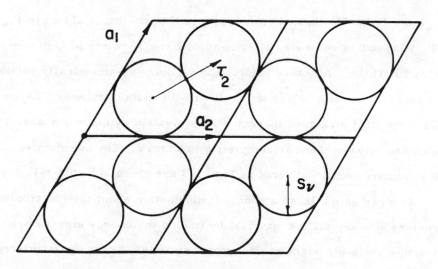

Figure 3-2. The muffin-tin sphere radius S_ν is usually chosen equal to half the nearest neighbor distance, as shown here for a two-dimensional crystal.

The basic vectors of the reciprocal lattice, defined by (2-5) are

$$\vec{b}_1 = \frac{1}{c} \hat{e}_z$$

$$\vec{b}_2 = \frac{1}{a} \hat{e}_x + \frac{1}{a\sqrt{3}} \hat{e}_y \tag{3-8}$$

$$\vec{b}_3 = \frac{2}{a\sqrt{3}} \hat{e}_y$$

for the HCP structure. The recips are given by

$$\vec{g}_i = 2\pi (n_1 \vec{b}_1 + n_2 \vec{b}_2 + n_3 \vec{b}_3) \tag{3-9}$$

where i represents the trio of integers n_1, n_2 and n_3. It is frequently convenient to abbreviate (3-9) by writing

$$\vec{g}_i = (n_1, n_2, n_3) \tag{3-10}$$

For the HCP structure the Brillouin zone (BZ) is enclosed by the planes which perpendicularly bisect the following recips: $(\pm 1, 0, 0)$, $(0, \pm 1, 0)$, $(0, 0, \pm 1)$, $(0, 1, -1)$ $(0, -1, 1)$. Half of the BZ is shown in Fig. 3-3. Also indicated is a smaller zone outlined by points of high symmetry ΓKMLHA. All other points in the BZ are symmetrically related to points in this zone, which we shall call the symmetry zone. In the BZ for the HCP structure there are 24 equivalent symmetry zones, and the choice between these is completely arbitrary. The coordinates of the symmetry points indicated in Fig. 3-3 are given in Table 3-1.

One can gain a large amount of information about the electronic structure of a crystalline material by finding the energy eigenvalues for states along the edges of the symmetry zone. This is particularly the case for semiconductors. Even for metals, for which there is considerable interest in the Fermi surface, information about general points inside the zone can usually be obtained by interpolating between the eigenvalues along the zone edges. However, as we shall see in the

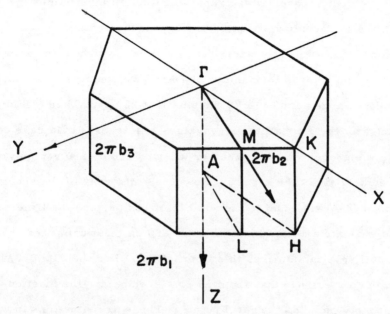

Figure 3-3. Basic vectors of the reciprocal lattice and the Brillouin zone for the hexagonal close-packed crystal structure.

Table 3-1. Coordinates of symmetry points in Fig. 3-3.

	$\hat{e}_x$	$\hat{e}_y$	$\hat{e}_z$
Γ	0	0	0
K	$\frac{4}{3}\frac{\pi}{a}$	0	0
M	$\frac{\pi}{a}$	$\frac{\pi}{a\sqrt{3}}$	0
L	$\frac{\pi}{a}$	$\frac{\pi}{a\sqrt{3}}$	$\frac{\pi}{c}$
H	$\frac{4}{3}\frac{\pi}{a}$	0	$\frac{\pi}{c}$
A	0	0	$\frac{\pi}{c}$

applications, it is frequently desirable to calculate eigenvalues for
points on a mesh evenly distributed throughout the symmetry zone. It
is then convenient to use the same set of recips throughout the zone.
If there were no limit to the number of recips we could use, we would
simply take a large number, like the smallest 200, and have confidence
that throughout the zone all the eigenvalues of interest would have converged to the proper values. Whether we used 180 or 250 recips would
not appreciably affect the results. However, the order of the secular
determinant (2-41) is equal to the number of recips, and the time required to evaluate a determinant of order 200 on most computers which
are currently available makes this impractical. For the IBM 360/50 it
has been our experience that about 30 or 40 recips are the most one
can reasonably include at general points. There are situations in which
as few as 20 or 25 recips are adequate for the entire symmetry zone.
The criterion for choosing a set of recips is to find the smallest number for which the eigenvalues throughout the zone are within a certain
tolerance of the converged values. The tolerance, of course, depends
on the particular application, but frequently 0.003 Ry is adequate.

In selecting a set of recips for the symmetry zone, we usually
begin by finding the completely converged eigenvalues at each of the
symmetry points. To illustrate this procedure let us consider the symmetry point K, as shown in Fig. 3-3 and 3-4. The most important
recips for a particular point are the ones which minimize $|\vec{k} + \vec{g}_i|$,
since the square of this quantity gives the kinetic energy contribution
in the plane wave region. These are the recips which are closest to the
point K' = -K as shown in Fig. 3-4. To simplify the discussion we will
ignore recips above and below the plane shown in Fig. 3-4 and treat
this as a two-dimensional reciprocal lattice. The most important recips

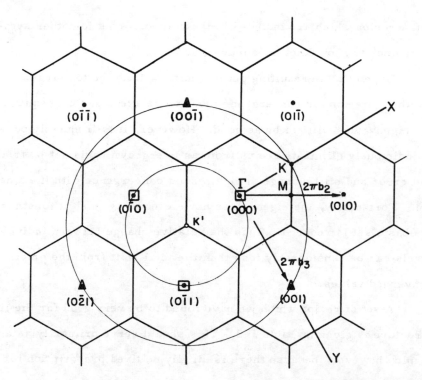

Figure 3-4. The basal plane ($\vec{b}_1 = 0$) of reciprocal lattice vectors for
the hexagonal close-packed structure. For the sym-
metry point K the vectors which minimize $\vec{k}_i = \vec{k} + \vec{g}_i$
are those nearest the opposing point K'.

for the point K are (000), (0$\bar{1}$0) and (0$\bar{1}$0). These are indicated by
small squares in Fig. 3-4 and are seen to be the closest to K'. The
next set of recips to be included (in this two-dimensional example) are
(00$\bar{1}$), (0$\bar{2}$1) and (001); these are indicated by small triangles in the
figure. In this manner we can continue to increase the basis set by
adding additional sets of recips. At each stage the energy eigenvalues
are determined, and this procedure is continued until the eigenvalues
have converged. This is done for each of the symmetry points in the
zone and a composite basis set consisting of all these recips is formed.
If the eigenvalues at a particular symmetry point have converged, the

extra recips which are included in the composite set for other symmetry points should not have much effect.

Hopefully the resulting set of recips will not be too large. If it
is, the criterion for convergence must be relaxed, and consequently
the eigenvalues will not be as good. However, it is frequently possible
to judiciously eliminate recips from an overgrown basis set by trial
and error and still manage to retain good convergence with the smaller
set. Fortunately, the eigenvalues have a tendency to shift together as
the basis set is reduced. Thus the relative change between individual
levels can be considerably less than the total shift from the original
converged values.

A set of recips which we have found to be very good for the HCP
structure is given in Table 3-2. This should serve primarily as an example, however, because there is simply no fixed prescription for the

Table 3-2. 32 "good" recips for the HCP crystal structure based on
$\vec{k}_i = \vec{k} + \vec{g}_i$ and determined from convergence studies at
the symmetry points listed in Table 3-1.

$$
\begin{array}{cccccccc}
 & & & (\overline{3}00) & & & & \\
(\overline{2}0\overline{1}) & (\overline{2}\overline{1}1) & (\overline{2}\overline{1}0) & (\overline{2}00) & & & & \\
(\overline{1}0\overline{1}) & (\overline{1}\overline{1}1) & (\overline{1}\overline{1}0) & (\overline{1}00) & (\overline{1}10) & (\overline{1}1\overline{1}) & (\overline{1}01) & (\overline{1}\overline{2}1) \\
(00\overline{1}) & (0\overline{1}1) & (0\overline{1}0) & (000) & (010) & (01\overline{1}) & (001) & (0\overline{2}1) \\
(10\overline{1}) & (1\overline{1}1) & (1\overline{1}0) & (100) & (110) & (11\overline{1}) & (101) & (1\overline{2}1) \\
 & (2\overline{1}1) & (2\overline{1}0) & & & & & \\
\end{array}
$$

best set of recips. Frequently a person is interested only in the states
in one region of the symmetry zone. This can significantly reduce the
number of recips needed for convergence. Another factor is the number of energy levels of interest. The higher levels require a larger
set of recips. Hence, if the number of electrons to be accomodated is
large, or if one is interested in excited states, it is necessary to solve
larger secular determinants.

At certain symmetry points and along some zone edges the secular determinant can be factored by the use of group theory. However, unless one is going to perform calculations many times for the same crystal structure and is interested only in points of high symmetry, the time required to learn and apply group theory is not merited. If a particular calculation calls primarily for eigenvalues at general points (for which one gets no assistance from group theory), then it is reasonable to leave the determinant unfactored for the occasional point which happens to have some symmetry. Of course, in some applications it is necessary to know the symmetry properties of the wave functions. These can be found by examining the expansion coefficients c_i in (2-7), but this requires rather lengthy calculations which are usually not merited unless some additional use is to be made of the wave functions. Through the use of group theory, information about the coefficients can be found which depends only on the symmetry properties of the crystal structure, thus eliminating the need for calculating the c_i. Fortunately, the information available from group theory has already been determined for many crystal structures (Luehrmann [33]).

MUFFIN-TIN POTENTIAL

The energy eigenvalues in a crystal are not too sensitive to the potential inside the muffin-tin spheres, and without much effort a reasonable potential can be constructed for these regions. In the central portion of the spheres the potential has atomic character. In the outer portion there is overlap from neighboring atoms, the most important contributions coming from nearest neighbors. To a large extent, this effect is automatically built into the muffin-tin by flattening the potential in the region between the spheres.

In this section we describe a method for constructing the muffin-tin potential which was suggested by Mattheiss [34]. It has been used successfully in many applications, particularly for metallic substances. In this approach the spherically symmetric contributions from neighboring atoms are superposed on the potential of a central atom. Consider, for example, the two dimensional muffin-tin shown in Fig. 3-5. The

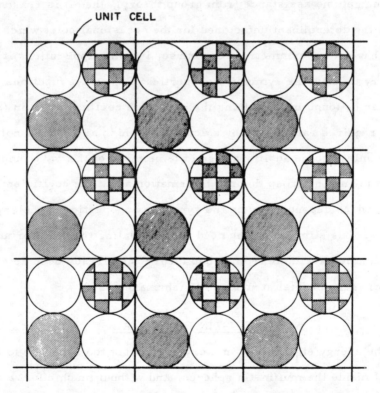

Figure 3-5. Hypothetical two-dimensional crystal with four atoms (three different kinds) per unit cell. In this example the muffin-tin spheres are all the same size.

patterns on the spheres indicate that in each unit cell there are three different types of atoms. Consider, for example, one of the "plain" spheres. The potential inside this sphere would be primarily that of the corresponding atom. There would be nearest neighbor overlap

from two "striped" atoms and two "checked" atoms, both located the
same distance from the central "plain" atom. A much smaller contribution would be expected from the next-nearest neighbors, four
"plain" atoms. Continuing in this manner we can specify the environ-
ment of a particular sphere by grouping the neighboring atoms according to type, number and distance from the central atom. This information is based entirely on crystal structure; results for some standard
structures are listed in Table 3-3.

The atomic potentials most frequently used in constructing the
muffin-tin potential are the results of Hartree-Fock-Slater self-consistent-field calculations. A very good discussion of this method and
a tabulation of results for all the elements is given by Herman and
Skillman [15]. Similar calculations based on the relativistic Dirac
equation have been performed by Liberman, et al [24]. For heavier
elements we prefer the relativistic atomic calculations, even for constructing a muffin-tin to be used in a nonrelativistic APW calculation.
When relativistic effects are included in a self-consistent calculation
there is a readjustment of the charge density near the origin which in
turn can appreciably affect the ordering of the outer levels. In Chapter
4 we discuss a method of including these same relativistic effects in the
APW calculation.

The effects of neighboring potentials are included by expanding
them in spherical harmonics about the origin of the central atom. Consider the point P in Fig. 3-6. It has spherical coordinates $(r_1, \hat{r}_1)$ and
$(r_2, \hat{r}_2)$ with respect to the two origins 1 and 2, respectively. We want
to expand the function

Table 3-3. Number of atoms and distance from central atom for some standard crystal structures.

FCC		BCC		Diamond		HCP	
Number	Distance†	Number	Distance†	Number	Distance†	Number	Distance‡
1	0	1	0	1	0	1	0
12	$1/\sqrt{2}$	8	$\sqrt{3}/2$	4	$\sqrt{3}/4$	6	$\sqrt{1/3 + b/4}$
6	1	6	1	12	$\sqrt{2}/2$	6	1
24	$\sqrt{6}/2$	12	$\sqrt{2}$	12	$\sqrt{11}/4$	6	$\sqrt{4/3 + b/4}$
12	$\sqrt{2}$	24	$\sqrt{11}/2$	6	1	2	$\sqrt{b}$
24	$\sqrt{10}/2$	8	$\sqrt{3}$	12	$\sqrt{19}/4$	12	$\sqrt{7/3 + b/4}$
8	$\sqrt{3}$	6	2	24	$\sqrt{24}/4$	6	$\sqrt{3}$
48	$\sqrt{14}/2$	24	$\sqrt{19}/2$	16	$\sqrt{27}/4$	12	$\sqrt{1 + b}$
6	2	24	$\sqrt{5}$	12	$\sqrt{2}$	6	2
36	$\sqrt{18}/2$	24	$\sqrt{6}$	24	$\sqrt{35}/4$	12	$\sqrt{13/3 + b/4}$
24	$\sqrt{5}$	32	$\sqrt{27}/2$	24	$\sqrt{40}/4$	12	$\sqrt{3 + b}$
24	$\sqrt{22}/2$	12	$\sqrt{8}$	12	$\sqrt{43}/4$	6	$\sqrt{1/3 + 9b/4}$
24	$\sqrt{6}$	48	$\sqrt{35}/2$	8	$\sqrt{3}$	6	$\sqrt{16/3 + b/4}$
72	$\sqrt{26}/2$	30	3	24	$\sqrt{51}/4$	12	$\sqrt{4 + b}$

† Distances in units of the lattice constant a

‡ $b = (c/a)^2$

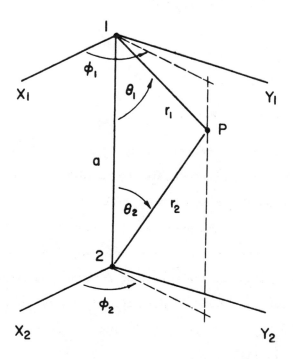

Figure 3-6.   The spherical coordinates of a point P as measured with
              respect to two origins separated by the distance a.

$$\psi_{\ell m}(r_1) = f_\ell(r_1)\, Y_{\ell m}(\hat{r}_1) \tag{3-11}$$

centered at origin 1, in terms of spherical harmonics centered at
origin 2,

$$\psi_{\ell m} = \sum_{\ell'=0}^{\infty} \sum_{m'=-\ell'}^{+\ell'} \alpha(\ell'm'|\ell m)\, Y_{\ell'm'}(\hat{r}_2) \tag{3-12}$$

Multiplying both sides of (3-12) by $Y_{\ell''m''}^*(\hat{r}_2)$ and integrating over the
angular variables yields

$$\alpha(\ell'm'|\ell m) = \int Y_{\ell'm'}^*(\hat{r}_2)\, \psi_{\ell m}(\hat{r}_1)\, d\hat{r}_2 \tag{3-13}$$

The variables $\vec{r}_1$ and $\vec{r}_2$, as can be seen in Fig. 3-6, satisfy the following:

$$r_1^{\,2} = a^2 + r_2^{\,2} - 2ar_2 \cos \theta_2 \tag{3-14}$$

$$\phi_1 = \phi_2 \tag{3-15}$$

$$r_1 \cos \theta_1 + r_2 \cos \theta_2 = a \tag{3-16}$$

$$r_1 \sin \theta_1 = r_2 \sin \theta_2 \tag{3-17}$$

where a is the distance between the two origins. The expansion coefficients in (3-3) have been tabulated by Löwdin[32]; for this reason the
method is frequently referred to as the Löwdin alpha expansion. Construction of the muffin-tin potential is a very specialized application of
this expansion however, and only a very simple form is required. The
simplication is twofold: the atomic potentials to be expanded are
spherically symmetric and only the spherically symmetric contributions
from neighboring atoms are to be retained in the muffin-tin. Hence,
with $\ell = m = o$, (3-11) becomes

$$\psi_{oo}(r_1) = \frac{1}{\sqrt{4\pi}} \, f(r_1) \tag{3-18}$$

Retaining only the $\ell' = m' = o$ term in (3-12) and using (3-13) we get

$$f(a \,|\, r_2) = \alpha(oo \,|\, oo) = \tfrac{1}{4} \pi \int f(r_1) \, d\hat{r}_2 \tag{3-19}$$

From (3-15) it is seen that r_1 does not depend on ϕ_2; hence the integration over this variable in (3-19) simply gives 2π. The remaining integration over θ_2 can be transformed by a change of variables to give

$$\alpha(oo \,|\, oo) = \tfrac{1}{2} \, \frac{1}{ar_2} \int_{|a-r_2|}^{a+r_2} r_1 \, f(r_1) \, dr_1 \tag{3-20}$$

where we have used (3-14) to get

$$\sin \theta_2 \, d\theta_2 = r_1 \, dr_1 / (ar_2) \tag{3-21}$$

and to determine the integration limits in (3-20). The final result from (3-19) is, therefore,

$$f(a|r_2) = \frac{1}{2ar_2} \int_{|a-r_2|}^{a+r_2} r_1 \, f(r_1) \, dr_1 \tag{3-22}$$

This gives the contribution at r_2, measured from origin 2, due to the function $f(r_1)$ centered at origin 1, the two origins being separated by the distance a.

In the method suggested by Mattheiss [34] the exchange and coulombic contributions to the muffin-tin potential are treated separately. The coulombic part is composed of contributions of the form

$$V_o(r) = 2Z/r - U_o(r) \tag{3-23}$$

where Z is the nuclear charge and $U_o(r)$ is the electronic contribution, i.e., the solution of Poisson's equation

$$\nabla^2 U_o(r) = -8\pi \, \rho_o(r) \tag{3-24}$$

based on the atomic electronic density

$$\rho_o(r) = \sum_{occupied} |\psi_{\ell m}|^2 \tag{3-25}$$

The procedure is to get $\rho_o(r)$ from atomic self-consistent-field calculations ([24], [15]) and then solve Poisson's equations (3-24) to get $U_o(r)$ and thus $V_o(r)$ in (3-23). The numerical solution of Poisson's equation is discussed in Appendix 1. Finally, the contributions from neighboring atoms are determined from (3-22) and the information in Table 3-3:

$$V_c(r) = V_o(r) + \sum_i^{neighbors} V_o(a_i|r) \quad \left(\begin{array}{c}\text{coulombic} \\ \text{contribution}\end{array}\right) \tag{3-26}$$

The exchange contribution is treated using Slater's free-electron exchange approximation [48]:

$$V_x(r) = -6 \left(\frac{3}{8\pi} \rho(r) \right)^{1/3} \quad \text{(exchange contribution)} \qquad (3\text{-}27)$$

where $\rho(r)$ is the crystal electronic density. This is approximated by adding to the atomic electronic density $\rho_o(r)$ the contributions from neighboring atoms; these are found by using (3-22). Thus

$$\rho(r) = \rho_o(r) + \overset{\text{neighbors}}{\underset{i}{\Sigma}} \rho_o(a_i | r) \qquad (3\text{-}28)$$

The exchange potential (3-27) is added to the coulombic contribution (3-26) to give

$$V_T(r) = V_c(r) + V_x(r) \qquad (3\text{-}29)$$

This is a spherically symmetric potential which, it is hoped, will be slowly varying in the region between the spheres. Inside the APW spheres the muffin-tin potential is taken to be

$$V(r) = V_T(r) - V_{AVG} \qquad (3\text{-}30)$$

where V_{AVG} is the average value of $V_T(r)$ in the region of constant potential between the spheres. By shifting the potential inside the spheres this amount, the constant becomes zero, as was assumed in the derivation of the matrix elements in Chapter 2. For monoatomic metals there is a rather straightforward procedure for finding V_{AVG} which has given useful results in several applications. However, for semimetals, semiconductors, ionic crystals and metallic alloys, it is not as easy to determine this constant with respect to the various po-tentials inside the spheres. Some of the methods which have been used for these more complicated materials have been discussed in the litera-ture.

For monoatomic metals the potential $V_T(r)$ is generally very flat in the region between the spheres and it is relatively easy to determine an appropriate average value.   Consider the unit cell shown in Fig. 3-7.

It is possible to impose a grid over the region outside the spheres and

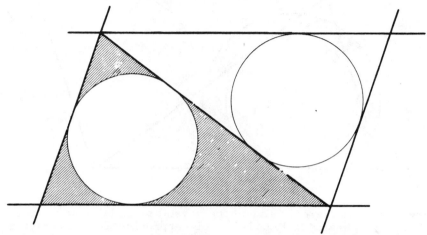

Figure 3-7.   A hypothetical unit cell showing the region over which the
crystal potential should be averaged and replaced by a
constant.

average the values of $V_T(r)$ found at each grid point.   A more conven-

ient method, which has been used with success in monoatomic metals,

is to simply perform a spherical average of $V_T(r)$ over the region be-

tween the APW sphere radius and the Wigner-Seitz sphere radius, as

shown in Fig. 3-8.   Thus

$$V_{AVG} = 3 \int_S^{r_o} V_T(r) \ r^2 \ dr/(r_o^3 - S^3) \qquad (3-31)$$

where S is the APW sphere radius and r_o is defined by

$$\frac{4}{3} \ \pi r_o^3 = \text{volume/atom} = \Omega_o / \text{atoms per unit cell} \qquad (3-32)$$

A computer program which we have used to calculate the muffin-tin po-

tential for monoatomic metals is described in Appendix 2.

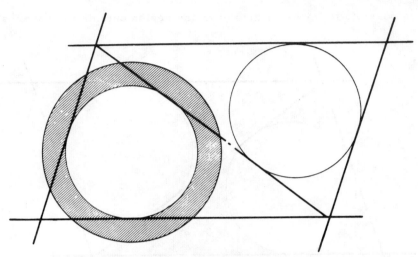

Figure 3-8.   The average value of the crystal potential over the region
indicated in Fig. 3-7 can be approximated by averaging
over a spherical region with the same volume. In many
applications this approximation is good because the potential outside the spheres is nearly constant.

LOGARITHMIC DERIVATIVES

The muffin-tin potential enters the APW matrix elements (2-68)

implicitly through the set of logarithmic derivatives evaluated at the

sphere radius S:

$$L_\ell (S, E) \equiv R'_\ell (S)/R_\ell (S) \tag{3-33}$$

These are determined from the radial Schrödinger equation (2-10) using

numerical techniques. For this purpose it is convenient to introduce

the independent variable

$$x = \log(\rho) \tag{3-34}$$

because it smoothly expands the radial scale near the origin where the

nodes of the wave function are close together. If we simultaneously

introduce the dependent variable

$$Y = \sqrt{\rho}\ R \tag{3-35}$$

then the radial equation (2-10) becomes

$$Y'' = \gamma Y \qquad\qquad (3-36)$$

where

$$\gamma = e^{2x} (V-E) + (\ell + \tfrac{1}{2})^2 \qquad\qquad (3-37)$$

This form of the differential equation has the advantages that no first derivative is present and that $\ell = 0$ does not require special treatment.

Near the origin of the radial coordinate $(x \to -\infty)$ the first term in (3-37) becomes negligible. The criterion for this is

$$e^x \, 8Z \ll 1 \qquad\qquad (3-38)$$

since near the nucleus the potential is $-2Z/\rho$, and $\ell = 0$ gives the smallest value for the second term in (3-37). If we consider $Z \leq 100$ this yields

$$e^{-x} \gg 800 \qquad\qquad (3-39)$$

which is reasonably satisfied for $x \leq -9$. Let us define x_1 as the value of x such that (3-38) is satisfied. Then for $x \approx x_1$ the differential equation (3-36) becomes

$$Y'' = (\ell + \tfrac{1}{2})^2 Y \qquad\qquad (3-40)$$

which has the solutions

$$Y(x) = Y(x_1) e^{\pm(\ell + \frac{1}{2})(x-x_1)} \qquad\qquad (3-41)$$

The boundary condition that Y be regular at the origin of the radial coordinate eliminates the solution with the negative sign. Thus

$$Y(x) = Y(x_1) e^{(\ell + 1)(x-x_1)} \qquad\qquad (3-42)$$

In terms of the new variables the logarithmic derivative (3-33) is

$$L_\ell = e^{-x} (Y'(x)/Y(x) - \tfrac{1}{2})$$ (3-43)

as can readily be proved using (3-34) and (3-35). Thus, we need to

determine the logarithmic derivative Y'/Y (the prime means derivative

with respect to x) at the value of x corresponding to the sphere radius

S;

$$x_J = \log (S)$$ (3-44)

In Fig. 3-9 an integration grid over the range of the variable x is

shown. Notice that x_J happens to correspond to a grid point in this

figure. It is convenient to choose the sphere radius slightly smaller

than half the nearest neighbor distance so that this will be the case.

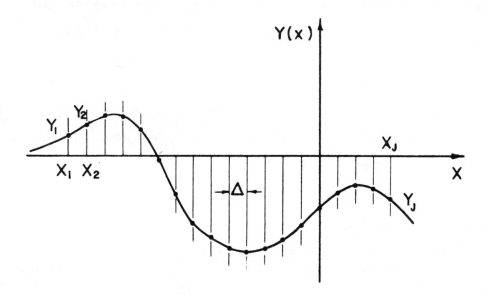

Figure 3-9.   The integration grid over the range of the variable x = log(r). x_1 corresponds to r → o, and x_J corresponds to r → ∞.

There are several methods of integrating the differential equa-

tion (3-36) outward from the boundary condition at $x = x_1$ to get Y'/Y

at x_J. We use the Milne method ([22], [17]), which is based on the following two equations:

$$Y_{n+1} = Y_n + Y_{n-2} - Y_{n-3} + \frac{\Delta^2}{4} (5Y_n'' + 2Y_{n-1}''$$

$$+ 5Y_{n-2}'') \tag{3-45}$$

$$Y_{n+1} = 2Y_n - Y_{n-1} + \frac{\Delta^2}{12} (Y_{n+1}'' + 10Y_n'' + Y_{n-1}'') \tag{3-46}$$

The first equation is used to predict the value Y_{n+1} based on values of Y_n, Y_{n-2} and Y_{n-3} at the preceding grid points and the second derivatives Y_n'', Y_{n-1}'', and Y_{n-2}'' determined from (3-36). Substituting this predicted value into (3-46) usually yields an improved value. This basic equation is used repeatedly until there is no change in the value of Y_{n+1}. This entire procedure is then repeated for the next grid point, and so on, until we have the values of Y_n near x_J. The first derivative is given by either of the following finite difference approximations [55]

$$Y_J' = (Y_{J+1} - Y_{J-1})/(2\Delta) \tag{3-47}$$

$$Y_J' = (Y_{J-2} - 8Y_{J-1} + 8Y_{J+1} - Y_{J+2})/(12\Delta) \tag{3-48}$$

$$Y_J' = (3Y_J - 4Y_{J-1} + Y_{J-2})/(2\Delta) \tag{3-49}$$

The second form (3-48) is the most accurate, but if Δ is small enough either (3-47) or (3-49) are also acceptable. The backward-difference formula (3-49) has the slight advantage that it only requires Y_n for $n \leq J$. However, it has been our experience that for $\Delta = 0.05$ it is necessary to use the more accurate form (3-48). A method which eliminates this problem of calculating the first derivative is discussed later in this section.

To get started on the above procedure it is necessary to have the values Y_1, Y_2, Y_3 and Y_4, in (3-45). The first value $Y_1 = Y(x_1)$ can be fixed arbitrarily since the logarithmic derivative Y'/Y is independent of the normalization. Then (3-42) can be used to calculate Y_2, Y_3 and Y_4. Alternatively, Y_2 can be calculated from (3-42) and then Y_3 and Y_4 can be calculated using (3-46). In fact, using (3-46) without the iteration procedure discussed in the Milne method is just a variant of the Noumerov method [22]. By substituting the differential equation (3-36) into (3-46) we get

$$Y_{n+1} = -(B_n Y_n + C_n Y_{n-1})/A_n \qquad (3-50)$$

where

$$A_n = 1 - \Delta^2 \gamma_{n+1}/12$$
$$B_n = -2 -5 \Delta^2 \gamma_n/6 \qquad (3-51)$$
$$C_n = 1 - \Delta^2 \gamma_{n-1}/12$$

We have found that using (3-50) with $\Delta = .05$ yields values of the logarithmic derivative in good agreement with the results of the more lengthy Milne method.

Either of the above methods requires the calculation of the derivative Y' by finite-difference approximations like (3-48). There is an alternate method in which this can be avoided. The radial equation (2-10) can be written

$$P''(\rho) = \mu P(\rho) \qquad (3-52)$$

where

$$\mu = -E + V + \ell(\ell+1)/\rho^2 \qquad (3-53)$$

and

$$P(\rho) = \rho R(\rho) \qquad (3-54)$$

Now if we define

$$Q = P' - (\ell+1)P/\rho \tag{3-55}$$

then

$$Q' = P'' - (\ell+1)P'/\rho + (\ell+1)P/\rho^2 \tag{3-56}$$

Solving (3-55) for P' yields

$$P'(\rho) = Q(\rho) + (\ell+1)P(\rho)/\rho \tag{3-57}$$

and substituting into (3-56) with (3-52) and (3-53) gives

$$Q'(\rho) = (V-E)\, P(\rho) - (\ell+1)\, Q(\rho)/\rho \tag{3-58}$$

From the definition (3-54) the logarithmic derivative can be written

$$R'(\rho)/R = P'(\rho)/P - 1/\rho \tag{3-59}$$

and from (3-55)

$$Q/P = P'(\rho)/P - (\ell+1)/\rho \tag{3-60}$$

Thus

$$R'(\rho)/R = Q/P + \ell/\rho \tag{3-61}$$

$Q(\rho)$ and $P(\rho)$ are given by the coupled first-order differential equations (3-57) and (3-58). The logarithmic derivative R'/R as given in (3-61) depends on these solutions only through the ratio Q/P.

In terms of the logarithmic variable $x = \log\rho$ the coupled equations (3-57) and (3-58) have the form

$$P'(x) = (\ell+1)\, P(x) + e^x\, Q(x) \tag{3-62}$$

$$Q'(x) = -(E-V)\, e^x\, P(x) - (\ell+1)Q(x) \tag{3-63}$$

In the limit as $x \to -\infty$, these become

$$P'(x) = (\ell+1)\, P(x) \qquad (x \approx x_1) \tag{3-64}$$

$$Q'(x) = -2Z\, P(x) - (\ell+1)\, Q(x) \qquad (x \approx x_1) \tag{3-65}$$

where the potential near the origin of the radial coordinate is $-2Z/\rho$.
If we assume solutions in the form

$$Q = A \, e^{ax} \qquad\qquad (3\text{-}66)$$

$$P = B \, e^{ax} \qquad\qquad (3\text{-}67)$$

then substituting into (3-64) and (3-65) yields $a = \ell+1$ and

$$A/B = -Z/(\ell+1) = Q/P \, \big|_{x \to -\infty} \qquad\qquad (3\text{-}68)$$

Thus the boundary condition at $x = x_1$ is satisfied by

$$P(x_1) = \text{arbitrary constant} \qquad\qquad (3\text{-}69)$$

$$Q(x_1) = -Z \, P(x_1)/(\ell+1) \qquad\qquad (3\text{-}70)$$

A convenient method for solving the coupled equations (3-62) and
(3-63) subject to the boundary conditions (3-69) and (3-70) is the Runge-
Kutta method [17]. If we use the notation

$$P'(x) = F(x, Q, P) \qquad\qquad (3\text{-}71)$$

$$Q'(x) = G(x, Q, P) \qquad\qquad (3\text{-}72)$$

then

$$P_{n+1} = P_n + \frac{\Delta}{6} (k_1 + 2k_2 + 2k_3 + k_4) \qquad\qquad (3\text{-}73)$$

and

$$Q_{n+1} = Q_n + \frac{\Delta}{6} (m_1 + 2m_2 + 2m_3 + m_4) \qquad\qquad (3\text{-}74)$$

where

$$k_1 = F(x_n, Q_n, P_n)$$

$$k_2 = F(x_n + \tfrac{1}{2}\Delta, \; Q_n + \tfrac{1}{2}k_1, \; P_n + \tfrac{1}{2}m_1)$$

$$k_3 = F(x_n + \tfrac{1}{2}\Delta, \; Q_n + \tfrac{1}{2}k_2, \; P_n + \tfrac{1}{2}m_2)$$

$$k_4 = F(x_n + \Delta, \; Q_n + k_3, \; P_n + m_3)$$

$$(3\text{-}75)$$

and a similar set of equations holds for m_1, m_2, m_3 and m_4 with F replaced by G on the right hand side of (3-75). The procedure is to use (3-69) and (3-70) to determine $P_1 = P(x_1)$ and $Q_1 = Q(x_1)$, x_1 being the value of x such that the approximations (3-64) and (3-65) are valid, i.e.

$$(\ell+1) \, P(x_1) >> e^{x_1} \, Q(x_1) \qquad (3-76)$$

and

$$V(x_1) >> E \qquad (3-77)$$

Using (3-70), the condition (3-76) can also be written

$$(\ell+1)^2 >> Z e^{x_1} \qquad (3-78)$$

This is essentially the same result given in (3-38). Using these values of x_1, P_1 and Q_1 in (3-73) and (3-74) yields P_2 and Q_2. This procedure is repeated for each of the grid points. The logarithmic derivative is then given by

$$L_\ell (S, \, E) = Q_J/P_J + \ell \, e^{-x_J} \qquad (3-79)$$

according to (3-61).

The logarithmic derivatives for Pb are shown in Fig. 3-10. These results were calculated using the computer program described in Appendix 3. Also shown on the figure are the free-electron results, that is, those using $V(r) = 0$ inside the spheres. In this special case the logarithmic derivative can be found analytically from the radial Schrödinger equation (2-10); the result is

$$L_\ell (S, \, E) = \sqrt{E} \; \mathscr{J}'_\ell (\sqrt{E} \, S) \, / \, \mathscr{J}_\ell (\sqrt{E} \, S) \qquad (3-80)$$

The logarithmic derivatives for Pb differ very little from the free-electron values as can be seen in Fig. 3-10. It can be seen from the APW matrix elements (2-59) and (2-60) that this results in energy

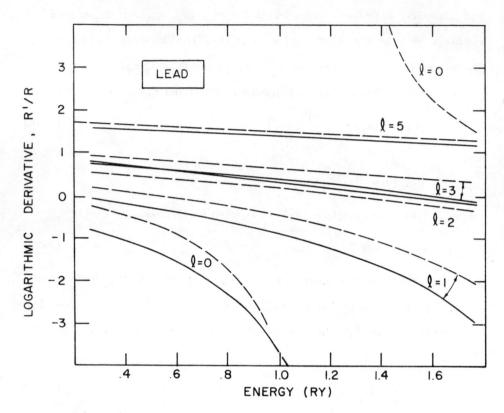

Figure 3-10.   Logarithmic derivatives as a function of energy.   Solid
               lines are for lead, and the dashed lines are for zero
               potential.

$$E = k_j^2 = (\vec{k} + \vec{g}_j)^2 \tag{3-81}$$

the free-electron result. The reason for this is that the factor

$$k_j \, \mathscr{J}'_\ell(k_j S)/\mathscr{J}_\ell(k_j S) - R'_\ell(S)/R_\ell(S) \tag{3-82}$$

which occurs in the summation in (2-60), can then be written

$$\sqrt{E} \, \mathscr{J}'_\ell(\sqrt{E}\, S)/\mathscr{J}_\ell(\sqrt{E}\, S) - R'_\ell(S)/R_\ell(S) \tag{3-83}$$

The first term is just the logarithmic derivative with V = o as given in

(3-80), and we have seen in Fig. 3-10 that for lead this is nearly equal

to R'/R. The resulting cancellation in (3-83) substantially reduces the contribution of the summation in (2-60). The remaining expression yields very small values for the off-diagonal matrix elements. Hence, the secular determinant will be essentially a product of diagonal terms of the form

$$(\Omega_{o} - 4\pi \sum_{\nu} S_{\nu}^{3}/3) (k_{j}^{2} - E) , \qquad (3-84)$$

and the requirement (2-41) that the determinant vanish yields the free-electron result (3-81).

The logarithmic derivatives for the element Zr are shown in Fig. 3-11. For the lower values of ℓ they differ substantially from the zero

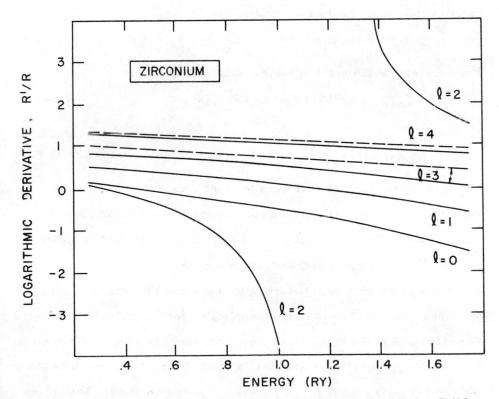

Figure 3-11. Logarithmic derivatives as a function of energy. Solid lines are for zirconium, and the dashed lines are for zero potential (also see Fig. 3-10).

potential results. For the energy range shown, there is no singularity
in the logarithmic derivative curve corresponding to $\ell = 0$. This result
is typical of the elements with partially filled d shells. The energy
bands of these transition elements depart radically from free-electron
results, as can be seen in several examples from the literature ([4], [10],
[35]).

SPHERICAL BESSEL FUNCTIONS AND LEGENDRE POLYNOMIALS

The Legendre polynomials which occur in the expression (3-68)
can be calculated from the recursion relationship

$$(\ell+1) \, P_{\ell+1}(x) = (2\ell+1) \, x \, P_{\ell}(x) - \ell P_{\ell-1}(x) \qquad (3\text{-}85)$$

The first two polynomials are found explicitly from

$$P_{0}(x) = 1 \text{ and } P_{1}(x) = x \qquad (3\text{-}86)$$

The recursion relation for spherical Bessel functions is

$$x \, \mathcal{J}_{\ell+1}(x) = (2\ell+1) \, \mathcal{J}_{\ell}(x) - x \mathcal{J}_{\ell-1}(x) \qquad (3\text{-}87)$$

or

$$x \mathcal{J}_{\ell}(x) = (2\ell+3) \mathcal{J}_{\ell+1}(x) - x \mathcal{J}_{\ell+2}(x) \qquad (3\text{-}88)$$

The first form, which is analogous to (3-85), cannot be used in the
same manner because it involves subtraction of numbers which are
nearly equal. This results in a rapid loss of accuracy for the higher ℓ
values. To avoid this a backward iteration based on (3-88) can be used,
but then it is not easy to get starting values since the analytical expressions analogous to (3-86) are too complicated for the higher ℓ values.
For all values of the argument x, however, there is a value of ℓ (call it
L) such that $j_{L}(x)$ becomes arbitrarily small for all $\ell \geq L$, and it is possible to set $j_{L}(x) = 0$ and $j_{L-1}(x)$ equal to a small constant. The values
of $j_{\ell}(x)$ for $\ell < L\text{-}1$ can then be calculated using (3-88). The first

numbers calculated in this manner are incorrect due to this arbitrary choice of initial values. The numbers get increasingly better, however, and by choosing L sufficiently large it is possible to get accurate results for the ℓ values of interest. Of course, in this procedure the normalization of the functions $j_\ell(x)$ is arbitrary. The resulting values must be scaled by an appropriate constant determined by either

$$j_0(x) = \sin x/x \qquad\qquad\qquad (3\text{-}89)$$

or

$$j_1(x) = (\sin x - x \cos x)/x^2 \qquad\qquad\qquad (3\text{-}90)$$

A computer program for calculating spherical Bessel functions is given in Appendix 4.

We have discussed each of the terms which occur in (2-59) and (2-68), and the calculation of these matrix elements should be straight-forward, except perhaps for a word about the summation in (2-68). In principle this includes all nonnegative integers, but in practice it can be truncated at $\ell = L$ where

$$j_L(KS) << j_0(KS) \qquad\qquad\qquad (3\text{-}91)$$

where K is the largest of the k_i. For most calculations it has been found that $L \approx 12$ is sufficient, although in many instances a smaller value can be used. In this respect the form of the matrix elements given in (2-60) is better than that in (2-68), since in the former there is some cancellation for the higher ℓ values (especially for NFE metals). However, this does not result in a significant simplification, and we usually prefer the form of the matrix elements given in (2-68).

SECULAR DETERMINANT AND EIGENVALUES

To find energy eigenvalues for a state with wave vector $\vec{k}$ the matrix elements are constructed and the determinant is examined as a function of the energy to find the zeros. A typical plot of the secular determinant is shown in Fig. 3-12. The roots are found either graphically or by interpolation schemes [17].

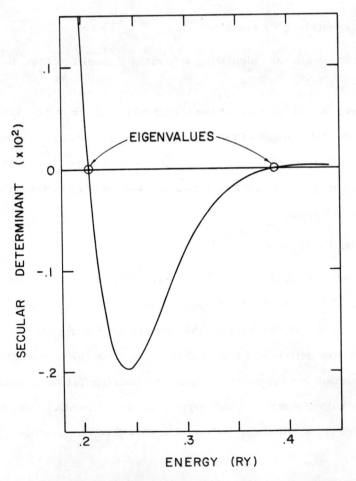

Figure 3-12. Secular determinant as a function of energy for zirconium at the symmetry point Γ.

The determinant of a large matrix can be evaluated by a sweep-out procedure which results in a matrix with only zeros on one side of the main diagonal. The determinant for this kind of matrix is simply the product of the diagonal elements. The procedure is best illustrated by an example. Given the matrix

$$M^{ij} = \begin{pmatrix} 2 & 4 & 6 \\ 4 & 6 & 16 \\ 6 & 16 & 32 \end{pmatrix}$$

(3-92)

we add -2 times each of the elements in row 1 to the corresponding elements in row 2. Similarly, we add -3 times row 1 to the third row. The result is

$$\begin{pmatrix} 2 & 4 & 6 \\ 0 & -2 & 4 \\ 0 & 4 & 14 \end{pmatrix}$$

(3-93)

which has zeros under the first diagonal element. The same procedure is applied to the second diagonal element. We add +2 times the elements in row 2 to be corresponding elements in row 3 to get

$$m^{ij} = \begin{pmatrix} 2 & 4 & 6 \\ 0 & -2 & 4 \\ 0 & 0 & 22 \end{pmatrix}$$

(3-94)

The determinant is 2(-2) (22) = -88.

The operations on a particular matrix element which result from applying this sweep-out procedure to the entire matrix are given by

$$m^{ij} = M^{ij} - \sum_{\mu=1}^{I-1} m^{i\mu} \, m^{\mu j}/m^{\mu\mu}$$

(3-95)

where I is the smaller of i or j. M^{ij} is the original APW matrix element and m^{ij} is the corresponding matrix element after the sweep-out procedure. Proceeding along each of the rows, the matrix elements above and including the main diagonal are each calculated as discussed in the previous section and then "triangularized" using (3-95). The product of the resulting diagonal elements gives the value of the determinant

$$\text{Det} \left| M^{ij} \right| = \pi_{\mu} \, m^{\mu \mu} \tag{3-96}$$

A computer program which constructs the APW matrix elements (2-59) and evaluates the determinant using the above procedure is discussed in Appendix 5.

EIGENFUNCTIONS

For each of the roots of the secular determinant the corresponding matrix elements M^{ij} can be used in (2-40) to find the expansion coefficients c_j. Since $\left| M^{ij} \right| = 0$ we can be sure that a nontrivial solution exists. To begin the solution the normalization is specified arbitrarily by setting

$$c_J = -1 \tag{3-97}$$

The value of J usually corresponds to the smallest of the diagonal elements M^{JJ}, although this is not essential. The simultaneous equations (2-40) are no longer homogeneous, and the constants $-M^{iJ}$ can be moved to the opposite side of the equations to give

$$\sum_{j \neq J} M^{ij} \, c_j = M^{iJ} \qquad (i=1, 2, \ldots M) \tag{3-98}$$

With the i = J equation eliminated, this yields a set of M-1 simultaneous, nonhomogeneous equations which can be written in matrix form as

$$Ax = b \tag{3-99}$$

where b is the column matrix consisting of the constants M^{iJ} (i ≠ J), x is the column matrix consisting of the coefficients c_j ($j \neq J$) and A is the

matrix M^{ij} with the jth row and column eliminated.   The solution of

(3-99) is

$$x = A^{-1} b \qquad\qquad (3-100)$$

where the matrix inversion can be accomplished using subroutines which

are available in most program libraries.   The coefficients c_j are related

to the components of the column matrix x according to

$$c_j = x_j \qquad (j < J)$$

$$c_J = -1 \qquad\qquad\qquad (3-101)$$

$$c_j = x_{j-1} \qquad (j > J)$$

If wave functions for different states $\vec{k}$ are to be combined in a particular

calculation, then the arbitrary normalization determined by setting

$c_J = -1$ is not adequate.   The normalization should be the same for each

state,

$$\int_{cell} |\phi_{\vec{k}}|^2 \, d\Omega = \sum_{i,j} c_i^* c_j \int_{cell} (\chi^i)^* \chi^j d\Omega = constant \qquad (3-102)$$

The overlap integral between the two APW's is readily found from (2-18)

and (2-19); the result is

$$\int_{cell} (\chi^i)^* \chi^j d\Omega = \Omega_o \delta_{ij} - 4\pi \sum_\nu S_\nu^2 e^{i\vec{k}_{ij} \cdot \vec{r}_\nu}$$

$$\left\{ \mathcal{J}_1(k_{ij}S_\nu)/k_{ij} - \sum_{\ell=o}^{\infty} (2\ell+1)P_\ell(\hat{k}_i \cdot \hat{k}_j) \right.$$

$$\left. \mathcal{J}_\ell(k_i S_\nu)\mathcal{J}_\ell(k_j S_\nu) I_\nu^{\ell} \right\} \qquad\qquad (3-103)$$

where

$$I_\nu^{\ell} = \int_0^{S_\nu} \rho^2 R_\ell^2(\rho)/(S_\nu^2 R_\ell^2(S_\nu)) \, d\rho \qquad\qquad (3\text{-}104)$$

The last integral can be related to the energy dependence of the log-arithmic derivatives at the boundary of the APW spheres [5]:

$$I_\nu^{\ell} = -\frac{\partial}{\partial E}\left[R'_\ell(S_\nu, E)/R_\ell(S_\nu, E)\right] \qquad\qquad (3\text{-}105)$$

SUMMARY

In this chapter we have dealt with the details of an APW calcula-tion. A few remarks about the general procedure might help to pull all of these together. In beginning a calculation the crystal structure and the associated reciprocal lattice are studied. The basic vectors of both real and reciprocal space are calculated, and the various input param-eters based on these are determined. These include the volume of the unit cell, the relative positions of the atoms within the unit cell, and the sizes of the APW spheres. If the crystal structure is different from FCC, BCC, diamond or HCP the distances to shells of atoms and the number of atoms in each shell is determined. The results of an atomic self-consistent field calculation are used to construct the muffin-tin potential. The reciprocal lattice is studied to determine a set of recips appropriate for the wave vectors of interest. Finally, the eigenvalues are determined by finding the zeros of the secular determinant based on the APW matrix elements.

4 RELATIVISTIC APW METHOD

The natural way to include relativistic effects in the APW formalism is to solve the Dirac equation based on the muffin-tin potential,

$$(\vec{\alpha} \cdot \vec{p} + \beta + 1 \text{ muffin-tin}) \, \phi(\vec{k}, \vec{r}) = W \, \phi(\vec{k}, \vec{r}) \qquad (4\text{-}1)$$

In this equation the units are specified by $m=c=\hbar=1$. These are the units used by Rose [43] in discussing the Dirac electron theory, and this text will be referenced frequently. Later in this section we will convert to atomic units with $e^2=2$, $m=\frac{1}{2}$ & $\hbar=1$. In (4-1) W is the total energy of the electronic state $\vec{k}$ including the rest energy mc^2 which is unity in the present units. The other terms have the following definitions:

$$\vec{p} = -i\vec{\nabla} \qquad (4\text{-}2)$$

$$\vec{\alpha} = \begin{pmatrix} 0 & \vec{\sigma} \\ \vec{\sigma} & 0 \end{pmatrix} \qquad (4\text{-}3)$$

$$\sigma_x = \begin{pmatrix} 0 & 1 \\ 1 & 0 \end{pmatrix} \qquad \sigma_y = \begin{pmatrix} 0 & -i \\ i & 0 \end{pmatrix} \qquad \sigma_z = \begin{pmatrix} 1 & 0 \\ 0 & -1 \end{pmatrix} \qquad (4\text{-}4)$$

73

$$\beta = \begin{pmatrix} 1 & 0 & 0 & 0 \\ 0 & 1 & 0 & 0 \\ 0 & 0 & -1 & 0 \\ 0 & 0 & 0 & -1 \end{pmatrix} \tag{4-5}$$

$$1 = \begin{pmatrix} 1 & 0 & 0 & 0 \\ 0 & 1 & 0 & 0 \\ 0 & 0 & 1 & 0 \\ 0 & 0 & 0 & 1 \end{pmatrix} \tag{4-6}$$

The variation function ϕ is expressed as a linear combination of four-component basis functions $\psi(\vec{k}_i, \vec{r})$

$$\phi(\vec{k}, \vec{r}) = \sum_{i=1}^{M} c_i \, \psi(\vec{k}_i, \vec{r}) \tag{4-7}$$

where $\vec{k}_i = \vec{k} + \vec{g}_i$. The expansion coefficients c_i are determined variationally. The basis functions ψ are constructed in a manner similar to that discussed in Chapter 2 for the nonrelativistic APW method. In fact, the similarity between the APW method and its relativistic generalization can be seen throughout the chapter.

In the zero potential region outside the spheres the solution of the Dirac equation (4-1) is [43]

$$H\psi(\vec{k}, \vec{r}) = k^o \, \psi(\vec{k}, \vec{r}) \tag{4-8}$$

where

$$k^o = (1 + k^2)^{\frac{1}{2}} \tag{4-9}$$

$$\psi(\vec{k}, \vec{r}) = \left(\frac{1 + k^o}{2k^o}\right)^{\frac{1}{2}} \begin{pmatrix} \chi(m) \\ \dfrac{\vec{\sigma} \cdot \vec{k}}{1 + k^o} \chi(m) \end{pmatrix} e^{i\vec{k} \cdot \vec{r}} \quad (m = \pm \tfrac{1}{2}) \tag{4-10}$$

and

$$\chi(+\tfrac{1}{2}) = \begin{pmatrix} 1 \\ 0 \end{pmatrix} , \quad \chi(-\tfrac{1}{2}) = \begin{pmatrix} 0 \\ 1 \end{pmatrix} \tag{4-11}$$

Notice that in the nonrelativistic limit, $k \ll 1$, the upper two components become

$$\psi(\vec{k}, \vec{r}) \approx e^{i\vec{k} \cdot \vec{r}} \chi(m) \tag{4-12}$$

and the lower two vanish. This is the nonrelativistic form of the wave function with spin included.

Inside a particular sphere the muffin-tin potential is spherically symmetric and the solutions of the Dirac equation with energy W' are [43]

$$\psi_{\kappa\mu}(\rho) = \begin{pmatrix} g_\kappa(\rho) \ \chi_\kappa^\mu \\[2mm] i \, f_\kappa(\rho) \ \chi_{-\kappa}^\mu \end{pmatrix} \tag{4-13}$$

where the radial functions satisfy the coupled equations

$$\frac{df}{d\rho} = (\kappa - 1)f/\rho - (W' - 1 - V)g \tag{4-14}$$

$$\frac{dg}{d\rho} = (W' - V + 1) f - (\kappa + 1)g/\rho \tag{4-15}$$

and the spin-angular functions χ_κ^μ are

$$\chi_\kappa^\mu = \sum_{m=\pm\frac{1}{2}} C(\ell \tfrac{1}{2} j; \mu - m, m) \ Y_{\ell, \mu - m}(\rho) \ \chi(m) \tag{4-16}$$

κ is any nonzero integer, positive or negative. The Clebsch-Gordan coefficients $C(\ell \tfrac{1}{2} j; \mu - m, m)$ are listed in Table 4-1. The spin-angular functions are orthonormal in the following sense:

$$\int \left(\chi_\kappa^\mu\right)^+ \chi_{\kappa'}^{\mu'} \, d\rho = \delta_{\mu\mu'} \delta_{\kappa\kappa'} \tag{4-17}$$

Table 4-1.   Clebsch-Gordan coefficients $C(\ell\,\tfrac{1}{2}\,j;m-m_2,m_2)$

	$m_2 = +\tfrac{1}{2}$	$m_2 = -\tfrac{1}{2}$
$j = \ell + \tfrac{1}{2}$	$\left(\dfrac{\ell + m + \tfrac{1}{2}}{2\ell + 1}\right)^{\tfrac{1}{2}}$	$\left(\dfrac{\ell - m + \tfrac{1}{2}}{2\ell + 1}\right)^{\tfrac{1}{2}}$
$j = \ell - \tfrac{1}{2}$	$-\left(\dfrac{\ell - m + \tfrac{1}{2}}{2\ell + 1}\right)^{\tfrac{1}{2}}$	$\left(\dfrac{\ell + m + \tfrac{1}{2}}{2\ell + 1}\right)^{\tfrac{1}{2}}$

The RAPW function inside a particular sphere can be chosen to be a
linear combination of the solutions (4-13),

$$\psi(\rho) = \sum_{\kappa,\,\mu} A_{\kappa\mu}
\begin{pmatrix}
g_\kappa(\rho) & \chi_\kappa^\mu \\[2mm]
i\,f_\kappa(\rho) & \chi_{-\kappa}^\mu
\end{pmatrix}
\tag{4-18}$$

The RAPW function has the form (4-10) outside the spheres and
the form (4-18) inside. Both are appropriate basis functions for the
respective regions, but they do not join up at the sphere boundaries. In
order to use these, a variational expression for the energy must be developed which permits the use of different functions inside and outside the
spheres. This is done in the next section and is merely a relativistic
generalization of the discussion given in Chapter 2. However, in order
to simplify the form of the matrix elements, we have the option of
choosing the expansion coefficients $A_{\kappa\mu}$ in (4-18) so that either the upper
two or the lower two components are continuous on the spherical boundaries. By choosing the upper two components to be continuous the resulting matrix elements reduce to those of the original APW method in
the nonrelativistic limit.

The expansion coefficients $A_{\kappa\mu}$ in (4-18) are chosen such that the
upper components match those in (4-10) by expanding the latter in terms
of the spin-angular functions (4-16). This expansion, which is a relativistic generalization of (2-16), is [43]

$$\psi^m(\vec{k}, \vec{r}) = e^{i\vec{k} \cdot \vec{r}_\nu} \sum_{\kappa, \mu} a^m_{\kappa\mu} \begin{vmatrix} \mathscr{I}_\ell(k\rho) & \chi^\mu_\kappa \\ \dfrac{ikS_\kappa}{1 + k^\circ} \mathscr{I}_{\ell'}(k\rho) & \chi^\mu_{-\kappa} \end{vmatrix}$$

(4-19)

where

$$a^m_{\kappa\mu} = 4\pi i^\ell \left(\frac{1 + k^\circ}{2k^\circ} \right)^{\frac{1}{2}} C(\ell \tfrac{1}{2} j; \mu - m, m) \; Y^*_{\ell, \mu-m}(\hat{k})$$

(4-20)

The expansion is centered on the νth sphere as shown in Fig. 2-3. S_κ takes on the value ± 1, according to whether κ is positive or negative. ℓ and ℓ' are related to κ by

$$\ell = \kappa, \quad \ell' = \kappa - 1, \quad j = \ell - \tfrac{1}{2} \quad (\kappa > 0)$$

$$\ell = -\kappa - 1, \quad \ell' = -\kappa, \quad j = \ell + \tfrac{1}{2} \quad (\kappa < 0)$$

(4-21)

For fixed κ, the μ summation is between j and $-j$. Comparison of the expansion (4-19) with (4-18) indicates that the choice

$$A^m_{\kappa\mu} = a^m_{\kappa\mu} \mathscr{I}_\ell(kS_\nu) \, e^{i\vec{k} \cdot \vec{r}_\nu} / g(S_\nu)$$

(4-22)

will match the upper components on the surface of the νth sphere.

In summary, the RAPW function is ($m = \pm \tfrac{1}{2}$)

$$\psi^m(\vec{k}, \vec{r}) = \left(\frac{1 + k^\circ}{2k^\circ} \right)^{\frac{1}{2}} \begin{vmatrix} \chi(m) \\ \dfrac{\vec{\sigma} \cdot \vec{k}}{1 + k^\circ} \chi(m) \end{vmatrix} e^{i\vec{k} \cdot \vec{r}}$$

(outside spheres)

(4-23)

$$\psi^m(\vec{k}, \vec{r}) = e^{i\vec{k} \cdot \vec{r}_\nu} \sum_{\kappa, \mu} a^m_{\kappa\mu} \mathscr{I}_\ell(kS_\nu) \begin{vmatrix} g_\kappa(\rho) & \chi^\mu_\kappa \\ i \, f_\kappa(\rho) & \chi^\mu_{-\kappa} \end{vmatrix} / g_\kappa(S_\nu)$$

(inside νth sphere)

(4-24)

VARIATIONAL EXPRESSION FOR THE ENERGY

A variational expression based on the Dirac Hamiltonian and valid for a trial function having different forms inside (region I) and outside (region II) of the APW spheres (see Fig. 2-4) has been presented by Loucks [29]:

$$W \int_{I+II} \phi^\dagger \phi d\Omega = \int_{I+II} \phi^\dagger H \phi d\Omega - \frac{i}{2} \int_{spheres} (\phi_{II} + \phi_{I})^\dagger \, \vec{\alpha} \cdot \hat{\rho}(\phi_{II} - \phi_{I}) dS \quad (4\text{-}25)$$

$\hat{\rho}$ is the unit vector in the direction of the outward normal for the spherical regions. The similarity between this expression and (2-20) is apparent. Only one surface term is needed in the relativistic case, however, the difference being due to the fact that the momentum operator occurs quadratically in the Schrödinger equation and only linearly in the Dirac Hamiltonian. To show that (4-25) is variational we write

$$\phi_I = \phi_t + \delta \phi_I, \quad \phi_{II} = \phi_t + \delta \phi_{II} \text{ and } W = W_t + \delta W \qquad (4\text{-}26)$$

where ϕ_t and W_t are the true solutions of the Dirac equation

$$H\phi_t = (\vec{\alpha} \cdot \vec{p} + \beta + 1 \text{ muffin-tin}) \, \phi_t = W_t \, \phi_t \qquad (4\text{-}27)$$

Substituting (4-26) into the left-hand side of (4-25) and retaining first order terms only yields

$$LHS = W_t \int_{II} (\phi_t^\dagger \phi_t + \phi_t^\dagger \delta \phi_{II} + \delta \phi_{II}^\dagger \phi_t) d\Omega$$

$$+ W_t \int_{I} (\phi_t^\dagger \phi_t + \phi_t^\dagger \delta \phi_I + \delta \phi_I^\dagger \phi_t) d\Omega$$

$$+ \delta W \int_{I+II} \phi_t^\dagger \phi_t \, d\Omega \qquad (4\text{-}28)$$

Similarly, substituting (4-26) in the right-hand side of (4-25) and using (4-27) yields

$$RHS = W_t \int_{II} (\phi_t^\dagger \phi_t + \delta \phi_{II}{}^\dagger \phi_t) d\Omega + \int_{II} \phi_t^\dagger H \delta \phi_{II} \, d\Omega$$

$$+ W_t \int_I (\phi_t^\dagger \phi_t + \delta \phi_I{}^\dagger \phi_t) d\Omega + \int_I \phi_t^\dagger H \delta \phi_I \, d\Omega$$

$$- i \int_{spheres} \phi_t^\dagger \vec{\alpha} \cdot \hat{\rho} \, (\delta \phi_{II} - \delta \phi_I) \, dS \qquad (4\text{-}29)$$

The terms involving the Dirac Hamiltonian require special attention because the integrations are over finite regions.

Consider the divergence theorem [16] applied to the vector $X^\dagger \vec{\alpha} Y$:

$$\int_{volume} \nabla \cdot (X^\dagger \vec{\alpha} Y) \, d\Omega = \int_{surface} X^\dagger \vec{\alpha} \cdot \hat{n} \, Y \, dS \qquad (4\text{-}30)$$

where $\hat{n}$ is the unit vector in the direction of the outward normal to the surface. X and Y are column matrices; for instance,

$$X = \begin{pmatrix} X_1 \\ X_2 \\ X_3 \\ X_4 \end{pmatrix} \qquad (4\text{-}31)$$

According to (4-3) each of the 3 components of the vector $\vec{\alpha}$ is a 4 x 4 matrix. Thus in (4-30) the matrix multiplication is of the form

$$(X_1{}^* X_2{}^* X_3{}^* X_4{}^*) \begin{pmatrix} \alpha_{11} & \alpha_{12} & \alpha_{13} & \alpha_{14} \\ \alpha_{21} & \alpha_{22} & \alpha_{23} & \alpha_{24} \\ \alpha_{31} & \alpha_{32} & \alpha_{33} & \alpha_{34} \\ \alpha_{41} & \alpha_{42} & \alpha_{43} & \alpha_{44} \end{pmatrix} \begin{pmatrix} Y_1 \\ Y_2 \\ Y_3 \\ Y_4 \end{pmatrix} = \sum_{i,j} X_i{}^* \alpha_{ij} Y_j \qquad (4\text{-}32)$$

where the α_{ij} are the matrix elements of either α_x, α_y or α_z. If we consider the x component of (4-30), the left-hand side can be written

$$\sum_{i,j} \int \frac{d}{dx} (X_i^* \alpha_{ij} Y_j) d\Omega = \sum_{i,j} \alpha_{ij} \int \left(X_i^* \frac{dY_j}{dx} + Y_j \frac{dX_i^*}{dx} \right) d\Omega \quad (4\text{-}33)$$

where α_{ij} are the matrix elements of α_x. Since $\alpha_{ij} = \alpha_{ji}^*$, as can be seen from (3-4), we can write (4-33) in the form

$$\sum_{i,j} \int \left(X_i^* \alpha_{ij} \frac{dY_j}{dx} + Y_j \alpha_{ji}^* \frac{dX_i}{dx} \right) d\Omega$$

$$= \left[\int (X^\dagger \vec{\alpha} \cdot \nabla Y + (Y^\dagger \vec{\alpha} \cdot \nabla X)^*) d\Omega \right]_x \quad (4\text{-}34)$$

Using this form for the left-hand side, (4-30) becomes

$$\int_{\text{volume}} X^\dagger \vec{\alpha} \cdot \nabla Y \, d\Omega = - \int_{\text{volume}} (Y^\dagger \vec{\alpha} \cdot \nabla X)^* d\Omega + \int_{\text{surface}} X^\dagger \vec{\alpha} \cdot \hat{n} Y dS \quad (4\text{-}35)$$

which, according to (4-2), is

$$\int_V X^\dagger \vec{\alpha} \cdot \vec{p} \, Y d\Omega = \int_V (Y^\dagger \vec{\alpha} \cdot \vec{p} \, X)^* d\Omega - i \int_S X^\dagger \vec{\alpha} \cdot \hat{n} \, Y \, dS \quad (4\text{-}36)$$

This can be used to evaluate the terms in (4-29) which involve the Dirac Hamiltonian. For instance,

$$\int_I \phi_t^\dagger H \delta \phi_I \, d\Omega = \int_I \phi_t^\dagger \vec{\alpha} \cdot \vec{p} \, \delta \phi_I \, d\Omega + \int \phi_t^\dagger (\beta + 1 \cdot V) \delta \phi_I d\Omega \quad (4\text{-}37)$$

From (4-5) and (4-6) it is seen that β and $1 \cdot V$ are symmetric, and hence that

$$\int \phi_t^\dagger (\beta + 1 \cdot V) \, \delta \phi_I \, d\Omega = \int (\delta \phi_I^\dagger (\beta + 1 \cdot V) \phi_t)^* d\Omega \quad (4\text{-}38)$$

Using this result and (4-36) in (4-37) yields

$$\int_I \phi_t^\dagger H \delta \phi_I \, d\Omega = W_t \int \phi_t^\dagger \, \delta \phi_I d\Omega - i \int_S \phi_t^\dagger \vec{\alpha} \cdot \hat{\rho} \, \delta \phi_I \, dS \quad (4\text{-}39)$$

Similarly, for the region outside the spheres we find

$$\int_{II} \phi_t^\dagger H \delta \phi_{II} \, d\Omega = W_t \int \phi_t^\dagger \, \delta \phi_{II} \, d\Omega + i \int_S \phi_t^\dagger \, \vec{\alpha} \cdot \hat{\rho} \, \delta \phi_{II} \, dS \qquad (4\text{-}40)$$

The sign of the surface term is different in (4-40) because $\hat{\rho}$ has the sense indicated for region I in Fig. 2-4, i.e., opposite to the outward normal for region II. There is no contribution from the surface of the unit cell because both the trial function and the true solution satisfy the Bloch condition. This was discussed in more detail in Chapter 2.

Substituting (4-39) and (4-40) into (4-29) and comparing the result with (4-28) yields

$$\delta W \int_{I + II} \phi_t^\dagger \phi_t \, d\Omega = 0 \qquad (4\text{-}41)$$

which completes the proof that (4-25) is indeed a variational expression for the energy, even if ϕ_I and ϕ_{II} do not match up at the sphere boundaries. In the following sections we apply this to RAPW functions for which only the lower two components do not match up. Although the proof is not included, it can also be shown that the variational expression (4-25) has the useful property that W is real for any trial wave function.

RAPW MATRIX ELEMENTS

The variation function $\phi(\vec{k}, \vec{r})$ is to be a linear combination of RAPW functions, each based on a different recip. The RAPW functions are given by (4-23) and (4-24) and have a different form for the two spin orientations $m = \pm \frac{1}{2}$. Both of these orientations must be included for each recip, and therefore the resulting basis set is twice as large as in the nonrelativistic case. Thus the expansion indicated in (4-7) should be written

$$\phi(\vec{k}, \vec{r}) = \sum_{i=1}^{M} \sum_{m=\pm\frac{1}{2}} c_i^m \, \psi^m(\vec{k}_i, \vec{r}) \qquad (4\text{-}42)$$

Using the variational expression (4-25) and following the same procedure outlined in Chapter 2 for the APW matrix elements, we can easily show that the coefficients c_i^m are given by

$$\sum_{j=1}^{M} \sum_{n=\pm\frac{1}{2}} M^{ij}\binom{n}{m} \, c_j^n = 0 \qquad \left(\begin{array}{l} i=1, 2, \ldots, M \\ m=\pm\frac{1}{2} \end{array}\right) \tag{4-43}$$

where

$$M^{ij}\binom{n}{m} = H^{ij}\binom{n}{m} + S^{ij}\binom{n}{m} - W\,\Delta^{ij}\binom{n}{m} \tag{4-44}$$

$$H^{ij}\binom{n}{m} = \int_{I+II} \psi^m(\vec{k}_i, \vec{r})^\dagger \, H \, \psi^n(\vec{k}_j, \vec{r}) \, d\Omega \tag{4-45}$$

$$\Delta^{ij}\binom{n}{m} = \int_{I+II} \psi^m(\vec{k}_i, \vec{r})^\dagger \, \psi^n(k_j, \vec{r}) \, d\Omega \tag{4-46}$$

and

$$S^{ij}\binom{n}{m} = -\frac{i}{2} \int_{\text{spheres}} \left[(\psi_{II}^m(\vec{k}_i, \vec{r}) + \psi_I^m(\vec{k}_i, \vec{r}))^\dagger \right.$$

$$\left. \vec{\alpha} \cdot \hat{\rho}\,(\psi_{II}^n(\vec{k}_j, \vec{r}) - \psi_I^n(\vec{k}_j, \vec{r})) \right] dS \tag{4-47}$$

The values of W allowed in (4-44) are given by the roots of the secular determinant

$$\text{Det } |M^{ij}\binom{n}{m}| = 0 \tag{4-48}$$

To find the explicit form of the matrix elements, it is convenient to consider the following combinations of terms:

$$H_I^{ij}\binom{n}{m} - W\,\Delta_I^{ij}\binom{n}{m} \tag{4-49}$$

$$H_{II}^{ij}\binom{n}{m} - W\,\Delta_{II}^{ij}\binom{n}{m} \tag{4-50}$$

$$S^{ij}\binom{n}{m} \tag{4-51}$$

The indices i, j, m, n will be supressed in the following discussion. If we choose the energy W' on which the form of the RAPW functions inside the spheres is based (see (4-14) and (4-15)) to be equal to the characteristic energy W, then the first term (4-49) is identically zero. This simplifies the form of the matrix elements, but makes them implicitly dependent on the characteristic energy through the form of the RAPW inside the spheres.

The integration in (4-50) is over the region outside the spheres. It is convenient to extend the integration throughout the entire unit cell while continuing to use the form of the RAPW function in the outer region. The expression (4-50) is found by subtracting from this result the resulting contribution due to the region inside the spheres. Thus

$$H_{II} - W\Delta_{II} = (H_{II} - W\Delta_{II})_{cell} - (H_{II} - W\Delta_{II})_{spheres} \tag{4-52}$$

According to (4-8) and (4-45), both of these terms are of the form

$$H_{II} - W\Delta_{II} = (k_j^o - W)\, \Delta_{II} \tag{4-53}$$

Using the form of the RAPW function in (4-23) we find

$$(\Delta_{II})_{cell} = \left(\frac{1 + k_i^o}{2k_i^o} \right)^{\frac{1}{2}} \left(\frac{1 + k_j^o}{2k_j^o} \right)^{\frac{1}{2}} \int_{cell} e^{i(\vec{k}_j - \vec{k}_i)\cdot\vec{r}} \, d\Omega$$

$$\left(\begin{matrix} X(m) \\ \dfrac{\vec{\sigma}\cdot\vec{k}_i}{1 + k_i^o} X(m) \end{matrix} \right)^{\dagger} \left(\begin{matrix} X(n) \\ \dfrac{\vec{\sigma}\cdot\vec{k}_j}{1 + k_j^o} X(n) \end{matrix} \right) \tag{4-54}$$

The integration over the cell gives $\Omega_o \delta_{ij}$ where Ω_o is the unit cell volume. The spinor multiplication is

$$(\chi(m)^{\dagger}, \; \chi(m)^{\dagger} \frac{\vec{\sigma} \cdot \vec{k}_i}{1 + k_i^{\;o}}) \begin{pmatrix} \chi(n) \\ \\ \frac{\vec{\sigma} \cdot \vec{k}_j}{1 + k_j^{\;o}} \quad \chi(n) \end{pmatrix}$$

$$= \delta_{mn} + \frac{\chi(m)^{\dagger} \vec{\sigma} \cdot \vec{k}_i \; \vec{\sigma} \cdot \vec{k}_j \; \chi(n)}{(1 + k_i^{\;o})(1 + k_j^{\;o})} \tag{4-55}$$

Using the relation [43]

$$\vec{\sigma} \cdot \vec{A} \; \vec{\sigma} \cdot \vec{B} = \vec{A} \cdot \vec{B} + i \, \vec{\sigma} \cdot (\vec{A} \times \vec{B}) \tag{4-56}$$

we have

$$\vec{\sigma} \cdot \vec{k}_i \; \vec{\sigma} \cdot \vec{k}_j = \vec{k}_i \cdot \vec{k}_j + i \, \vec{\sigma} \cdot (\vec{k}_i \times \vec{k}_j) \tag{4-57}$$

Combining these results yields for (4-54)

$$(\Delta_{II})_{cell} = \Omega_{o} \left(\frac{1 + k_i^{\;o}}{2 k_i^{\;o}} \right) \left(1 + \frac{k_i^{\;2}}{(1 + k_i^{\;o})^2} \right) \; \delta_{mn} \, \delta_{ij}$$

$$= \Omega_{o} \, \delta_{ij} \, \delta_{mn} \tag{4-58}$$

The second term in (4-52) is the same as (4-54) except the integration is over the spheres. We have seen in Chapter 2 that

$$\int_{\nu\text{-sphere}} e^{i\vec{k}_{ij} \cdot \vec{r}} \, d\Omega = e^{i\vec{k}_{ij} \cdot \vec{r}_\nu} \; 4\pi \, S_\nu^{\;2} \mathcal{J}_1(k_{ij}S_\nu)/k_{ij} \tag{4-59}$$

where

$$\vec{k}_{ij} = \vec{k}_j - \vec{k}_i \tag{4-60}$$

Therefore,

$$(\Delta_{II})_{\text{spheres}} = \xi^{ij}\binom{n}{m}\sum_{\nu} 4\pi S_{\nu}^{2} e^{i\vec{k}_{ij}\cdot\vec{r}_{\nu}} \mathscr{J}_{1}(k_{ij}S_{\nu})/k_{ij} \qquad (4\text{-}61)$$

where

$$\xi^{ij}\binom{n}{m} = \left(\frac{1+k_{i}^{0}}{2k_{i}^{0}}\right)^{\frac{1}{2}}\left(\frac{1+k_{j}^{0}}{2k_{j}^{0}}\right)^{\frac{1}{2}}\left(\left[1+\frac{\vec{k}_{i}\cdot\vec{k}_{j}}{(1+k_{i}^{0})(1+k_{j}^{0})}\right]\delta_{mn}\right.$$

$$\left. +i\,\frac{\vec{k}_{i}\times\vec{k}_{j}\cdot(m|\vec{\sigma}|n)}{(1+k_{i}^{0})(1+k_{j}^{0})}\right) \qquad (4\text{-}62)$$

and

$$\left(\pm\tfrac{1}{2}\,|\,\vec{\sigma}\,|\,\pm\tfrac{1}{2}\right) = \pm\,\hat{e}_{z}\,, \quad \left(\pm\tfrac{1}{2}\,|\,\vec{\sigma}\,|\,\mp\tfrac{1}{2}\right) = \hat{e}_{x}\mp i\,\hat{e}_{y} \qquad (4\text{-}63)$$

The results (4-61), (4-58) and (4-53) can be combined with (4-52) to give the result for the expression (4-50).

Next the surface integral (4-51), which is defined in (4-47), will be evaluated. The differential surface element is $dS = S_{\nu}^{2}d\hat{\rho}$ and the radial functions are evaluated at $\rho = S_{\nu}$. Using ψ_{II} as given in (4-24) and ψ_{I} in the expanded form (4-19), the last factor in the surface integral becomes

$$\psi_{II}^{n}(k_{j},S_{\nu}) - \psi_{I}^{n}(k_{j},S_{\nu}) = ie^{i\vec{k}_{j}\cdot\vec{r}_{\nu}}\sum_{\kappa,\mu} a_{\kappa\mu}^{nj}$$

$$\left(\left[\frac{k_{j}S_{\kappa}}{1+k_{j}^{0}}\mathscr{J}_{\ell'}(k_{j}S_{\nu}) - \frac{\mathscr{J}_{\ell}(k_{j}S_{\nu})f_{\kappa}(S_{\nu})}{g_{\kappa}(S_{\nu})}\right]\chi_{-\kappa}^{\mu}\right) \qquad (4\text{-}64)$$

According to (4-47) this is to be operated on by

$$\vec{\alpha}\cdot\hat{\rho} = \begin{array}{cc} 0 & \vec{\sigma}\cdot\hat{\rho} \\ \vec{\sigma}\cdot\hat{\rho} & 0 \end{array} \qquad (4\text{-}65)$$

and $\vec{\sigma}\cdot\hat{\rho}$ applied to the spin-angular function gives [43]

$$\vec{\sigma} \cdot \hat{\rho} \quad \chi^{\mu}_{-\kappa} = - \chi^{\mu}_{\kappa} \tag{4-66}$$

Thus

$$\vec{\alpha} \cdot \hat{\rho} (\psi_{II} - \psi_I) = - i \, e^{i \vec{k}_j \cdot \vec{r}_\nu} \sum_{\kappa, \mu} a^{nj}_{\kappa\mu} \begin{pmatrix} \begin{bmatrix} \quad \end{bmatrix} \chi^{\mu}_{\kappa} \\ \\ 0 \end{pmatrix} \tag{4-67}$$

where the square bracket contains the same terms as in (4-64). The remaining factor in (4-47) is

$$(\psi_{II} + \psi_I)^{\dagger} = e^{-i \vec{k}_i \cdot \vec{r}_\nu} \sum_{\kappa, \mu} a^{mi\dagger}_{\kappa\mu} \begin{pmatrix} 2 \mathcal{J}_\ell(k_i S_\nu) \chi^{\mu}_{\kappa} \\ \\ \text{Lower Component} \end{pmatrix}^{\dagger} \tag{4-68}$$

In multiplying this by (4-67) there is a contribution only from the upper components. In performing the angular integration $d\hat{\rho}$, the orthonormality of the spin-angular functions (4-17) reduces the surface integral (4-47) to

$$S^{ij}(^n_m) = e^{i \vec{k}_{ij} \cdot \vec{r}_\nu} \, 4\pi \, S_\nu^2 \sum_{\kappa} D^{ij}_{\kappa}(^n_m) \, \mathcal{J}_\ell(k_i S_\nu)$$

$$\begin{pmatrix} \dfrac{\mathcal{J}_\ell(k_j S_\nu) \, f_\kappa(S_\nu)}{g_\kappa(S_\nu)} - \begin{pmatrix} \dfrac{k_j S_\kappa}{1 + k_j^o} \end{pmatrix} \mathcal{J}_{\ell'}(k_j S_\nu) \end{pmatrix} \tag{4-69}$$

where

$$D^{ij}_{\kappa}(^n_m) = \frac{1}{4\pi} \sum_{\mu} a^{mi\dagger}_{\kappa\mu} a^{nj}_{\kappa u} = \left(\frac{1 + k_i^o}{2 k_i^o} \right)^{\frac{1}{2}} \left(\frac{1 + k_j^o}{2 k_j^o} \right)^{\frac{1}{2}}$$

$$4\pi \sum_{\mu} C(\ell \tfrac{1}{2} j; \mu - m, m) C(\ell \tfrac{1}{2} j; \mu - n, n)$$

$$Y^*_{\ell, \mu - n}(\hat{k}_j) \, Y_{\ell, \mu - m}(\hat{k}_i) \tag{4-70}$$

It is convenient at this point to convert from relativistic units $(m = c = \hbar = 1)$ to atomic units $(m = \frac{1}{2}, \hbar = 1, e^2 = 2)$ and to simplify some terms by dropping very high order relativistic corrections which are not important for the electronic states in a crystal. The unit conversions are indicated in Table 4-2 [43]. It follows from the definition of the fine structure constant,

$$\alpha = e^2/(\hbar c) \approx 1/137 \qquad\qquad (4\text{-}71)$$

that the speed of light in atomic units is

$$c = 2/\alpha \approx 2(137) \qquad\qquad (4\text{-}72)$$

Table 4-2. Conversion of units

	$m = 1$ $c = 1$ $\hbar = 1$	m c $\hbar$	$m = \frac{1}{2}$ $\hbar = 1$ $e^2 = 2$
Energy	W	W/mc^2	$2W/c^2$
Wave vector	k	$\hbar k/mc$	$2k/c$
Length	ρ	$mc\rho/\hbar$	$c\rho/2$
	relativistic	cgs	atomic

The results listed in Table 4-2 can be used to convert the various terms occurring in the matrix elements. For instance, from (4-53) we have

$$k_j^o - W = (1 + k_j^2)^{\frac{1}{2}} - (1 + E) \rightarrow \left(1 + \frac{4k_j^2}{c^2}\right)^{\frac{1}{2}} - \left(1 + \frac{2E}{c^2}\right) \qquad (4\text{-}73)$$

where E is the energy relative to the rest energy, that is $W = E + mc^2$. For wave vectors corresponding to the electronic states in a crystal, k_j is much less than c; hence (4-73) can be simplified to

$$k_j^o - W \rightarrow 2(k_j^2 - E)/c^2 \tag{4-74}$$

Similarly, the terms occurring in (4-62) become

$$\left(\frac{1 + k^o}{2k^o}\right)^{\frac{1}{2}} \rightarrow \left(\frac{1 + \left(1 + \frac{4k^2}{c^2}\right)^{\frac{1}{2}}}{2\left(1 + \frac{4k^2}{c^2}\right)^{\frac{1}{2}}}\right)^{\frac{1}{2}} \approx 1 \tag{4-75}$$

and

$$\frac{k}{1 + k^o} \rightarrow \frac{2k/c}{1 + \left(1 + \frac{4k^2}{c^2}\right)^{\frac{1}{2}}} \approx k/c \tag{4-76}$$

The approximation $k_j \ll c$ is very good. It amounts to neglecting relativistic effects in the region between the spheres. This is reasonable
since the velocities of the electrons in a crystal are an appreciable fraction of the speed of light only near the nuclei where the potential energy
is very large. Thus, all the relativistic effects are contained in f_κ and
g_κ, the radial functions inside the spheres, and no approximations have
been made in this region. In this regard, it is evident that $\xi^{ij}\binom{n}{m}$ in
(4-62) can be approximated by δ_{mn}.

If the units in the volume terms (Ω_o and S_ν^2/k) and the surface
term S_ν^2 are also converted,

$$\Omega_o \rightarrow c^3 \Omega_o/8$$
$$S_\nu^2 \rightarrow c^2 S_\nu^2/4 \tag{4-77}$$

then the RAPW matrix element (4-44) becomes

$$M^{ij}\binom{n}{m} = (k_j^2 - E)\left\{\Omega_o \delta_{ij} - 4\pi \sum_\nu S_\nu^2 e^{i\vec{k}_{ij}\cdot\vec{r}_\nu} \mathscr{J}_1(k_{ij}S_\nu)/k_{ij}\right\}\delta_{mn}$$

$$+ 4\pi \sum_\nu S_\nu^2 e^{i\vec{k}_{ij}\cdot\vec{r}_\nu} \sum_\kappa D_\kappa^{ij}\binom{n}{m}\mathscr{J}_\ell(k_iS_\nu)\mathscr{J}_\ell(k_jS_\nu)$$

$$\left(\frac{cf_\kappa(S_\nu)}{g_\kappa(S_\nu)} - \frac{S_\kappa k_j \mathscr{J}_{\ell'}(k_jS_\nu)}{\mathscr{J}_\ell(k_jS_\nu)}\right)$$

$$(4\text{-}78)$$

after dropping a common factor $c/4$. From (4-70) and (4-75),

$$D_\kappa^{ij}\binom{n}{m} = 4\pi \sum_\mu C(\ell\tfrac{1}{2}j;\mu-n, n) C(\ell\tfrac{1}{2}j;\mu-m, m)$$

$$Y_{\ell,\,\mu-n}^*(\hat{k}_j)\, Y_{\ell,\,\mu-m}(\hat{k}_i) \tag{4-79}$$

and in Appendix 6 it is shown that

$$D_\kappa^{ij}\binom{+}{+} = |\kappa|\,P_\ell(\hat{k}_i\cdot\hat{k}_j) + iS_\kappa(\hat{k}_i\times\hat{k}_j)_z P_\ell'(\hat{k}_i\cdot\hat{k}_j) \tag{4-80}$$

$$D_\kappa^{ij}\binom{-}{+} = iS_\kappa P_\ell'(\hat{k}_i\cdot\hat{k}_j)\left[(\hat{k}_i\times\hat{k}_j)_x - i(\hat{k}_i\times\hat{k}_j)_y\right] \tag{4-81}$$

It can also be shown that

$$D_\kappa^{ij}\binom{-}{-} = D_\kappa^{ij}\binom{+}{+}^* \tag{4-82}$$

and

$$D_\kappa^{ij}\binom{+}{-} = -D_\kappa^{ij}\binom{-}{+}^* \tag{4-83}$$

The radial functions in (4-78) satisfy the coupled equations (4-14) and (4-15). These are repeated here in atomic units:

$$\frac{d(cf)}{d\rho} = (\kappa - 1)cf/\rho - (E-V)g \tag{4-84}$$

$$\frac{dg}{d\rho} = \left(\frac{E - V}{c^2} + 1\right) cf - (\kappa + 1)g/\rho \tag{4-85}$$

It is interesting to compare these equations with the nonrelativistic results (3-57) and (3-58). If we define

$$cf \equiv Q/\rho \quad , \quad g = P/\rho \tag{4-86}$$

and let $c \to \infty$, then (4-84) and (4-85) are equivalent to (3-57) and (3-58)
with $\kappa = -(\ell + 1)$ as given in (4-21). Thus

$$\frac{cf}{g} = \frac{Q}{P} = \frac{R'}{R} - \ell/\rho = \frac{R'}{R} + (\kappa + 1)/\rho \tag{4-87}$$

according to (3-61). Also, it is interesting to note the similarity between the matrix elements in (4-78) and the nonrelativistic results (2-59)
and (2-60).

PRACTICAL ASPECTS OF THE RAPW METHOD

In this section we will discuss only those aspects of the RAPW ma-
trix elements (4-78) which are unique to the relativistic formalism.
The nonrelativistic APW matrix elements have already been discussed in
Chapter 3. In (4-80) it is necessary to calculate the derivatives of the
Legendre polynomials, $P'_\ell(x)$. These can be related to the Legendre
polynomials which are also needed in the matrix elements [1]:

$$P'_\ell(x) = \ell(-x P_\ell(x) + P_{\ell-1}(x))/(1 - x^2) \tag{4-88}$$

This relationship is indeterminant for $x = \pm 1$, and for these special
cases it reduces to

$$P'_\ell(\pm 1) = \frac{1}{2} (\pm 1)^{\ell+1} \ell(\ell+1) \tag{4-89}$$

The similarity between the first-order coupled equations (4-84) and (4-85) and the nonrelativistic equations (3-57) and (3-58) has already been noted. Using (4-86) and transforming to the logarithmic coordinate $x = \log \rho$, (4-84) and (4-85) become

$$P' = e^x \left(\frac{(E-V)}{c^2} + 1 \right) Q - \kappa P \qquad\qquad (4\text{-}90)$$

$$Q' = \kappa Q - e^x (E - V) P \qquad\qquad (4\text{-}91)$$

It is obvious that as $c \to \infty$ these reduce to the nonrelativistic results (3-62) and (3-63) with $\kappa < 0$ (4-21). An accurate method of solving (4-90) and (4-91) is based on a combination of the Runge-Kutta and Milne methods. The former has been discussed in Chapter 3 and is used to get the starting values for the Milne method. The initial values are determined from the boundary condition at the origin of the radial coordinate. By examing (4-90) and (4-91) in the limit as $x \to -\infty$ it can be shown that [43]

$$\frac{Q}{P} = \frac{cf}{g} = c \; \frac{\kappa + \sqrt{\kappa^2 - (2Z/c)^2}}{(2Z/c)} \qquad (x \approx x_1) \qquad (4\text{-}92)$$

where Z is the nuclear charge, and the value of x_1 (which specifies the range of validity of the approximation (4-92)) has been discussed in Chapter 3. The procedure we follow is to fix either Q or P arbitrarily at x_1 and use (4-92) to determine the other. These initial values are used in the Runge-Kutta method to get the starting values for the Milne method. The form of the Milne method appropriate to coupled first-order equations is based on the following equations [1]:

$$P_{n+1} = P_{n-5} + \frac{3\Delta}{10} (11 P'_n - 14 P'_{n-1} + 26 P'_{n-2} - 14 P'_{n-3}$$

$$+ 11 P'_{n-4}) \qquad\qquad (4\text{-}93)$$

$$P_{n+1} = P_{n-3} + \frac{2\Delta}{45}(7P'_{n+1} + 32P'_n + 12P'_{n-1} + 32P'_{n-2}$$

$$+ 7P'_{n-3}) \hspace{3cm} (4-94)$$

and two similar equations with P replaced by Q. An iteration based on equations of the form (4-94) for both P and Q is continued until the calculated values stabilize. A computer program using the above procedures for calculating cf/g is discussed in Appendix 7. In Fig. 4-1 we show some results for the element thorium.

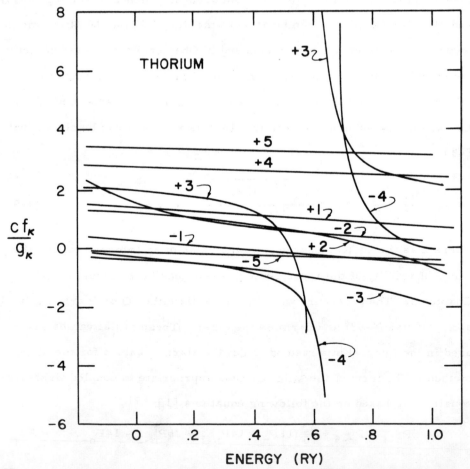

Fig. 4-1. The energy dependence of cf/g for metallic thorium.

All the other terms in the RAPW matrix elements (4-78) have been discussed in Chapter 3. The procedure for calculating these matrix elements is essentially the same as in the nonrelativistic case except that the κ summation is over both positive and negative integers (zero excluded). We usually take $\kappa \leq 10$, but there are situations (NFE metals) when fewer terms are required. According to (4-21) we note that $\kappa = -1$ corresponds to $\ell = 0$. For $\ell > 0$ there are two corresponding values of κ, one positive and one negative. For instance, $\kappa = -3$ and $\kappa = +2$ correspond to $\ell = 2$. In order to include the two values of κ corresponding to each ℓ, it is desirable to always include one more term in the negative sum than in the positive one. A computer program for calculating the RAPW matrix elements and evaluating the secular determinant are described in Appendix 8.

As indicated in (4-42) the basis set must include a RAPW function corresponding to both spin orientations for each recip. The resulting matrix is, therefore, twice as big as in the nonrelativistic case and has the form indicated in Fig. 4-2. The determinant can be evaluated using exactly the same procedure discussed in Chapter 3. However, due to the special form of the RAPW matrix elements there are certain simplifications possible which substantially reduce these calculations. They result from the relations (4-82) and (4-83) and from the requirement that the matrix in Fig. 4-2 be Hermitian. The latter is not obvious from (4-78), but there are alternate forms of these matrix elements from which it can easily be seen [29].

The equations (4-82) and (4-83) give the relationship between the matrix elements corresponding to the spin combinations possible for the same pair of recips. This is indicated in Fig. 4-3. It can be seen that

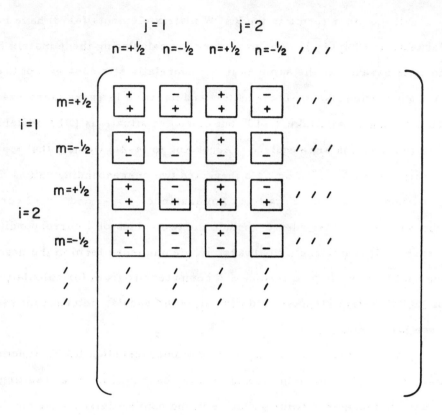

Figure 4-2. Form of the matrix in the RAPW method. The indices i
            and j are labels for the reciprocal lattice vectors; the
            indices m and n are labels for the two spin orientations.

the additional requirement of Hermiticity simplifies the matrix elements

in the 2 x 2 matrices along the main diagonal. In applying the triangular-

ization procedure (3-95) to a matrix of this form, it is found that the

second row does not change because of the zero matrix element in the

second column. Even more important, after the third and fourth rows

have been triangularized using (3-95) the resulting matrix elements have

the form indicated in Fig. 4-4. Hence, it is not necessary to triangular-

ize the even rows since these matrix elements (both before and after

triangularization) can be related to the matrix elements in the odd rows.

Not only does this reduce the number of matrix elements which must be

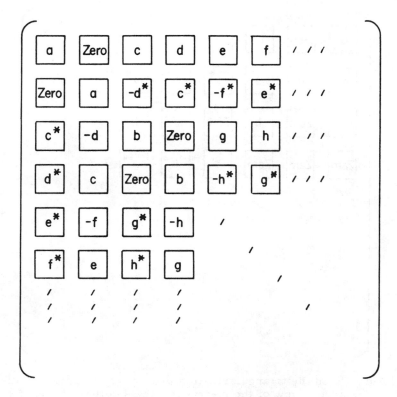

Figure 4-3.   The RAPW matrix elements in the even rows are related
              to those in the odd rows corresponding to the same pair
              of reciprocal lattice vectors, as shown for c and d. The
              additional requirement of Hermiticity produces pairs of
              equal elements along the main diagonal and zeros for some
              of the neighboring elements.

calculated, but it also eliminates the intrinsic double degeneracy due to

spin-doubling of the basis set. We see in Fig. 4-3 that each of the main

diagonal elements will occur twice. This is also true of the triangular-

ized matrix in Fig. 4-4. By considering only the odd rows the deter-

minant is a product of the form ab'... instead of aab'b'..., thus elimin-

ating the double degeneracy. Of course, this is an advantage in practice

since the determinant changes sign for singly degenerate roots making

them easier to find with the computer.

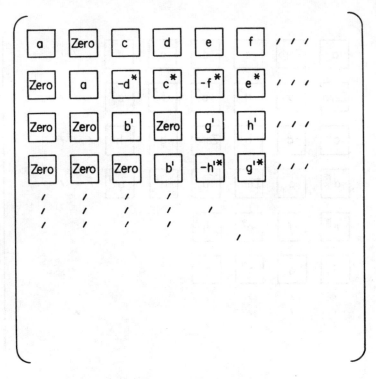

Figure 4-4.   When the triangularization procedure is applied to the
second row of the matrix in Fig. 4-3 there is no change.
After successive pairs of rows are triangularized the elements in the even rows are still found to be related to
those in the preceding odd rows in the same way as before.

It is convenient to write (3-95) in terms of the matrix elements
in the odd rows only.   If we let α and β refer to the rows and columns
as shown in Fig. 4-3 then

$$m_{\alpha\beta} = M_{\alpha\beta} - \sum_{\mu=1}^{\alpha-1} m^{*}_{\mu\alpha} m_{\mu\beta}/m_{\mu\mu} \qquad (\alpha \text{ odd}) \qquad (4\text{-}95)$$

The $M_{\alpha\beta}$ are the original matrix elements, and the $m_{\alpha\beta}$ are the values
after triangularization.   For the first row we take $m_{\alpha\beta} = M_{\alpha\beta}$.   This
equation is to be applied one row at a time to each of the matrix elements
to right of and including the main diagonal.   The sum can be split into
even and odd parts:

$$m_{\alpha\beta} = M_{\alpha\beta} - \sum_{\mu \text{ odd}}^{\alpha-2} m^*_{\mu\alpha} m_{\mu\beta} / m_{\mu\mu}$$

$$- \sum_{\mu \text{ even}}^{\alpha-1} m^*_{\mu\alpha} m_{\mu\beta} / m_{\mu\mu} \qquad (\alpha \text{ odd}) \qquad (4\text{-}96)$$

Let us consider for definiteness that β is odd. Then, in the summation with μ even, we have from (4-83)

$$\sum_{\mu \text{ even}}^{\alpha-1} m^*_{\mu\alpha} m_{\mu\beta} / m_{\mu\mu}$$

$$= \sum_{\mu \text{ even}}^{\alpha-1} (-m^*_{\mu-1, \alpha+1})^* (-m^*_{\mu-1, \beta+1}) / m_{\mu-1, \mu-1}$$

$$(\alpha, \beta \text{ odd}) \qquad (4\text{-}97)$$

If we let $\mu \rightarrow \mu - 1$ in the right-hand side, this can be combined with the odd summation in (4-96) to give

$$m_{\alpha\beta} = M_{\alpha\beta} - \sum_{\mu \text{ odd}}^{\alpha-2} (m^*_{\mu\alpha} m_{\mu\beta} + m^*_{\mu, \beta+1} m_{\mu, \alpha+1}) / m_{\mu\mu}$$

$$(\alpha, \beta \text{ odd}) \qquad (4\text{-}98)$$

Similarly, using (4-82), it can be shown that for β even

$$m_{\alpha\beta} = M_{\alpha\beta} - \sum_{\mu \text{ odd}}^{\alpha-2} (m^*_{\mu\alpha} m_{\mu\beta} - m^*_{\mu, \beta-1} m_{\mu, \alpha+1}) / m_{\mu\mu}$$

$$\binom{\alpha \text{ odd}}{\beta \text{ even}} \qquad (4\text{-}99)$$

In Appendix 8 computer programs for constructing the RAPW matrix elements and evaluating the secular determinant are discussed.

Appendix 1

NUMERICAL SOLUTION OF POISSON'S EQUATION

We want to find the electrostatic potential $V(r)$ consistent with Poisson's equation (atomic units),

$$\nabla^2 V(r) = -8\pi\, \rho(r) \tag{A1-1}$$

where ρ is the electronic density

$$\rho = \sum_{\text{occupied}} |\psi|^2 \tag{A1-2}$$

The electronic densities for all the elements have been calculated relativistically by Liberman, et al [24]. It is convenient to make the following change in variables:

$$x = \log r \tag{A1-3}$$

$$W = e^{\frac{x}{2}} V \tag{A1-4}$$

The first change (A1-3) expands the scale near the origin where the nodes of the atomic functions in (A1-2) are close together. The second change (A1-4) is such that the resulting differential equation has no first derivative term. Poisson's equation (A1-1) becomes

$$W'' = \frac{1}{4} W - g \tag{A1-5}$$

where

$$g = 8\pi e^{\frac{5}{2} x} \rho \tag{A1-6}$$

In order to approximate (A1-5) by a set of finite-difference equations, a Taylor series expansion of W about an arbitrary point is considered. We have

$$W(x \pm \Delta) = W(x) \pm \Delta W'(x) + \frac{\Delta^2}{2!} W''(x) \pm \frac{\Delta^3}{3!} W'''(x)$$

$$+ \frac{\Delta^4}{4!} W^{iv}(x) \pm \ldots \tag{A1-7}$$

where W', W'', W'''... are the first, second, third, etc. derivatives of W. Adding $W(x+\Delta)$ and $W(x-\Delta)$ from (A1-7) yields

$$W(x+\Delta) + W(x-\Delta) - 2W(x) = \Delta^2 W''(x) + \frac{\Delta^4}{12} W^{iv}(x) + \ldots \tag{A1-8}$$

By taking the second derivative of (A1-8) and neglecting the highest order term, we find

$$\Delta^2 W^{iv}(x) = W''(x+\Delta) + W''(x-\Delta) - 2W''(x) \tag{A1-9}$$

Using (A1-5) to determine the second derivatives in (A1-9), the result can be substituted into (A1-8) to give

$$A W_{j+1} + B W_j + A W_{j-1} + D_j = 0 \tag{A1-10}$$

where

$$A = 1 - \Delta^2/48 \tag{A1-11}$$

$$B = -2(1 + 5\Delta^2/48) \tag{A1-12}$$

$$D_j = \Delta^2 (g_{j+1} + 10 \, g_j + g_{j-1})/12 \tag{A1-13}$$

The indices refer to grid points on an integration mesh as shown in Fig. (A1-1), i.e.,

$$W_j = W(x_j), \quad W_{j+1} = W(x_j+\Delta), \quad \text{etc} \tag{A1-14}$$

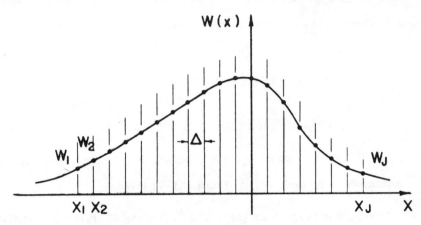

Figure A1-1   The integration grid over the range of the variable
$x = \log(r)$. x_1 corresponds to $r \to 0$, and x_J corresponds
to $r \to \infty$.

Each value of W_j is related to the two neighboring values according to (A1-10). This results in a tridiagonal system of linear equations. To approach the solution of these equations the following recursion relation is introduced:

$$W_j = E_j + W_{j+1}/F_j \qquad\qquad (A1-15)$$

If E_j and F_j were known for each grid point and if W_J had been specified by the appropriate boundary condition (see Fig. A1-1), then (A1-15) could be used to calculate W_j for $j = J, J-1, J-2, \ldots 1$. The boundary conditions are discussed later. To find expressions for E_j and F_j the recursion relation (A1-15) is substituted into the finite difference equation (A1-10) to give

$$AW_{j+1} + B\,(E_j + W_{j+1}/F_j) + A(E_{j-1} + W_j/F_{j-1}) + D_j = 0 \qquad (A1-16)$$

In order to get an expression involving only W_{j+1}, the term W_j in (A1-16) can be eliminated by using (A1-15) again. The result is

$$W_{j+1} \left\{ A + B/F_j + A/(F_{j-1} F_j) \right\} +$$

$$\left\{ BE_j + A(E_{j-1} + E_j/F_{j-1}) + D_j \right\} = 0 \qquad (A1-17)$$

This can be satisfied for all j by taking

$$A + B/F_j + A/(F_{j-1} F_j) = 0 \qquad (A1-18)$$

and

$$BE_j + A(E_{j-1} + E_j/F_{j-1}) + D_j = 0 \qquad (A1-19)$$

The first of these equations can be solved for F_j to give

$$F_j = - (B/A + 1/F_{j-1}) \qquad (A1-20)$$

and the second equation yields

$$E_j = - \frac{(D_j + AE_{j-1})}{A(B/A + 1/F_{j-1})} = (D_j/A + E_{j-1})/F_j \qquad (A1-21)$$

The constants A and B occurring in these equations are given by (A1-11) and (A1-12), respectively, and depend only on the interval Δ between the grid points of the integration mesh. According to (A1-13) and (A1-6) the D_j can be calculated from the values of the electronic density ρ tabulated for each of the grid points.

If the boundary conditions at r = 0 is specified, the values of E_1 and F_1 can be determined. Then (A1-20) and (A1-21) can be used to calculate E_j and F_j for j = 2, 3, 4, ... J-1. Finally, the boundary condition at r = ∞ (in practice this corresponds to x_J in Fig. (A1-1) is used to specify W_J, and then the W_j for j = J-1, J-2, ...1 are calculated using (A1-15) and the values of E_j and F_j.

In the atomic case the electronic density is limited to a finite region and for large r we can take $\rho \rightarrow o$. According to (A1-6) this leads to $g \to 0$, and in this limit the solution of (A1-5) is

$$W = A e^{\pm \frac{x}{2}} \qquad (g \to 0) \qquad\qquad\qquad (A1-22)$$

The constant A can be determined from a simple result of elec-

trostatics. For a neutral atom the total number of electrons is equal

to the nuclear charge Z. Therefore, since the electronic density is

spherically symmetric, the potential at an outside point is

$$V(r) = 2Z/r \qquad (r \text{ large}) \qquad\qquad\qquad (A1-23)$$

Using the definitions (A1-3) and (A1-4) this becomes

$$W = 2Z e^{-x/2} \qquad\qquad\qquad (A1-24)$$

which is consistent with (A1-22). Thus, the value of W_J is given by

$$W_J = 2Z e^{-x_J/2} \qquad\qquad\qquad (A1-25)$$

where it is practical to take x_J to be the smallest value of x outside

the region in which ρ is finite (negligible compared to maximum value).

The boundary condition at $r = 0$ follows from a consideration of

(A1-5) in the limit as $x \to -\infty$. Again, according to (A1-6), we have

$g \to 0$ and the solution of (A1-5) is of the form (A1-22). In order for W

to remain finite in this limit, it is necessary to take

$$W = A e^{+x/2} \qquad\qquad\qquad (A1-26)$$

This can be used to relate the W_j at two neighboring points. Using the

symbols in Fig. A1-1 we have

$$W_2 = A e^{x_2/2} = A e^{(x_1+\Delta)/2} = e^{\Delta/2} W_1 \qquad\qquad (A1-27)$$

Also, from (A1-15) with $j = 1$, it is seen that

$$W_2 = F_1 W_1 - F_1 E_1 \qquad\qquad\qquad (A1-28)$$

Thus, by choosing

$$E_1 = 0 \qquad\qquad\qquad (A1-29)$$

and

$$F_1 = e^{\Delta/2} \qquad\qquad\qquad (A1-30)$$

the proper behavior at $r = o$ is assured. These conditions and the recursion relations (A1-20) and (A1-21) are sufficient to calculate all the
values of E_j and F_j for $j = 1, 2, \ldots, J\text{-}1$. The result (A1-25) and repeated application of (A1-15) then completes the numerical solution of
Poisson's equation.

The above procedure for solving Poisson's equation has been pro-
gramed for the computer as a subroutine and is listed below. It has
been specialized in the following ways: $\Delta = .05$, $x_1 = -8.8$ and the
input is in the form

$$PSQ = 4\pi r^2 \rho = r^2 R^2 \qquad\qquad\qquad (A1-31)$$

where R is the radial part of the wave function ψ in (A1-2).

```
      SUBROUTINE POISON(PSQ,Z,J,W)
      DIMENSION PSQ(250),W(250),E(250),F(250)
      A=1.-.0025/48.
C                                           (EQ. A1.11)
      B=-2.-.025/48.
C                                           (EQ. A1.12)
      EDL=EXP(.025)
      C=.0025/6.
      C2=-B/A
      E(1)=0.
C                                           (EQ. A1.29)
      F(1)=EXP(.025)
C                                           (EQ. A1.30)
      X=-8.75
      ITOP=J-1
      DO 5 I=2,ITOP
      D=C*EXP(.5*X)*(EDL*PSQ(I+1)+10.*PSQ(I)+PSQ(I-1)/EDL)
C                                           (EQS. A1.13, A1.6)
      F(I)=C2-1./F(I-1)
C                                           (EQ. A1.20)
      E(I)=(D/A+E(I-1))/F(I)
C                                           (EQ. A1.21)
    5 X=X+.05
      W(J)= 2.*Z*EXP(-.5*X)
      DO 6 I=1,ITOP
      JV=J-I
    6 W(JV)=E(JV)+W(JV+1)/F(JV)
C                                           (EQ. A1.15)
      RETURN
      END
```

Appendix 2

MUFFIN-TIN POTENTIAL PROGRAM

The computer program listed below is based on the discussion
of the muffin-tin potential given in Chapter 3. The input and output
statements involve the following variables.

Variable	Symbol used in Chapter 3
XAD[†]	Distances to shells of atoms (in units of the lattice constant a) as given in Table 3-3 for FCC, BCC and diamond structures (HCP is already contained in the program).
NA[†]	Number of atoms in each of the shells. These are also given in Table 3-3 and must be in the same order as the input for XAD i. e., FCC, BCC, diamond and HCP. (Note that HCP is included here but not in XAD.)
NAME(I)	A title card containing the name of the atomic species in the first 16 columns.
SIGW	$p^2 = 4\pi r^2 \rho$ from the relativistic self-consistent field calculations of Liberman, et al [24]. This is called "RHO(r) AT END" on their output. The first part of our program converts their data to a log scale with $x_1 = -8.8$ and $\Delta x = 0.05$, which we use throughout.

[†]This program has been set up so that the input for FCC, BCC,
Diamond and HCP crystal structures must be included in each application. The information in Table 3-3 can be punched on computer cards
and considered part of the muffin-tin program. The input parameter
LAT is used to specify the crystal structure for a particular application. For special crystal structures additional input (see XNA and AD
above) must be included.

Z | Atomic number

JRI | Index of grid point corresponding to the APW sphere radius on a log scale with x_1 = -8.8 and $\Delta x = 0.05$ (see Fig. 3-8).

LAT | Used to specify lattice structure of crystal:

LAT	STRUCTURE
1	FCC
2	BCC
3	Diamond
4	HCP
5	other*

OMA | Volume per atom (atomic units)

A | Lattice constant (atomic units); not needed if LAT = 5.

C | Lattice constant (atomic units); needed only for HCP crystal structure.

*XNA | This input is needed only if crystal structure is different from the four already included. It is the number of atoms in each shell, same as NA above.

*AD | This input is needed only if crystal structure is different from the four already included. It consists of the distances to the shells of atoms given in XNA; same as XAD described above except it is given in atomic units, i.e., the lattice constant a is included.

VINT | V_{AVG} (Equation (3-31))

BGXMT | $V(r)$, the muffin-tin potential shifted so that V = 0 between the spheres. This output is both printed and punched on cards. The independent variable is on a log scale with x_1 = -8.8 and $\Delta x = 0.05$.

```
C     INTEGRATED  WABER/MUFFIN TIN  W/ CRYSTAL STRUCTURE
      DIMENSION XW(500), SIGW(500),PSQ(250),W(250),AA(250),AB(250),
     1AACR(250), ABCR(250),BGXMT(250),XNA(14), AD(14),NA(4,15),R(15),
     2XAD(3,15),NAME(4)
      DO 50 I=1,3
   50 READ (1,51)(XAD(I,J),J=1,14)
   51 FORMAT (8F10.8)
      DO 75 I=1,4
   75 READ (1,81)(NA(I,J),J=1,14)
   81 FORMAT (14I5)
C
C     INTERPOLATING WABERS SIGMA OVER TO PSQ
      RW1=1.19685E-04
      RWNP=3.603288
      RWN=3.492427
      NSIG=421
      DXW=ALOG(RWNP)-ALOG(RWN)
      XW(1)=ALOG(RW1)
      READ (1,61)(NAME(I),I=1,4)
   61 FORMAT(4A4)
      READ (1,6)(SIGW(J),J=1,NSIG)
    6 FORMAT(8E10.3)
      XL=-8.8
      DXL=.05
    8 JW=2
      XW(2)=XW(1)+DXW
      JL=1
   12 IF (XL-XW(JW))10,10,11
   11 IF (JW-NSIG)14,13,13
   14 JW=JW+1
      XW(JW)=XW(JW-1)+DXW
      GO TO 12
   10 PSQ(JL)= SIGW(JW-1)+(XL-XW(JW-1))*(SIGW(JW)-SIGW(JW-1))/DXW
      IF (JL-250)15,13,13
   15 JL=JL+1
      XL=XL+DXL
      GO TO 12
C
C     LATTICE  CALCULATIONS
   13 READ (1,80)Z,JRI,LAT
   80 FORMAT(1F10.6,2I5)
      READ (1,51)OMA,A,C
      IF (LAT-4)82,400,101
C
C        HCP CRYSTAL STRUCTURE
C
  400 B=C/A
      BS=B*B
      R(1)=0.
      R(2)=1./3.+BS/4.
      R(3)=1.
```

```
           R(4)=4./3.+BS/4.
           R(5)=BS
           R(6)=7./3.+BS/4.
           R(7)=3.
           R(8)=1.+BS
           R(9)=4.
           R(10)=13./3.+BS/4.
           R(11)=3.+BS
           R(12)=1./3.+(9.*BS)/4.
           R(13)=16./3.+BS/4.
           R(14)=4.+BS
           DO 2 I=1,14
         2 AD(I)=SQRT(R(I))
           GO TO 52
C
C          FCC, BCC, AND DIAMOND CRYSTAL STRUCTURES
C
        82 DO 62 I=1,14
        62 AD(I)=XAD(LAT,I)
        52 DO 83 I=1,14
        83 XNA(I)=NA(LAT,I)
           DS=A
           DO 20 J=2,14
        20 AD(J)=DS*AD(J)
           GO TO 503
C
C          SPECIAL CRYSTAL STRUCTURES
C
       101 READ (1,51)(XNA(I),I=1,14)
           READ (1,51)(AD(I),I=1,14)
C
C          MUFFIN TIN SEGMENT
C
       503 I=225
        84 IF (PSQ(I)-1.E-10)85,86,86
        86 I=I+1
           GO TO 84
        85 JJCHI=I
           CALL POISON (PSQ,Z,JJCHI,W)
C                                             (SEE APPENDIX 1)
           X=-8.8
           DO 108 J=1,JJCHI
           CE=EXP(-.5*X)
           AA(J)=CE*(-2.*Z*CE+W(J))
C                                   (ATOMIC ELECTROSTATIC POTENTIAL)
           AB(J)=PSQ(J)*EXP(-2.*X)
C                                   (4*PI* ATOMIC ELECTRONIC DENSITY)
       108 X=X+.05
           RO=(.75*OMA/3.141593)**(1./3.)
           XJRI=JRI
           XJXB=.05*(XJRI-1.)-8.8
```

```
      RI=EXP(XJXB)
      CI=3./(RO*RO*RO-RI*RI*RI)
      XT=ALOG(RO)
      JXT=1.+20.*(XT+8.8)
      JTOP=JXT+1
      CALL SUMAX(AA,AACR,JJCHI,XNA,AD,JTOP)
C                                    (EQ 3.26 BASED ON EQ 3.22)
      CALL SUMAX(AB,ABCR,JJCHI,XNA,AD,JTOP)
C                                    (EQ 3.28 BASED ON EQ 3.22)
      CP=3.*(3./(2.*3.141593)**2)**(1./3.)
C
C
C         CALCULATING  AVERAGE POTENTIAL BY EQ. 3.31
C
      YJXT=JXT
      XJXT=.05*(YJXT-1.)-8.8
      G=XT-XJXT
      FR=CI*EXP(3.*(XJXT+.05))*(AACR(JXT+1)-CP*ABCR(JXT+1)**(1./3.))
      FL=CI*EXP(3.*XJXT)*(AACR(JXT)-CP*ABCR(JXT)**(1./3.))
      VINT=.5*G*((2.-20.*G)*FL+20.*G*FR)
      XJXB=XJXB-.05
      JXB=JRI-1
  109 JXB=JXB+1
      IF (JXB-JXT)110,111,111
  110 XJXB=XJXB+.05
      FR=CI*EXP(3.*(XJXB+.05))*(AACR(JXB+1)-CP*ABCR(JXB+1)**(1./3.))
      FL=CI*EXP(3.*XJXB)*(AACR(JXB)-CP*ABCR(JXB)**(1./3.))
      VINT=VINT+.025*(FR+FL)
      GO TO 109
  111 X=-8.8
      DO 112 J=1,JTOP
  113 BGXMT(J)= AACR(J)-CP*ABCR(J)**(1./3.)-VINT
  112 X=X+.05
      WRITE (3,1170)RI,(NAME(I),I=1,4)
 1170 FORMAT(a1      RESULTS FOR MUFFIN-TIN WITH       RI=aF7.4,20X,4A4//)
      WRITE (3,117)VINT,Z,JRI,LAT
  117 FORMAT(a VINT=aE17.8,a      Z=aF10.2,a    JRI=aI5,a    LAT=aI3//)
      WRITE (3,115)BGXMT
  115 FORMAT (5E20.8)
      WRITE (2,116)BGXMT
  116 FORMAT (5E16.8)
      STOP 88
      END
```

```
      SUBROUTINE SUMAX(CHIAT,CHICRY,JJCHI,XNA,AD,JTOP)
C
C     THIS PERFORMS EQ.3.22 AND SUMS OVER 14 NEAREST SHELLS OF ATOMS)
C
      DIMENSION CHIAT(250),CHICRY(250),XNA(15),AD(15),STOR(250,15)
      XJJCHI=JJCHI
      TOPX=.05*(XJJCHI-1.)-8.8
      DO 6 J=1,JTOP
    6 STOR(J,1)=CHIAT(J)
      JA=2
    7 X=-8.8
      I=1
    8 XINT=0.
      ET=EXP(X)
   31 BLX=ALOG(AD(JA)-ET)
      IF (BLX-TOPX)9,50,50
    9 JBL=2.+20.*(BLX+8.8)
      XJBL=JBL
      XBL=.05*(XJBL-1.)-8.8
      G=XBL-BLX
      XINT=XINT+.5*G*(CHIAT(JBL)*(2.-20.*G)*EXP(2.*XBL)+20.*G*CHIAT(JBL
     1-1)*EXP(2.*(XBL-.05)))
      TLX=ALOG(AD(JA)+ET)
      IF (TLX-TOPX)10,11,11
   11 JTL=JJCHI
      GO TO 40
   10 JTL=1.+20.*(TLX+8.8)
      IF (JTL-JBL)12,13,13
   12 FZN=CHIAT(JTL)*EXP(2.*(XBL-.05))
      FZ3=CHIAT(JBL)*EXP(2.*XBL)
      FZ2=FZN+20.*(FZ3-FZN)*(TLX-XBL+.05)
      FZ1=FZN+20.*(FZ3-FZN)*(BLX-XBL+.05)
      XINT=.5*(FZ1+FZ2)*(TLX-BLX)
      GO TO 50
   13 XJTL=JTL
      XTL=.05*(XJTL-1.)-8.8
      C=TLX-XTL
      XINT=XINT+.5*C*(CHIAT(JTL)*(2.-20.*C)*EXP(2.*XTL)+CHIAT(JTL+1)*
     120.*C*EXP(2.*(XTL+.05)))
   40 IF (JTL-JBL)50,50,14
   14 XINT=XINT+.5*(CHIAT(JBL)*EXP(2.*XBL)+CHIAT(JBL+1)*EXP(2.*(XBL+
     1.05)))*.05
      JBL=JBL+1
      IF (JBL-JTL)15,50,50
   15 XBL=XBL+.05
      GO TO 14
   50 STOR(I,JA)=.5*XINT*XNA(JA)/(AD(JA)*ET)
   32 IF (I-JTOP)16,17,17
   16 I=I+1
      X=X+.05
      GO TO 8
```

```
17 IF (JA-14)19,20,20
19 JA=JA+1
   GO TO 7
20 I=1
21 JA=1
   CHICRY(I)=0.
22 CHICRY(I)=CHICRY(I)+STOR(I,JA)
   IF (JA-14)23,24,24
23 JA=JA+1
   GO TO 22
24 IF (I-JTOP)25,26,26
25 I=I+1
   GO TO 21
26 RETURN
   END
```

Appendix 3

LOGARITHMIC DERIVATIVE SUBROUTINE

In Chapter 3 we discussed several methods of calculating the logarithmic derivatives (3-33). In this section some computer programs based on these methods are presented. The main program is coded to calculate the logarithmic derivatives by two different methods, the Noumerov method based on (3-50) and a composite method using both the Runge-Kutta and Milne methods. The energy dependence of the logarithmic derivatives based on the Noumerov method are fit by polynomials. Results calculated from the polynomial expansions are then compared with the original Noumerov results and the results from the composite Runge-Kutta-Milne method. It has been our experience that the polynomial expansions of the Noumerov results have always compared favorably with the more accurate results from the composite method, and hence the expansion coefficients are used as input to the APW program discussed in Appendix 5.

The input and output variables associated with these programs are listed below.

TEXT   Title card giving atomic species, etc. (80 columns)

BGX   Muffin-tin potential; output of program discussed in Appendix 2.

JRI

Index of the grid point corresponding to the APW sphere radius on a log scale with x_1 = -8.8 and $\Delta x = 0.05$ (see Fig. 3-8).

MAXL

Maximum value of ℓ in the summations in (2-60) and (2-68).

NE, BE, and ES

The energy range over which the logarithmic derivatives are to be fit by polynomials is specified by NE, BE, and ES. BE is the lower limit of the energy range. ES is the increment in the energy and NE is the number of such increments between the lower and upper limits of the energy range.

NDEG

The degree of the polynomials used to fit the energy dependence of the logarithmic derivatives. We have found 7th degree polynomials to be adequate in most cases. Runs can be made using polynomials of different degree by including more than one input card corresponding to statement 200.

QC, QD

The polynomial coefficients which fit the energy dependence of the logarithmic derivatives are both printed and punched on cards. The output is in the order of increasing ℓ values. For each ℓ there are two groups of polynomial coefficients: the first (QC) is used to fit the radial function R, the second (QD) to fit the derivative of the radial function. The equation for the logarithmic derivative is then given by

$$L_\ell(E) = R'_\ell / R_\ell = \sum_{i=o}^{NDEG} (QC)_i E^i \Big/ \sum_{i=o}^{NDEG} (QD)_i E^i$$

The programs listed below are based on a logarithmic scale with $x_1 = -8.8$ and $\Delta x = 0.05$ (see Fig. 3-8).

```
C     LOGARITHMIC DERIVATIVE PROGRAM
      DIMENSION BGX(250),Y(250),EX(80),AN(20,80),R(20,80),RP(20,80),
     1QA(10),QB(10),RY(80),RYP(80),W(80),DIF(80),TEXT(20),ANS(80),
     2QC(10),QD(10),ANF(20),FG(20,80),DI(20,80),SUMP(4),SUMR(4)
      DOUBLE PRECISION QA,QB
      READ(1,3)TEXT
    3 FORMAT(20A4)
      READ(1,5)BGX
    5 FORMAT(5E16.8)
      READ(1,7)JRI,MAXL,NE,BE,ES
    7 FORMAT(3I5,2F10.6)
C     NOUMEROV METHOD
      DAC=2.083333E-04
      DB=2.083333E-03
      NL=MAXL+1
      DO 41 I=1,NL
      XL=I-1
      Q=(XL+0.5)*(XL+0.5)
      E=BE-ES
      DO 41 J=1,NE
      E=E+ES
      YJM1=1.E-20
      YJ=EXP(.05*(XL+.5))*YJM1
C                                               EQ. 3.42 WITH X-X₁ =.05
      SGM1=Q+EXP(-17.6)*(BGX(1)-E)
C                                               EQ. 3.37 WITH X=-8.80
      SG=Q+EXP(-17.5)*(BGX(2)-E)
C                                               EQ. 3.37 WITH X=-8.75
      X=-8.8
      Y(1)=YJM1
      Y(2)=YJ
      DO 38 K=1,JRI
      X=X+0.05
      EEF=EXP(2.*(X+.05))
      SGP1=Q+EEF*(BGX(K+2)-E)
C                                               EQ. 3.37
      A=1.-DAC*SGP1
      B=-2.-DB*SG
      C=1.-DAC*SGM1
C                                               EQ. 3.51
      YJP1=-(B*YJ+C*YJM1)/A
C                                               EQ. 3.50
      Y(K+2)=YJP1
      YJM1=YJ
      YJ=YJP1
      SGM1=SG
   38 SG=SGP1
      XJRI=X-0.05
      R(I,J)=EXP(-0.5*XJRI)*Y(JRI)
C                                               R, RADIAL FUNCTION
```

```
      YP=(Y(JRI-2)-8.*Y(JRI-1)+8.*Y(JRI+1)-Y(JRI+2))/.6
C                                             EQ. 3.48
      RP(I,J)=EXP(-1.5*XJRI)*(YP-0.5*Y(JRI))
C                                             R', DERIVATIVE OF RADIAL FUNCTION
       AN(I,J)=RP(I,J)/R(I,J)
C                                             EQ. 3.43
   41 EX(J)=E
      DO 100 JC=1,NE
      EQ=EX(JC)
      CALL DLOGDR(BGX,EQ,MAXL,JRI,ANF)
C
C                                             CALLS LOGARITHMIC DERIVATIVE
C                                             SUBROUTINE   BASED ON COUPLED
C                                             FIRST ORDER EQUATIONS
C
      DO 100 IC=1,NL
      FG(IC,JC)=ANF(IC)
  100 DI(IC,JC)=ANF(IC) - AN(IC,JC)
  200 READ(1,45)NDEG
   45 FORMAT(I5)
      IF(NDEG)201,201,46
   46 ND1=NDEG+1
      WRITE (2,66)NDEG
   66 FORMAT(I5)
      DO 75 I=1,NL
      DO 47 J=1,NE
      W(J)=1.
      RY(J)=R(I,J)
   47 RYP(J)=RP(I,J)
      CALL OPLSPA(NDEG,NE,EX,RY,W,QA,0.0)
C     POLYNOMIAL FIT OF R
      CALL OPLSPA(NDEG,NE,EX,RYP,W,QB,0.0)
C     POLYNOMIAL FIT OF R
      DO 50 K1=1,ND1
      QC(K1)=QA(K1)
   50 QD(K1)=QB(K1)
      DO 58 JA=1,NE
      ANR=QC(1)
      ANP=QD(1)
      DO 56 K=2,ND1
      XE=EX(JA)**(K-1)
      ANR=ANR+QC(K)*XE
   56 ANP=ANP+QD(K)*XE
      ANS(JA)=ANP/ANR
C                LOGARITHMIC DERIVATIVE FROM POLYNOMIAL FIT
   58 DIF(JA)=AN(I,JA)-ANS(JA)
      WRITE(3,60)TEXT
   60 FORMAT(1H1,20A4)
      IA=I-1
C                PRINTS AND PUNCHES POLYNOMIAL COEFFICIENTS
      WRITE(3,63)IA
   63 FORMAT(1H0,43H COEFF. TO PSI AND PSI@(LOW TO HIGH) FOR L=,I3)
```

```
      WRITE(3,65)(QC(KA),KA=1,ND1)
   65 FORMAT(1H0,4HPSI ,6E16.8)
      WRITE(3,67)(QD(KB),KB=1,ND1)
   67 FORMAT(1H0,4HPSI∂,6E16.8)
      WRITE(2,68)(QC(KA),KA=1,ND1)
      WRITE(2,68)(QD(KB),KB=1,ND1)
   68 FORMAT(5E16.8)
C
C   ROOT MEAN SQUARE ANALYSIS OF VARIOUS METHODS
C
      MP=1
      M1=1
      M2=NE/4
  120 SUMA=0.0
      SUMB=0.0
      DO 101 MQ=M1,M2
      SUMA=SUMA+DIF(MQ)*DIF(MQ)
  101 SUMB=SUMB+DI(I,MQ)*DI(I,MQ)
      SUMP(MP)=SQRT(SUMA/(M2-M1+1))
      SUMR(MP)=SQRT(SUMB/(M2-M1+1))
      M1=M2+1
      M2=M2+NE/4
      MP=MP+1
      IF(MP-4)120,120,102
  102 STOA=0.0
      STOB=0.0
      DO 103 MR=1,4
      STOA=STOA+SUMP(MR)/4.*SUMP(MR)
  103 STOB=STOB+SUMR(MR)/4.*SUMR(MR)
      STOC=SQRT(STOA)
      STOD=SQRT(STOB)
      WRITE(3,110)
  110 FORMAT(1H0,50H ROOT MEAN SQ.        DLOGDR-RAT.POL.      F/G-DLOGDR)
      DO 112 MST=1,4
  112 WRITE(3,113)MST,SUMP(MST),SUMR(MST)
  113 FORMAT(1H0,I2,11H.QUARTER    ,2E20.8)
      WRITE(3,115)STOC,STOD
  115 FORMAT(1H0,13H   TOTAL     ,2E20.8)
      WRITE(3,69)
   69 FORMAT(1H0,110H  E=              DLOGDR=                RAT.POL.=
     1       DIFF.=         F/G=                F/G - DLOGDR=)
      DO 71 JB=1,NE
   71 WRITE(3,72)EX(JB),AN(I,JB),ANS(JB),DIF(JB),FG(I,JB),DI(I,JB)
   72 FORMAT(1H ,F10.6,5E20.8)
   75 CONTINUE
      GO TO 200
  201 STOP
      END
```

```
      SUBROUTINE DLOGDR(BGX,E,LM,JRI,ANS)
C     COUPLED EQUATIONS - MILNE METHOD (STARTS WITH RUNGE-KUTTA)
      DIMENSION BGX(250),ANS(30),SXK(4),SXM(4),P(250),Q(250),PP(200),
     1QP(250)
      TEST=1.E+4
      DX=.05
      XJRI=JRI
      XI=.05*(XJRI-1.)-8.8
      RI=EXP(XI)
      HO=-BGX(1)*EXP(-8.8)
C                                                -R*V(R)= +2Z FOR X=-8.8
      MXKAP=LM+1
   48 DO 95 K=1,MXKAP
C                                                K= L+1
      XK=-K
      AOB=.5*HO/XK
C                                                Q/P FOR X=-8.8 (EQ.3.68)
      CB=EXP(-8.8)
      TC=(E-BGX(1))*CB
    8 P(1)=1.E-20
C                                                EQ. 3.69
      Q(1)= AOB*P(1)
C                                                EQ. 3.71
      PP(1)=Q(1)*CB-XK*P(1)
C                                                EQ. 3.62
      QP(1)=XK*Q(1)-TC*P(1)
C                                                EQ. 3.63
   11 X=-8.8
      N=1
   25 IK=0
      XC=X
      BGC=BGX(N)
      WC=Q(N)
      UC=P(N)
   20 IK=IK+1
      T=EXP(XC)
      TC=(E-BGC)*T
   12 SXK(IK)=DX*(-XK*UC+WC*T)
C                                                k_i IN EQ. 3.75
      SXM(IK)=DX*(XK*WC-TC*UC)
C                                                m_i IN ANALOGOUS EQUATION
   15 GO TO (16,17,18,19),IK
   16 XC=XC+.5*DX
      UC=UC+.5*SXK(1)
      WC=WC+.5*SXM(1)
      BGC=.5*(BGC+BGX(N+1))
      GO TO 20
   17 UC=UC+.5*(SXK(2)-SXK(1))
      WC=WC+.5*(SXM(2)-SXM(1))
      GO TO 20
```

```
 18 XC=XC+.5*DX
    UC=UC+SXK(3)-.5*SXK(2)
    WC=WC+SXM(3)-.5*SXM(2)
    BGC=BGX(N+1)
    GO TO 20
 19 Q(N+1)=Q(N)+(SXM(1)+2.*SXM(2)+2.*SXM(3)+SXM(4))/6.
C                                        EQ. 3.74
    P(N+1)=P(N)+(SXK(1)+2.*SXK(2)+2.*SXK(3)+SXK(4))/6.
C                                        EQ. 3.73
    PP(N+1)=T*Q(N+1)-XK*P(N+1)
C                                        EQ. 3.62
    QP(N+1)=XK*Q(N+1)-TC*P(N+1)
C                                        EQ. 3.63
 24 X=X+DX
    N=N+1
    IF (N-6)25,26,26
 26 X=X+DX
    T=EXP(X)
    TC=(E-BGX(N+1))*T
 27 UNP=P(N-5)+.015*(11.*PP(N)-14.*PP(N-1)+26.*PP(N-2)-14.*PP(N-3)+11.
   1*PP(N-4))
C                                        EQ. 4.92
    WNP=Q(N-5)+.015*(11.*QP(N)-14.*QP(N-1)+26.*QP(N-2)-14.*QP(N-3)+11.
   1*QP(N-4))
C                                        ANALOGOUS EQUATION
    NIT=0
 33 PP(N+1)=T*WNP-XK*UNP
C                                        EQ. 3.62
    QP(N+1)=XK*WNP-TC*UNP
C                                        EQ. 3.63
    UNP2=P(N-3)+(7.*PP(N+1)+32.*PP(N)+12.*PP(N-1)+32.*PP(N-2)+7.*PP(N-
   13))/450.
C                                        EQ. 4.93
    WNP2=Q(N-3)+(7.*QP(N+1)+32.*QP(N)+12.*QP(N-1)+32.*QP(N-2)+7.*QP(N-
   13))/450.
C                                        ANALOGOUS EQUATION
    IF (ABS(TEST*(UNP2-UNP))-ABS(UNP2))30,30,31
 30 IF (ABS(TEST*(WNP2-WNP))-ABS(WNP2))32,32,31
 31 IF (NIT-5)81,32,81
 81 NIT=NIT+1
    WNP=WNP2
    UNP=UNP2
    GO TO 33
 32 Q(N+1)=WNP2
    P(N+1)=UNP2
    N=N+1
    IF (N-JRI)26,34,34
 34 ANS(K)=Q(N)/P(N)-(1.+XK)/RI
C                                        EQ. 3.61
 95 CONTINUE
 46 RETURN
    END
```

```
      SUBROUTINE OPLSPA (NDEG,NPTS,X,Y,W,Q,TUWYLO)
C
C     POLYNOMIAL FITTING PROGRAM
C
      DIMENSION  X(1),  Y(1),  W(1)
      DOUBLE PRECISION Q(1), PN(11), PN1(10), SUM(4), B, C, PNX, TMP
      IF (TUWYLO)  2,1,2
   1  N=0
      C=0.
      PN(1)=1.0
      GO TO 6
   2  C=-SUM(3)/SUM(4)
   3  B=-SUM(1)/SUM(3)
      SUM(4)=SUM(3)
      N=N+1
      PN1(N)=0.
      PN(N+1)=0.
      DO 4    J=1,N
      TMP=PN(J)
      PN(J)=B*PN(J)+C*PN1(J)
   4  PN1(J)=TMP
      DO 5    J=1,N
   5  PN(J+1)=PN(J+1)+PN1(J)
   6  DO 7    K=1,3
   7  SUM(K)=0.0
      DO 11   I=1,NPTS
      PNX=1.0
      J=N
   8  IF (J)   10,10,9
   9  PNX=PN(J)+PNX*X(I)
      J=J-1
      GO TO 8
  10  SUM(1)=SUM(1)+W(I)*X(I)*PNX*PNX
      SUM(2)=SUM(2)+W(I)*Y(I)*PNX
  11  SUM(3)=SUM(3)+W(I)*PNX*PNX
      Q(N+1)=SUM(2)/SUM(3)
      IF (N)   3,3,12
  12  DO 13   J=1,N
  13  Q(J)=Q(J)+Q(N+1)*PN(J)
      IF (N-NDEG)  2,14,14
  14  RETURN
      END
```

Appendix 4

SPHERICAL BESSEL FUNCTION SUBROUTINE

The subroutine listed in this Appendix is used to calculate spherical Bessel functions. It is based on the method discussed in Chapter 3. The variables occurring in the argument list are defined below.

FJ, X, N   The Bessel function $j_\ell (x)$ is stored in
                        $FJ(\ell + 1)$ for $\ell = 0, 1, 2 \ldots N$.

JCK   Dimension of FJ in the main program. It should be at least three times the maximum value of N.

```
      SUBROUTINE BESSH(N,X,FJ,JCK)
      DIMENSION FJ(1)
      IF (N)1,7,7
   1  WRITE (3,2)
   2  FORMAT (33H1 ERROR, N SHOULD NOT BE NEGATIVE)
      STOP 88
   7  IF (X)8,11,10
   8  WRITE (3,9)
   9  FORMAT (33H1 ERROR, X SHOULD NOT BE NEGATIVE)
      STOP 88
  10  IF (X-.00000001)11,25,25
  11  FJ(1)=1.0
      IF (N)1,15,12
  12  MM=N+1
      DO 13 M=2,MM
  13  FJ(M)=0.0
  15  RETURN
  25  FNC=1.04*X+6.5
      TST=4.21*ALOG10(X)+3.0
      IF (2.0-TST)27,26,26
  26  DELTA=2.0
      GO TO 28
  27  DELTA=TST
  28  FN=N
      IF (FN-FNC)29,29,30
  29  FNS=FNC+DELTA
      GO TO 31
  30  FNS=FN+DELTA
  31  NS=FNS+1.0
      IF (NS+2-JCK)313,313,310
 310  WRITE (3,311)
 311  FORMAT (30H1ERROR, NS+2 EXCEEDS DIMENSION)
      WRITE (3,312)NS,JCK,N,X
 312  FORMAT (1HJ4X3HNS=I11,5X10HDIMENSION=I11,5X2HN=I11,5X2HX=E20.8)
      STOP 88
 313  FJ(NS+1)=0.0
      FJ(NS)=1.0E-45
      M=NS-1
      FM=M-1
  32  FJ(M)=((2.0*FM+3.0)/X)*FJ(M+1)-FJ(M+2)
      IF (ABS(FJ(M))-1.0E40)320,56,56
 320  IF (M-1)34,34,33
  33  M=M-1
      FM=FM-1.0
      GO TO 32
  34  IF (X-0.02)35,36,36
  35  SER=1.0-X**2/6.0+X**4/120.0
      CON=FJ(1)/SER
      JJ=1
      GO TO 39
  36  SER=SIN(X)
```

```
      IF (ABS(SER)-.1)37,38,38
   37 IF (X-.11)38,38,380
   38 CON=X*FJ(1)/SER
      JJ=1
      GO TO 39
  380 CON1=X*FJ(1)/SER
      FJ(1)=FJ(1)/CON1
      CON=X*FJ(2)/(SER/X-COS(X))
      JJ=2
   39 MM=N+1
      DO 40 M=JJ,MM
   40 FJ(M)=FJ(M)/CON
      RETURN
   56 JJ=M+1
      DO 57 J=JJ,NS
   57 FJ(J)=FJ(J)*1.0E-40
      GO TO 32
      END
```

Appendix 5

APW PROGRAMS

The computer programs described in this Appendix are used to calculate the APW secular determinant as a function of energy for lattices with either one or two identical atoms per unit cell. In the main program the calculations which depend only on the wave vector of the electron $\vec{k}$, i. e., on the point in the Brillouin zone, are performed. In the subroutine STDET the energy dependent part of the matrix elements is calculated and the determinant evaluated. A discussion of these subjects is given in Chapter 3. The input and output variables are defined below.

BAX, BAY, BAZ	The x, y, and z components of the vector separating the two atoms in the unit cell. For the HCP structure this is given by $\vec{\tau}_2$ in Equation (3-3). If there is only one atom per unit cell these are zero.
$\emptyset$M3	Volume occupied by two atoms. For crystal structures with two atoms per unit cell this is Ω_o given in Equation (3-2); for only one atom per unit cell, two times Ω_o must be used.
MAXL	Maximum value of ℓ in the summations in (2-60) and (2-68).
JRI	Index of the grid point corresponding to the APW sphere radius on a log scale with $x_1 = -8.8$ and $\Delta x = 0.05$. (See Fig. 3-8.)

NDEG   Degree of the polynomials used to fit the
                            energy dependence of the logarithmic
                            derivatives. (See Appendix 3.)

NBAS   Number of recips used in the APW ex-
                            pansion.

QP, QPP   Polynomial coefficients used to fit energy
                            dependence of the logarithmic derivatives.
                            This is punched card output of the pro-
                            gram described in Appendix 3 where the
                            variables are called QC and QD, respec-
                            tively.

BKX, BKY, BKZ   The x, y, and z components of the recips
                            used in the APW expansion.

SKX, SKY, SKZ   The x, y, and z components of the wave

                            vector $\vec{k}$.

EBOT, ETOP, DELE   The determinant is calculated for ener-
                            gies ranging from EBOT to ETOP in in-
                            crements equal to DELE.

E, DET   The output is energy E and the secular
                            determinant DET.

```
C        APW DETERMINANT AS A FUNCTION OF ENERGY
         DIMENSION BKX(50),BKY(50),BKZ(50),SKIM(50),SKIX(50),SKIY(50),
        1SKIZ(50),ANS(20),FJL(50,20),FJ(100),QP(10,20),
        2QPP(10,20),FJ1(50,50),STR(50,50),DOT(50,50)
         COMMON NBAS,MAXL,C4,SKIM,SKIX,SKIY,SKIZ,FJL,ANS,RI,BAX,BAY,BAZ,
        1FJ1,STR,DOT
         READ (1,2)BAX,BAY,BAZ,OM3,MAXL,JRI,NDEG,NBAS
       2 FORMAT(4F10.6,4I5)
         XJRI=JRI
         RI=EXP(.05*(XJRI-1.)-8.8)
C                                       APW SPHERE RADIUS S
         NL=MAXL+1
         ND1=NDEG+1
         DO 10 L1=1,NL
         READ(1,1)(QP(JA,L1),JA=1,ND1)
      10 READ(1,1)(QPP(JB,L1),JB=1,ND1)
       1 FORMAT(5E16.8)
C                                       POLYNOMIAL COEFFICIENTS FOR ENERGY
C                                       DEPENDENCE OF LOGARITHMIC DERIVATIVES
      40 READ (1,3)(BKX(J),BKY(J),BKZ(J),J=1,NBAS)
       3 FORMAT(3E20.8)
C                                       RECIPROCAL LATTICE VECTORS  $\vec{g}_i$
         C4=4.*3.1415927E0*RI*RI/OM3
      11 READ(1,4)SKX,SKY,SKZ
       4 FORMAT(3F10.6)
C                                       WAVE VECTOR  $\vec{k}$
         WRITE(3,203)SKX,SKY,SKZ
     203 FORMAT(5X,11H KX,KY,KZ= 3F15.8)
         DO 100 I=1,NBAS
         SKIX(I)=SKX+BKX(I)
         SKIY(I)=SKY+BKY(I)
         SKIZ(I)=SKZ+BKZ(I)
C                                       COMPONENTS OF  $\vec{k}_i = \vec{k} + \vec{g}_i$
         SKIM(I)=SQRT(SKIX(I)*SKIX(I)+SKIY(I)*SKIY(I)+SKIZ(I)*SKIZ(I))
C                                       MAGNITUDE OF  $\vec{k}_i$
         X=SKIM(I)*RI
         CALL BESSH(MAXL,X,FJ,100)
C                                       SPHERICAL BESSEL FUNCTION SUBROUTINE
C                                       (SEE APPENDIX 4)
         DO 100 JL=1,NL
     100 FJL(I,JL)=FJ(JL)
         DO 500 I=1,NBAS
         IT=I+1
         DO 500 J=IT,NBAS
         DOT(I,J)=SKIX(I)*SKIX(J)+SKIY(I)*SKIY(J)+SKIZ(I)*SKIZ(J)
C                                       $\vec{k}_i \cdot \vec{k}_j$
         DKM=SQRT(SKIM(I)*SKIM(I)+SKIM(J)*SKIM(J)-2.*DOT(I,J))
C                                       $|\vec{k}_{ij}|$
```

```
      AR=DKM*RI
      FJ1(I,J)=(SIN(AR)/AR-COS(AR))/AR/DKM
C                                              j_1(|k_ij|S)/|k_ij|
      DKX=SKIX(J)-SKIX(I)
      DKY=SKIY(J)-SKIY(I)
      DKZ=SKIZ(J)-SKIZ(I)
C                                         COMPONENTS OF k_ij
      CAP=BAX*DKX+BAY*DKY+BAZ*DKZ
  500 STR(I,J)=2.*COS(.5*CAP)
C                                         Σ e^{ik_ij·r_ν}; THE STRUCTURE FACTOR
      READ(1,201) EBOT,ETOP,DELE          ν
  201 FORMAT(3F10.6)
      WRITE(3,204) DELE,EBOT,ETOP
  204 FORMAT(2X,5HDELE=F10.6,10X,5HEBOT=F10.6,10X,5HETOP=F10.6)
      E=EBOT
      IF(DELE)5,5,202
C                                         POLYNOMIAL EXPRESSIONS FOR R AND R'
  202 DO 70 IL=1,NL
      ANR=QP(1,IL)
      ANP=QPP(1,IL)
      DO 71 K=2,ND1
      XE=E**(K-1)
      ANR=ANR+QP(K,IL)*XE
   71 ANP=ANP+QPP(K,IL)*XE
   70 ANS(IL)=ANP/ANR
C                                         LOGARITHMIC DERIVATIVES
      CALL STDET(E,DET)
C                                         SUBROUTINE FOR EVALUATING SECULAR
C                                         DETERMINANT
      WRITE(3,72)E,DET
   72 FORMAT(20X,2E20.8)
      E=E+DELE
      IF(ETOP-E)11,11,202
    5 STOP 88
      END
```

```
      SUBROUTINE STDET(EP,DET)
      DIMENSION SKIM(50),SKIX(50),SKIY(50),SKIZ(50),FJL(50,20),ANS(20),
     1D(50,50),FPL(20),FJ1(50,50),STR(50,50),DOT(50,50)
      COMMON NBAS,MAXL,C4,SKIM,SKIX,SKIY,SKIZ,FJL,ANS,RI,BAX,BAY,BAZ,
     1FJ1,STR,DOT
      DET=1.
      N=MAXL+1
      DO 49 I=1,NBAS
      CT=(SKIM(I)*SKIM(I)-EP)*(1.-2.*C4*RI/3.)
      SUM1=FJL(I,1)*FJL(I,1)*ANS(1)
      DO 12 L=2,N
      XL1=L-1
   12 SUM1=SUM1+(2.*XL1+1.)*FJL(I,L)*FJL(I,L)*ANS(L)
      SUM2=2.*C4*SUM1+CT
C                                      DIAGONAL MATRIX ELEMENTS
C                                      (EQS. 2.59 AND 2.68)
      IF(I-1)19,19,14
   14 DO 18 NA=2,I
   18 SUM2=SUM2-D(NA-1,I)*D(NA-1,I)/D(NA-1,NA-1)
C                                      TRIANGULARIZATION PROCEDURE (EQ. 3.95)
   19 D(I,I)=SUM2
      DET=DET*SUM2
C                                      DETERMINANT IS PRODUCT OF DIAGONAL
C                                      ELEMENTS (EQ. 3.96)
      JA=I+1
      IF(JA-NBAS)25,25,51
   25 DO 49 J=JA,NBAS
      IF(SKIM(I))31,31,30
   30 IF(SKIM(J))31,31,33
   31 CSK=1.
      GO TO 34
   33 CSK=DOT(I,J)/SKIM(I)/SKIM(J)
   34 FPL(1)=1.
      FPL(2)=CSK
      SUM3=FJL(I,1)*FJL(J,1)*ANS(1)
      SUM3=SUM3+3.*FJL(I,2)*FJL(J,2)*CSK*ANS(2)
      DO 41 L=3,N
      XL2=L-1
      FPL(L)=(2.*XL2-1.)*CSK*FPL(L-1)/XL2-(XL2-1.)*FPL(L-2)/XL2
   41 SUM3=SUM3+(2.*XL2+1.)*FJL(I,L)*FJL(J,L)*FPL(L)*ANS(L)
      SUM4=C4*(SUM3+FJ1(I,J)*(EP-DOT(I,J)))*STR(I,J)
C                                      NON-DIAGONAL MATRIX ELEMENTS
C                                      (EQS. 2.59 AND 2.68)
      IF(I-1)49,49,43
   43 DO 48 NB=2,I
   48 SUM4=SUM4-D(NB-1,I)*D(NB-1,J)/D(NB-1,NB-1)
C                                      TRIANGULARIZATION PROCEDURE (EQ. 3.95)
   49 D(I,J)=SUM4
   51 RETURN
      END
```

Appendix 6

SIMPLIFICATION OF THE COEFFICIENTS $D_\kappa^{ij}\binom{n}{m}$

The coefficients $D_\kappa^{ij}\binom{n}{m}$ occur in the relativistic APW matrix
elements (4-78). According to (4-79) they are given by

$$D_\kappa^{ij}\binom{n}{m} = 4\pi \sum_\mu C(\ell \tfrac{1}{2} j; \mu - n, n)\, C(\ell \tfrac{1}{2} j; \mu - m, m)$$

$$Y^*_{\ell, \mu - n}(\hat{k}_j)\, Y_{\ell, \mu - m}(\hat{k}_i) \tag{A6-1}$$

In this Appendix it is shown that

$$D_\kappa^{ij}\binom{+}{+} = |\kappa|\, P_\ell(\hat{k}_i \cdot \hat{k}_j) + iS_\kappa\, (\hat{k}_i \times \hat{k}_j)_z\, P'_\ell(\hat{k}_i \cdot \hat{k}_j) \tag{A6-2}$$

$$D_\kappa^{ij}\binom{-}{+} = iS_\kappa\, P'_\ell(\hat{k}_i \cdot \hat{k}_j)\left[(\hat{k}_i \times \hat{k}_j)_x - i(\hat{k}_i \times \hat{k}_j)_y \right] \tag{A6-3}$$

which are the results stated in (4-80) and (4-81).

Let us first consider the case $n = m = + \tfrac{1}{2}$ which leads to (A6-2).
For definiteness we assume that $\kappa > 0$. From (4-21) and Table 4-1, we
have

$$C(\ell \tfrac{1}{2} j; \mu - \tfrac{1}{2}, \tfrac{1}{2}) = -\left(\frac{\ell - \mu + \tfrac{1}{2}}{2\ell + 1} \right)^{\tfrac{1}{2}} \tag{A6-4}$$

Substituting into (A6-1) yields

$$D = \frac{4\pi}{2\ell + 1} \sum_{\mu} (\ell - \mu + \tfrac{1}{2}) \, Y^*_{\ell, \mu - \frac{1}{2}}(\hat{k}_j) \, Y_{\ell, \mu - \frac{1}{2}}(\hat{k}_i) \qquad (A6-5)$$

The summation includes all the integers between -j and +j, and j = $\ell - \tfrac{1}{2}$ for $\kappa > 0$. Hence, by defining m = $\mu - \tfrac{1}{2}$ we can write equation (A6-5) as

$$D = \frac{4\pi}{2\ell + 1} \sum_{m = -\ell}^{+\ell} (\ell - m) \, Y^*_{\ell m}(\hat{k}_j) \, Y_{\ell m}(\hat{k}_i) \qquad (A6-6)$$

The upper limit corresponding to μ = +j is actually m = ℓ -1. However, because the factor ℓ -m vanishes with m = ℓ, this extra term can be included without changing the value of D. If the summation in (A6-6) is divided into two parts, the first term can be simplified using the addition theorem (2-58). We get

$$D = \ell \, P_\ell (\hat{k}_i \cdot \hat{k}_j) - \frac{4\pi}{2\ell + 1} \sum_{m=-\ell}^{+\ell} m \, Y^*_{\ell m}(\hat{k}_j) \, Y_{\ell m}(\hat{k}_i) \qquad (A6-7)$$

The second term can also be simplified by the addition theorem, but it is necessary to introduce the operator

$$L_z = - i \frac{\partial}{\partial \phi} \qquad (A6-8)$$

which corresponds to the z component of angular momentum in quantum mechanics. It is known (Powell and Craseman [42]) that

$$L_z \, Y_{\ell m}(\hat{k}) = m \, Y_{\ell m}(\hat{k}) \qquad (A6-9)$$

if ϕ is the azimuthal angle of $\hat{k}$ as shown in Fig. A6-1. Applying L_z to both sides of the addition theorem (2-58) (with i and j interchanged) yields

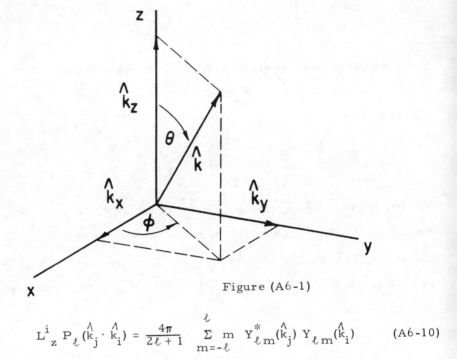

Figure (A6-1)

$$L_z^i \, P_\ell \, (\hat{k}_j \cdot \hat{k}_i) = \frac{4\pi}{2\ell + 1} \sum_{m=-\ell}^{\ell} m \, Y_{\ell m}^*(\hat{k}_j) \, Y_{\ell m}(\hat{k}_i) \qquad \text{(A6-10)}$$

where the superscript on L_z^i indicates that the derivative is with respect to the azimuthal angle of $\hat{k}_i$. The effect of this operator on the Legendre polynomial can be seen by writing

$$\hat{k}_j \cdot \hat{k}_i = \cos \theta_j \cos \theta_i + \sin \theta_j \sin \theta_i \cos(\phi_i - \phi_j) \qquad \text{(A6-11)}$$

where θ_i is the polar angle of $\hat{k}_i$, etc. Thus

$$L_z^i \, P_\ell \, (\hat{k}_j \cdot \hat{k}_i) = - i \, P_\ell' (\hat{k}_j \cdot \hat{k}_i) \sin \theta_j \sin \theta_i \sin(\phi_j - \phi_i)$$

$$= - i \, (\hat{k}_i \times \hat{k}_j)_z \, P_\ell' (\hat{k}_i \cdot \hat{k}_j) \qquad \text{(A6-12)}$$

This subscript on the cross product indicates the z component. Using this result and (A6-10), the expression (A6-7) becomes

$$D = \ell P_\ell (\hat{k}_i \cdot \hat{k}_j) + i \, (\hat{k}_i \times \hat{k}_j)_z \, P_\ell' (\hat{k}_i \cdot \hat{k}_j) \qquad \text{(A6-13)}$$

According to (4-21) for $\kappa > 0$ we have $\ell = \kappa$; hence (A6-13) agrees with (A6-2).

The above procedure can be carried out for $\kappa < 0$ and also yields the result (A6-2). The details will not be discussed. Instead we turn to the second result (A6-3) in which $n = -\frac{1}{2}$ and $m = +\frac{1}{2}$. Again we consider the case $\kappa > 0$. Substituting from Table 4-1 into (A6-1) yields

$$D = -\frac{4\pi}{2\ell + 1} \sum_{\mu} (\ell + \mu + \tfrac{1}{2})^{\frac{1}{2}} (\ell - \mu + \tfrac{1}{2})^{\frac{1}{2}}$$

$$Y^*_{\ell, \mu + \frac{1}{2}}(\hat{k}_j) \, Y_{\ell, \mu - \frac{1}{2}}(\hat{k}_i) \qquad\qquad (A6\text{-}14)$$

If we define $m = \mu + \frac{1}{2}$, this becomes

$$D = -\frac{4\pi}{2\ell + 1} \sum_{m = -\ell + 1}^{\ell} (\ell + m)^{\frac{1}{2}} (\ell - m + 1)^{\frac{1}{2}}$$

$$Y^*_{\ell m}(\hat{k}_j) \, Y_{\ell, m-1}(\hat{k}_i) \qquad\qquad (A6\text{-}15)$$

The lower limit can be extended to $-\ell$, the extra term being zero because of the factor $(\ell + m)^{\frac{1}{2}}$. A more useful form of this can be found by applying the following operator to the addition theorem:

$$L_- = e^{-i\phi} \left(-\frac{\partial}{\partial \theta} + i \cot \theta \, \frac{\partial}{\partial \phi} \right) \qquad\qquad (A6\text{-}16)$$

This is the familiar angular momentum lowering operator (Dicke and Wittke [9]), and it has the following property:

$$L_- Y_{\ell m} = (\ell + m)^{\frac{1}{2}} (\ell - m + 1)^{\frac{1}{2}} Y_{\ell, m-1} \qquad\qquad (A6\text{-}17)$$

Applying this operator to both sides of the addition theorem (2-58) (with i and j interchanged) yields

$$L^i_- P_\ell(\hat{k}_j \cdot \hat{k}_i) = \frac{4\pi}{2\ell + 1} \sum_{m=-\ell}^{\ell} (\ell+m)^{\frac{1}{2}}(\ell-m+1)^{\frac{1}{2}}$$

$$Y^*_{\ell m}(\hat{k}_j)\, Y_{\ell,\,m-1}(\hat{k}_i) \tag{A6-18}$$

where the superscript indicates that the derivatives in (A6-16) are with respect to the angular coordinates of $\vec{k}_i$. It is clear from (A6-18) and (A6-15) that

$$D = -L^i_- P_\ell(\hat{k}_j \cdot \hat{k}_i) \tag{A6-19}$$

Using (A6-11) we see that

$$L^i_- P_\ell(\hat{k}_j \cdot \hat{k}_i) = e^{-i\phi_i}\, P'_\ell(\hat{k}_j \cdot \hat{k}_i)\left(-\frac{\partial}{\partial\theta_i} + i\cot\theta_i \frac{\partial}{\partial\phi_i}\right)(\hat{k}_j \cdot \hat{k}_i)$$

$$= -iP'_\ell(\hat{k}_i \cdot \hat{k}_j)\left\{(\hat{k}_i x \hat{k}_j)_x - i(\hat{k}_i x \hat{k}_j)_y\right\} \tag{A6-20}$$

Therefore

$$D = iP'_\ell(\hat{k}_i \cdot \hat{k}_j)\left\{(\hat{k}_i x \hat{k}_j)_x - i(\hat{k}_i x \hat{k}_j)_y\right\} \tag{A6-21}$$

which agrees with (A6-3). The result for $\kappa < 0$ can be found by essentially the same procedure, but the details will not be discussed.

Appendix 7

cf_κ/g_κ SUBROUTINE

The computer program listed below is a relativistic generalization of the program DLOGDR in Appendix 3. It is based on equations (4-90) and (4-91), and the method of solution is discussed in Chapter 4. The starting values are found using the Runge-Kutta method. In the remainder of the calculation the Milne method is used. The variables occurring in the argument list are defined below.

E	Energy for which cf/g is to be calculated.
JRI	Index of the grid point corresponding to the APW sphere radius on a log scale with $x_1 = -8.8$ and $\Delta x = 0.05$. (see Fig. 3-8).
MXKAP	Maximum value of κ in the summation in (4-78).
RATFG(κ, J)	Storage location for cf_κ/g_κ. J = 1 for $\kappa > 0$ and J = 2 for $\kappa < 0$.
BGX	Muffin-tin potential; output of program discussed in Appendix 2.

```
      SUBROUTINE FOVRG(E,JRI,MXKAP,RATFG,BGX)
C                                    SUBROUTINE FOR CALCULATING CF/G
      DIMENSION BGX(250),RATFG(20,2),SXK(4),SXM(4),P(250),Q(250),PP(250)
     1,QP(250)
      COMMON OM1,OM3,C
      TEST=1.E+4
      CIN=1./C/C
      DX=.05
      HOC=-BGX(1)*EXP(-8.8)/C
      LLMN=1
      ISN=1
   48 DO 95 K=1,MXKAP
      XK=K*ISN
      IF (ABS(HOC/XK)-.05)5,5,6
    5 U=(XK+ABS(XK))/HOC-.5*HOC/ABS(XK)
      GO TO 7
    6 U=(XK+SQRT(XK*XK-HOC*HOC))/HOC
    7 TC=EXP(-8.8)
    8 P(1)=1.E-20
      Q(1)=C*U*1.E-20
C                                                      EQ. 4.92
      PP(1)=TC*(CIN*(E-BGX(1))+1.)*Q(1)-XK*P(1)
C                                                      EQ. 4.90
      QP(1)=XK*Q(1)-TC*(E-BGX(1))*P(1)
C                                                      EQ. 4.91
C                                    RUNGE-KUTTA METHOD
   11 X=-8.8
      N=1
   25 IK=0
      XC=X
      BGC=BGX(N)
      WC=Q(N)
      UC=P(N)
   20 IK=IK+1
      T=EXP(XC)
   12 SXK(IK)=DX*(-XK*UC+T*WC*(CIN*(E-BGC)+1.))
      SXM(IK)=DX*(XK*WC-T*(E-BGC)*UC)
   15 GO TO (16,17,18,19),IK
   16 XC=XC+.5*DX
      UC=UC+.5*SXK(1)
      WC=WC+.5*SXM(1)
      BGC=.5*(BGC+BGX(N+1))
      GO TO 20
   17 UC=UC+.5*(SXK(2)-SXK(1))
      WC=WC+.5*(SXM(2)-SXM(1))
      GO TO 20
   18 XC=XC+.5*DX
      UC=UC+SXK(3)-.5*SXK(2)
      WC=WC+SXM(3)-.5*SXM(2)
      BGC=BGX(N+1)
      GO TO 20
```

```
   19 Q(N+1)=Q(N)+(SXM(1)+2.*SXM(2)+2.*SXM(3)+SXM(4))/6.
      P(N+1)=P(N)+(SXK(1)+2.*SXK(2)+2.*SXK(3)+SXK(4))/6.
      PP(N+1)=T*Q(N+1)*(CIN*(E-BGC)+1.)-XK*P(N+1)
      QP(N+1)=XK*Q(N+1)-T*(E-BGC)*P(N+1)
   24 X=X+DX
      N=N+1
      IF (N-6)25,26,26
C
C                                  MILNE METHOD
C
   26 X=X+DX
      T=EXP(X)
   27 UNP=P(N-5)+.015*(11.*PP(N)-14.*PP(N-1)+26.*PP(N-2)-14.*PP(N-3)+11.
     1*PP(N-4))
      WNP=Q(N-5)+.015*(11.*QP(N)-14.*QP(N-1)+26.*QP(N-2)-14.*QP(N-3)+11.
     1*QP(N-4))
      NIT=0
   33 PP(N+1)=T*(CIN*(E-BGX(N+1))+1.)*WNP-XK*UNP
      QP(N+1)=XK*WNP-T*(E-BGX(N+1))*UNP
      UNP2=P(N-3)+(7.*PP(N+1)+32.*PP(N)+12.*PP(N-1)+32.*PP(N-2)+7.*PP(N-
     13))/450.
      WNP2=Q(N-3)+(7.*QP(N+1)+32.*QP(N)+12.*QP(N-1)+32.*QP(N-2)+7.*QP(N-
     13))/450.
      IF (ABS(TEST*(UNP2-UNP))-ABS(UNP2))30,30,31
   30 IF (ABS(TEST*(WNP2-WNP))-ABS(WNP2))32,32,31
   31 IF (NIT-5)81,32,81
   81 NIT=NIT+1
      WNP=WNP2
      UNP=UNP2
      GO TO 33
   32 Q(N+1)=WNP2
      P(N+1)=UNP2
      N=N+1
      IF (N-JRI)26,34,34
   34 RATFG(K,LLMN)=Q(N)/P(N)
   95 CONTINUE
      IF (ISN)46,46,47
   47 ISN=-ISN
      LLMN=2
      GO TO 48
   46 RETURN
      END
```

Appendix 8

RELATIVISTIC APW PROGRAMS

The computer programs listed below are used to calculate the secular determinant as a function of energy using the relativistic APW method. They are specialized to either one or two identical atoms per unit cell, but can be easily modified for other applications. The basic program is the subroutine RELEP. The dummy main program and the two subroutines SUB1 and SUB2 are used to circumnavigate storage restrictions on the IBM 360/50 computer. [†] The input and output variables occurring in RELEP are described below.

C	Speed of light; in atomic units ($e^2 = 2$, $m = 1/2$, $h = 2\pi$) it is 274.0746. To get nonrelativistic results use $C = 10^6$.
NAME(I)	A 16 column word used to identify the calculation on the output.
RI	APW sphere radius based on JRI (see below). RI = EXP(-8.8 + (JRI - 1)/20).
NBAS	Number of reciprocal lattice vectors.

[†]Notice that in subroutine SUMRI an array called SUMRE(I, J, K) is not completely dimensioned. It is stored, however, in the top of Common and overflows into the above locations. This is a convenient way to store a large array in the IBM 360/50 computer. We have found that if the top of Common is located at 40K (words) there is room to accomodate the programs, Common storage, and the overflow above Common. Our computer has about 60K (words) total storage.

MXKAP

Maximum value of kappa in summation given in 4.78.

KBAS

Number of atoms per unit cell (either one or two; if two, both must be same atomic species).

JRI

Index of the grid point corresponding to the APW sphere radius on a log scale with x_1 = -8.8 and Δx = 0.05 (see Fig. 3-8).

ØM1

Volume of APW sphere divided by volume of unit cell

BGX

Muffin-tin potential; output of program discussed in Appendix 2. In the version of the programs listed below the values of cf/g are calculated each time by integrating the differential equations. Frequently, however, we fit the energy dependence with polynomials and read in the corresponding coefficients instead of BGX (see Appendix 3). The programs can easily be modified to accomodate this change.

COMENT(I)

A 120 column title used to identify the calculation on the output.

RNX, RNY, RNZ

x, y and z components of the vector separating the two atoms in the unit cell. If KBAS = 1 these must be zero.

BKX, BKY, BKZ

x, y and z components of the reciprocal lattice vectors.

SKX, SKY, SKZ

x, y and z components of the wave vector $\vec{k}$.

IBAS

Number of sets of input data corresponding to the same wave vector but different energy ranges.

BE, TE, DELE

The secular determinant is evaluated for the energy range between BE and TE in increments equal to DELE.

EP, DET

The output is energy and the secular determinant.

```
C        DUMMY MAIN, SUB1, AND SUB2 ARE USED TO PROVIDE SPACE FOR ARRAYS

C        DUMMY MAIN
         DIMENSION   S(8000)
         CALL SUB1(S)
         END



         SUBROUTINE SUB1 (S)
         DIMENSION   S(1),    D(8000)
         CALL SUB2 (S)
         END



         SUBROUTINE SUB2 (S)
         DIMENSION   S(1),    D(2000)
         CALL RELEP (S)
         END



       SUBROUTINE RELEP (SUMIM)
       DIMENSION BKX(50),BKY(50),BKZ(50),BGX(250),RATFG(20,2),
      1 GIM(40,40), NAME(4),COMENT(30),  FGP(20),    FGM(20),
      2ONIJ(1275), RE(40,40),   SUMIM(11,40,1),            DETS(100),
      3 E(100), SKIM(50),BE(20),TE(20), DELE(20),FE(20)
       COMMON OM1, OM3, C, NBAS, MXKAP, RI, RNX, RNY, RNZ, KBAS
       READ (1,1)C,(NAME(I),I=1,4),RI,NBAS,MXKAP,KBAS,JRI,OM1
     1 FORMAT(E15.8,4A4,9X,F10.5,4I5,F10.6)
       READ (1,3)BGX
     3 FORMAT (5E16.8)
       READ (1,5)(COMENT(I),I=1,30)
     5 FORMAT(20A4)
       READ (1,40)RNX,RNY,RNZ
    40 FORMAT(3F10.5)
       READ (1,4)(BKX(J),BKY(J),BKZ(J),J=1,NBAS)
     4 FORMAT(3E20.8)
    21 READ (1,2)SKX,SKY,SKZ,IBAS
     2 FORMAT(3F10.4,I5)
       IF (IBAS)11,20,11
    20 STOP 88
    11 READ (1,17)(BE(J),TE(J),DELE(J),J=1,IBAS)
    17 FORMAT(3F10.4)
       OM3=1.
       DO 22 J=1,IBAS
    22 FE(J)=TE(J)-DELE(J)/10
       WRITE (3,8)(NAME(I),I=1,4),SKX,SKY,SKZ
     8 FORMAT(@1 RESULTS FROM REL E PLOTTER FOR    @4A4,@    AT      KX=@
      1F8.5,@      KY=@F8.5,@       KZ=@F8.5//)
```

```
      WRITE (3,51)(COMENT(I),I=1,30)
   51 FORMAT(30A4//)
      WRITE (3,9)C,RI,NBAS,MXKAP,KBAS,JRI
    9 FORMAT(a    C=aE16.8,a     RI=aF10.5,a     NBAS=aI4,a     MXKAP=a
   1I4,a    KBAS=aI3,a     JRI=aI5//)
      WRITE (3,10)
   10 FORMAT(a              ENERGY           DETERMINANTa//)
      CALL CANDS(SKX,SKY,SKZ,ONIJ, SKIM, RE, GIM,           SUMIM,
   1 BKX, BKY, BKZ)
C                                   CALCULATION OF THOSE QUANTITIES IN THE
C                                   MATRIX ELEMENTS WHICH DO NOT DEPEND ON
C                                   THE ENERGY
      I=0
   19 I=I+1
      EP=BE(I)
      DO 6 M=1,100
      CALL FOVRG (EP,JRI,MXKAP,RATFG,BGX)
C                                   CALCULATION OF CF/G FOR PARTICULAR
C                                   ENERGY
      CALL COPLE (MXKAP,RATFG,FGP,FGM)
      CALL RESUM (ONIJ, DET, RE, GIM,        SUMIM , EP,        SKIM,
   1  FGP, FGM)
C                                   CALCULATION OF MATRIX ELEMENTS AND
C                                   DETERMINANT
      WRITE (3,7)EP,DET
    7 FORMAT(F15.5,5X,E20.8)
      DETS(M)=DET
      E(M)=EP
      IF (EP-FE(I))12,18,18
   18 IF (I-IBAS)19,21,21
   12 EP=EP+DELE(I)
    6 CONTINUE
      END
```

```
      SUBROUTINE CANDS(SKX,SKY,SKZ,ONIJ, SKIM, RE, GIM, SUMIM,
     1 BKX, BKY, BKZ)
C                                       CALCULATES ENERGY INDEPENDENT TERMS IN
C                                       MATRIX ELEMENTS
      DIMENSION BKX(50),BKY(50),BKZ(50),COART(1275), RE(40,40),
     1 ONIJ(1275), FJ(30,50), GIM(40,40),  SUMIM(11,40,1),
     2          SKIX(50),SKIY(50),SKIZ(50),SKIM(50)
      COMMON OM1, OM3, C, NBAS, MXKAP, RI, RNX, RNY, RNZ, KBAS
      XBAS=KBAS
      DO 1 I=1,NBAS
      SKIX(I)=SKX+BKX(I)
      SKIY(I)=SKY+BKY(I)
      SKIZ(I)=SKZ+BKZ(I)
C                                       COMPONENTS OF K
      SKIM(I)=SQRT(SKIX(I)*SKIX(I)+SKIY(I)*SKIY(I)+SKIZ(I)*SKIZ(I))
C                                       MAGNITUDE OF K
      XA=SKIM(I)*RI
      CALL BESSH(MXKAP,XA,I,FJ,30)
C                                       SPHERICAL BESSEL FUNCTION SUBROUTINE
C                                       (NOTICE THAT FJ IS DOUBLY SUBSCRIPTED
C                                       BESSH MUST CORRESPOND.)
    1 CONTINUE
      N=0
      DO 4 I=1,NBAS
      DO 3 J=I,NBAS
      N=N+1
      IF (I-J)5,2,2
C                                       DIAGONAL TERMS
    2 COART(N)=XBAS*OM1*3./RI
      ONIJ(N)=-OM1*XBAS+OM3
    3 CONTINUE
    4 CONTINUE
C                                       NON-DIAGONAL TERMS
      CALL SUMRI (FJ , COART, SKIX, SKIY, SKIZ, SKIM, RE, GIM,
     1        SUMIM)
      RETURN
    5 DKX=BKX(J)-BKX(I)
      DKY=BKY(J)-BKY(I)
      DKZ=BKZ(J)-BKZ(I)
C                                       COMPONENTS OF K
      DKM=SQRT(DKX*DKX+DKY*DKY+DKZ*DKZ)*RI
      ARG=(DKX*RNX+DKY*RNY+DKZ*RNZ)/XBAS
      COAR=COS(ARG)
      COART(N)=XBAS*COAR*OM1*3./RI
      ONIJ(N)=-3.*OM1*(SIN(DKM)/DKM-COS(DKM))/(DKM*DKM)*XBAS*COAR
      GO TO 3
      END
```

```
      SUBROUTINE BESSH(N,X,IP,FJ,JCK)
C                                    SPHERICAL BESSEL FUNCTION SUBROUTINE
C                                    FOR DOUBLY SUBSCRIPTED FJ
      DIMENSION FJ(30,1)
      IF (N)1,7,7
    1 WRITE (3,2)
    2 FORMAT (33H1 ERROR, N SHOULD NOT BE NEGATIVE)
      STOP 88
    7 IF (X)8,11,10
    8 WRITE (3,9)
    9 FORMAT (33H1 ERROR, X SHOULD NOT BE NEGATIVE)
      STOP 88
   10 IF (X-.00000001)11,25,25
   11 FJ(1,IP)=1.0
      IF (N)1,15,12
   12 MM=N+1
      DO 13 M=2,MM
   13 FJ(M,IP)=0.0
   15 RETURN
   25 FNC=1.04*X+6.5
      TST=4.21*ALOG10(X)+3.0
      IF (2.0-TST)27,26,26
   26 DELTA=2.0
      GO TO 28
   27 DELTA=TST
   28 FN=N
      IF (FN-FNC)29,29,30
   29 FNS=FNC+DELTA
      GO TO 31
   30 FNS=FN+DELTA
   31 NS=FNS+1.0
      IF (NS+2-JCK)313,313,310
  310 WRITE (3,311)
  311 FORMAT (30H1ERROR, NS+2 EXCEEDS DIMENSION)
      WRITE (3,312)NS,JCK,N,X
  312 FORMAT (1HJ4X3HNS=I11,5X10HDIMENSION=I11,5X2HN=I11,5X2HX=E20.8)
      STOP 88
  313 FJ(NS+1,IP)=0.0
      FJ(NS,IP)=1.0E-45
      M=NS-1
      FM=M-1
   32 FJ(M,IP)=((2.0*FM+3.0)/X)*FJ(M+1,IP)-FJ(M+2,IP)
      IF (ABS(FJ(M,IP))-1.0E40)320,56,56
  320 IF (M-1)34,34,33
   33 M=M-1
      FM=FM-1.0
      GO TO 32
   34 IF (X-0.02)35,36,36
   35 SER=1.0-X**2/6.0+X**4/120.0
      CON=FJ(1,IP)/SER
      JJ=1
      GO TO 39
```

```
   36 SER=SIN(X)
      IF (ABS(SER)-.1)37,38,38
   37 IF (X-.11)38,38,380
   38 CON=X*FJ(1,IP)/SER
      JJ=1
      GO TO 39
  380 CON1=X*FJ(1,IP)/SER
      FJ(1,IP)=FJ(1,IP)/CON1
      CON=X*FJ(2,IP)/(SER/X-COS(X))
      JJ=2
   39 MM=N+1
      DO 40 M=JJ,MM
   40 FJ(M,IP)=FJ(M,IP)/CON
      RETURN
   56 JJ=M+1
      DO 57 J=JJ,NS
   57 FJ(J,IP)=FJ(J,IP)*1.0E-40
      GO TO 32
      END
```

```
      SUBROUTINE XDETR (A,B,D)
C                                    CALCULATES DETERMINANT
      DIMENSION    A(50,1),    B(50,1)
      COMMON OM1, OM3, C, NBAS
      D=1.
      DO 4 I=2,NBAS
      IM1=I-1
      DO 3 NU=1,IM1
      FR=A(NU,I)/A(NU,NU)
      FI=B(NU,I)/A(NU,NU)
      SR=A(I,NU)/A(NU,NU)
      SI=B(I,NU)/A(NU,NU)
      DO 2 J=I,NBAS
      A(I,J)=A(I,J)-FR*A(NU,J)-FI*B(NU,J)-SR*A(J,NU)-SI*B(J,NU)
      IF (J-I)2,2,1
    1 B(I,J)=B(I,J)-FR*B(NU,J)+FI*A(NU,J)-SI*A(J,NU)+SR*B(J,NU)
      A(J,I)=A(J,I)-FR*A(J,NU)-FI*B(J,NU)+SR*A(NU,J)+SI*B(NU,J)
      B(J,I)=B(J,I)-FR*B(J,NU)+FI*A(J,NU)+SI*A(NU,J)-SR*B(NU,J)
    2 CONTINUE
    3 CONTINUE
    4 CONTINUE
      DO 5 I=1,NBAS
      D=D*A(I,I)
    5 CONTINUE
      RETURN
      END
```

```
      SUBROUTINE SUMRI(FJ,COART,SKIX,SKIY,SKIZ,SKIM,RE,GIM,SUMIM)
      DIMENSION    FJ(30,1),      COART(1275),    SKIX(50),    SKIY(50),
    1 SKIZ(50),   SKIM(50),   RE(40,40),   GIM(40,40),   SUMRE(11,40,1),
    2 SUMIM(11,40,1),    PLX(14),    DPLX(14)
      COMMON OM1, OM3, C, NBAS, MXKAP, RI, RNX, RNY, RNZ, KBAS,SUMRE
      L=0
      PLX(1)=1.
      DPLX(1)=0.
      DO 9 II=1,NBAS
      DO 8 JS=II,NBAS
      L=L+1
      PRO=SKIM(II)*SKIM(JS)
      IF (PRO)1,1,10
    1 CX=0.
      CY=0.
      CZ=0.
      GO TO 5
   10 CX=(SKIY(JS)*SKIZ(II)-SKIZ(JS)*SKIY(II))/PRO
      CY=(SKIZ(JS)*SKIX(II)-SKIX(JS)*SKIZ(II))/PRO
      CZ=(SKIX(JS)*SKIY(II)-SKIY(JS)*SKIX(II))/PRO
      UDOT=(SKIX(II)*SKIX(JS)+SKIY(II)*SKIY(JS)+SKIZ(II)*SKIZ(JS))/PRO
      IF (ABS(UDOT)-.9999)3,11,11
   11 DO 2 LTM=2,MXKAP
      LUP=LTM-1
      XL=LUP
      PLX(LTM)=(UDOT)**LUP
    2 DPLX(LTM)=.5*XL*(XL+1.)*PLX(LTM)*UDOT
      GO TO 5
    3 PLX(2)=UDOT
      DPLX(2)=1.
      DO  4 LTX=3,MXKAP
      XL=LTX-1
      PLX(LTX)=((2.*XL-1.)*UDOT*PLX(LTX-1)-(XL-1.)*PLX(LTX-2))/XL
    4 DPLX(LTX)=XL*(PLX(LTX-1)-UDOT*PLX(LTX))/(1.-UDOT*UDOT)
    5 POL1=PLX(1)*FJ(1,II)*FJ(2,JS)
      POL2=DPLX(1)*FJ(1,II)*FJ(2,JS)
      DO 6 K=2,MXKAP
      KP1=K+1
      GK=K
      KM1=K-1
      GKM=KM1
      POL1=POL1+PLX(K)*FJ(K,II)*(GK*FJ(KP1,JS)-GKM*FJ(KM1,JS))
      POL2=POL2+DPLX(K)*FJ(K,II)*(FJ(KP1,JS)+FJ(KM1,JS))
    6 CONTINUE
      POL1=POL1*COART(L)*SKIM(JS)
      POL2=POL2*COART(L)*SKIM(JS)
      RE(JS,II)=CY*POL2
      RE(II,JS)=POL1
      GIM(JS,II)=CX*POL2
      GIM(II,JS)=CZ*POL2
```

```
      DO 7 K=1,MXKAP
      SUM1=FJ(K,II)*FJ(K,JS)*COART(L)
      SUM2=SUM1*DPLX(K)
      SUMRE(K,JS,II)=SUM2*CY
      SUMRE(K,II,JS)=SUM1*PLX(K)
      SUMIM(K,JS,II)=SUM2*CX
      SUMIM(K,II,JS)=SUM2*CZ
    7 CONTINUE
    8 CONTINUE
    9 CONTINUE
      RETURN
      END
```

```
      SUBROUTINE COPLE (MX,Y,FGP,FGM)
      DIMENSION   Y(20,1),   FGP(1),   FGM(1)
      FGP(1)=Y(1,2)
      FGM(1)=Y(1,2)
      DO 1 K=2,MX
      GK=K
      KM1=K-1
      GM=KM1
      FGP(K)=GK*Y(K,2)+GM*Y(KM1,1)
      FGM(K)=Y(K,2)-Y(KM1,1)
    1 CONTINUE
      RETURN
      END
```

```
      SUBROUTINE RESUM (ONIJ ,DET, RE, GIM,SUMIM,EP,SKIM,FGP,FGM)
C                                CALCULATES MATRIX ELEMENTS
      DIMENSION    ONIJ(1275),   RE(40,40),   GIM(40,40),   SUMRE(11,40,1),
     1 SUMIM(11,40,1),  XME(50,50),    RATFG(20,1),    SKIM(1),    ENG(50),
     2   XMI(50,50),    FGP(1),    FGM(1)
      COMMON OM1, OM3, C, NBAS, MXKAP, RI, RNX, RNY, RNZ, KBAS,SUMRE
      DO 1 L=1,NBAS
    1 ENG(L)=SKIM(L)*SKIM(L)-EP
      L=0
      DO 10 II=1,NBAS
      DO 9 JS=II,NBAS
      L=L+1
      XME1=ONIJ(L)*ENG(JS)
      CORE1=0.
      CORE2=0.
      COIM1=0.
      COIM2=0.
      DO 2 K=1,MXKAP
      CORE1=CORE1+SUMRE(K,II,JS)*FGP(K)
      CORE2=CORE2+SUMRE(K,JS,II)*FGM(K)
      COIM1=COIM1+SUMIM(K,II,JS)*FGM(K)
      COIM2=COIM2+SUMIM(K,JS,II)*FGM(K)
    2 CONTINUE
      RE1=CORE1+RE(II,JS)
      RE2=CORE2+RE(JS,II)
      GIM1=COIM1+GIM(II,JS)
      GIM2=COIM2+GIM(JS,II)
      XMI(JS,II)=GIM2
      XMI(II,JS)=GIM1
      XME(JS,II)=RE2
      XME(II,JS)=XME1+RE1
    9 CONTINUE
   10 CONTINUE
      CALL XDETR (XME, XMI, DET)
C                                CALCULATES DETERMINANT
      RETURN
      END
```

REFERENCES

1. Abramowitz, M. and Stegun, I. A., <u>Handbook of Mathematical Functions</u>. Applied Mathematics Series, 55, National Bureau of Standards, Washington, D. C. (1965).

2. Antoncik, E., "The Electron Theory of Metallic Aluminum," <u>Czech, J. Phys</u>., 2, 18 (1953).

3. Burdick, G. A., "Topology of the Fermi Surface of Cu," <u>Phys. Rev. Letters</u>, 7, 156 (1961).

4. Burdick, G. A., "Energy Band Structure of Cu," <u>Phys. Rev</u>., 129, 138 (1963).

5. Callaway, J., <u>Energy Band Theory</u>. Academic Press, New York (1964).

6. Chodorow, M. I., "The Band Structure of Metallic Copper," <u>Phys. Rev</u>., 55, 675 (1939).

7. Conklin, J. B., Jr., Johnson, L. E., and Pratt, G. W., Jr., "Energy Bands in PbTe," <u>Phys. Rev</u>., 137, A1282 (1965).

8. Dahl, J. P. and Switendick, A. C., "Energy Bands in Cuprous Oxide," <u>J. Phys. Chem. Solids</u>, 27, 931 (1966).

9. Dicke, R. H. and Wittke, J. P., <u>Quantum Mechanics</u>. Addison-Wesley, Reading, Massachusetts (1960).

10. Dimmock, J. O. and Freeman, A. J., "Band Structure and Magnetism of Gadolinium Metal," <u>Phys. Rev. Letters</u>, 13, 750 (1964).

11. Ern, V. and Switendick, A. C., "Electronic Band Structure of TiC, TiN and TiO," <u>Phys. Rev</u>., 137, A1927 (1965).

12. Freeman, A. J., Dimmock, J. O., and Watson, R. E., "Fermi Surface, Magnetic Ordering, and Electrical Properties of Rare Earth Metals," <u>Phys. Rev. Letters</u>, 16, 94 (1966).

13. Freeman, A. J., Furdyna, A. M., and Dimmock, J. O., "Electronic Band Structure, Fermi Surface, and Magnetic Properties of Palladium Metal," <u>J. Appl. Phys</u>., 37, 1256 (1966).

14. Harrison, W. A., <u>Pseudopotentials in the Theory of Metals</u>. Benjamin, New York (1966).

15. Herman, F. and Skillman, S., <u>Atomic Structure Calculations</u>. Prentice-Hall, Inc., Englewood Cliffs, New Jersey (1963).

146

16. Hildebrand, F. B., Advanced Calculus for Engineers. Prentice-Hall, Englewood Cliffs, New Jersey (1949).

17. Hildebrand, F. B., Introduction to Numerical Analysis. McGraw-Hill, New York (1956).

18. Howarth, D. J., "Application of the APW Method to Copper," Phys. Rev., 99, 469 (1955).

19. Johnson, L. E., Conklin, J. B., Jr., and Pratt, G. W., Jr., "Relativistic Effects in the Band Structure of PbTe," Phys. Rev. Letters, 11, 538 (1963).

20. Jones H., Brillouin Zones and Electronic States in Crystals. North-Holland, Amsterdam (1962).

21. Keeton, S. C. and Loucks, T. L., "Relativistic Energy Bands for Thorium, Actinium and Lutetium," Phys. Rev., 146, 429 (1966).

22. Kunz, K. S., Numerical Analysis. McGraw-Hill, New York (1957).

23. Leigh, R. S., "The APW and Related Methods for Crystal Eigenvalue Problems," Proc. Phys. Soc. (London), A69, 388 (1956).

24. Liberman, D., Waber, J. T., and Cromer, D. T., "Self-Consistent-Field Dirac-Slater Wave Functions for Atoms and Ions I. Comparison with Previous Calculations," Phys. Rev., 137, A27 (1965).

25. Lloyd, P., "Pseudo-Potential Models in Theory of Band Structure," Proc. Phys. Soc. (London), 86, 825 (1965).

26. Loucks, T. L., "Relativistic Energy Bands for Tungsten," Phys. Rev. Letters, 14, 693 (1965).

27. Loucks, T. L., "Relativistic Energy Bands for Lead by the Relativistic APW Method," Phys. Rev. Letters, 14, 1072 (1965).

28. Loucks, T. L., "Fermi Surfaces of Cr, Mo and W by the APW Method," Phys. Rev., 139, A1181 (1965).

29. Loucks, T. L., "Relativistic Electronic Structure in Crystals I. Theory," Phys. Rev., 139, A1333 (1965).

30. Loucks, T. L., "Relativistic Electronic Structure in Crystals. II. Fermi Surface of Tungsten," Phys. Rev., 143, 506 (1966).

31. Loucks, T. L., "Fermi Surface and Positron Annihilation in Yttrium," Phys. Rev., 144, 504 (1966).

32. Löwdin, P. O., "Quantum Theory of Cohesive Properties of Solids," Adv. Phys., 5, 1 (1956).

33. Luehrmann, A. W., "Crystal Symmetries of Plane-Wave-Like Functions I. Symmorphic Space Groups," Adv. Phys., (to be published)

34. Mattheiss, L. F., "Energy Bands for Solid Argon," Phys. Rev., 133, A1399 (1964).

35. Mattheiss, L. F., "Energy Bands for the Iron Transition Series," Phys. Rev., 134, A970 (1964).

36. Mattheiss, L. F., "Energy Bands for V_3X Compounds," Phys. Rev., 138, A112 (1965).

37. Mattheiss, L. F., "Fermi Surface in Tungsten," Phys. Rev., 139, A1893 (1965).

38. Mattheiss, L. F. and Watson, R. E., "Estimate of the Spin-Orbit Parameter ξ_{5d} in Tungsten," Phys. Rev. Letters, 13, 526 (1964).

39. Mott, N. F. and Jones, H., The Theory of the Properties of Metals and Alloys, Clarendon Press, Oxford, 1936; reprinted by Dover, New York (1958).

40. Onodera, Y., Okazaki, M., and Inui, T., "Relativistic Energy Bands of KI," J. Phys. Soc. Japan, 21, 816 (1966).

41. Pauling, L. and Wilson, E. B., Introduction to Quantum Mechanics. McGraw-Hill, New York (1935).

42. Powell, J. L. and Craseman, B., Quantum Mechanics. Addison-Wesley, Reading, Mass. (1961).

43. Rose, M. E., Relativistic Electron Theory. John Wiley, New York (1961).

44. Saffren, M. M. and Slater, J. C., "An Augmented Plane Wave Method for the Periodic Potential Problem II," Phys. Rev., 92, 1126 (1953).

45. Schlosser, H. and Marcus, P. M., "Composite Wave Variational Method for Solution of Energy Band Problem in Solids," Phys. Rev., 131, 2529 (1963).

46. Scop, Peter M., "Band Structure of Silver Chloride and Silver Bromide," Phys. Rev., 139, A934 (1965).

47. Slater, J. C., "Wave Functions in a Periodic Potential," Phys. Rev., 51, 846 (1937).

48. Slater, J. C., "A Simplification of the Hartree-Fock Method," Phys. Rev., 81, 385 (1951).

49. Slater, J. C., "An Augmented Plane Wave Method for the Period Potential Problem," Phys. Rev., 92, 603 (1953).

50. Slater, J. C., "Energy Band Calculations by the APW Method," Advances in Quantum Chemistry, Academic Press, New York, Vol. 1, p. 35 (1964).

51. Slater, J. C., Quantum Theory of Molecules and Solids, Vol. 2, McGraw-Hill, New York (1965).

52. Slater, J. C., "Green's Function Method in the Energy-Band Problem," Phys. Rev., 145, 599 (1966).

53. Smith, R. A., Wave Mechanics of Crystalline Solids. John Wiley, New York (1961).

54. Snow, E. C., Waber, J. T., and Switendick, A. C., "Effect of Assumed Electronic Configuration on the Electronic Band Structure of Nickel," J. Appl. Phys., 37, 1342 (1966).

55. Southwell, R. V., Relaxation Methods in Theoretical Physics. Oxford, Clarendon Press (1946).

56. Soven, P., "Relativistic Band Structure and Fermi Surface of Thallium. I," Phys. Rev., 137, A1706 (1965).

57. Switendick, A. C., "Self-Consistent Energy Band Calculations for Cr. I. Charge and Spin Densities," J. Appl. Phys., 37, 1022 (1966).

58. Terrell, J. H., "The Fermi Surface of Beryllium," Phys. Letters, 8, 149 (1964).

59. Trlifaj, M., "Electron Theory of Metallic Magnesium," Czech. J. Phys., 1, 110 (1952).

60. Williams, R. W., Loucks, T. L., and Mackintosh, A. R., "Positron Annihilation and the Electronic Structure of Rare Earth Metals," Phys. Rev. Letters, 16, 168 (1966).

61. Wood, J. H., "Wave Functions for Iron d Band," Phys. Rev., 117, 714 (1960).

62. Wood, J. H., "Energy Bands in Fe via the APW Method," Phys. Rev., 126, 517 (1962).

63. Wood, J. H., "Gallium Energy Bands and Fermi Surface via the APW Method," Phys. Rev., 146, 432 (1966).

64. Wyckoff, R. W. G., Crystal Structures, Vol. 1. Interscience, New York (1963).

65. Ziman, J. M., Principles of the Theory of Solids. Cambridge University Press, London (1964).

66. Ziman, J. M., "The T Matrix, the K Matrix, d Bands and ℓ-Dependent Pseudo-Potentials in the Theory of Metals," Proc. Phys. Soc. (London), 86, 337 (1965).

MAY 15, 1937

PHYSICAL REVIEW

VOLUME 51

Wave Functions in a Periodic Potential

J. C. SLATER*

Institute for Advanced Study, Princeton, New Jersey

(Received March 24, 1937)

A new method for approximating the solutions of the problem of the motion of an electron in a periodic potential, as a crystal lattice, is suggested. The potential is supposed to be spherically symmetrical within spheres surrounding the atoms, constant outside. The wave function is expanded in spherical harmonics and radial solutions of the wave equation within the spheres, and in plane waves outside the spheres, joining continuously at the surface. A single unperturbed function consists of a single plane wave outside the spheres, together with the necessary spherical functions within the spheres. The matrix components of energy are set up between these unperturbed functions, and the secular equation set up. This equation involves the energy explicitly, and also implicitly through the ratio of the slope of the various radial functions to the functions themselves at the surfaces of the spheres, and must be solved numerically. It is hoped that the method will be useful for comparatively low energy excited electrons, for which the usual method of expansion in plane waves converges too slowly.

INTRODUCTION

THE first step in the solution of the wave mechanical problem of the motions of electrons in a crystal is to replace the other

* On leave from the Massachusetts Institute of Technology, Cambridge, Massachusetts.

electrons by a static distribution of charge, and to treat the motion of one electron in this static, periodic potential field. The potential is of a particular sort: Near each nucleus, it approaches the potential near the corresponding atom as it would be if isolated from its neighbors, the

151

potential energy of an electron becoming negatively infinite as the nucleus is approached. The potential is spherically symmetrical around a nucleus. Between atoms, the potential varies much less rapidly, making a continuous joining with the potentials near the various nuclei. It involves no great inaccuracy to idealize this potential in the following way: we assume spheres surrounding the various nuclei, the sphere around the nth nucleus having a radius R_n (these radii will naturally be equal if the atoms are all alike). We suppose that within each sphere, the potential is spherically symmetrical, so that within the nth sphere it may be taken to be $U_n(|r-r_n|)$, where r is the radius vector to an arbitrary point, r_n the radius vector to the nth nucleus. Outside all the spheres, we suppose the potential to be constant, and to get continuity of the potential we assume that each of the potentials U_n reduces to this constant value at the radius R_n. In particular, to simplify matters, we shall adjust the zero of potential so that the constant region between atoms is at zero potential. The present paper is devoted to a general formulation of the solution of such a boundary value problem, on the assumption that the atoms are arranged in a regular crystal, and to methods of approximating to the solution.

We seek a solution of energy E. Within any one of the spheres, the wave equation is one of spherical symmetry. Then it can be solved quite rigorously by well-known methods. We separate variables in spherical coordinates with respect to the nucleus. If these coordinates are $|r-r_n|$, θ, ϕ, the wave function is

$$\sum_{l=0}^{\infty} \sum_{m=-l}^{l} A_{lm} P_l^{|m|}(\cos\theta) \exp(im\phi) u_{nl}(|r-r_n|). \quad (1)$$

Here u_{nl} satisfies the equation

$$-\frac{1}{r^2}\frac{d}{dr}\left(r^2\frac{du_{nl}}{dr}\right) + \left(\frac{l(l+1)}{r^2} + U_n\right) u_{nl} = E u_{nl}. \quad (2)$$

The radial function u_{nl} of course depends on the energy E as a parameter, but we shall not indicate that in the notation, since it is understood throughout. There are two independent solutions of (2) for any energy value E. Of these, one is regular at the origin, the other regular at infinity, the two coinciding for the characteristic values of E. Since in general we are not dealing with characteristic values of E, and since we are interested in the interior of the sphere, we choose the functions regular at the origin. Then any series of the form (1), with arbitrary coefficients A_{lm}, satisfies the differential equation within the sphere.

Of course, outside the sphere, and up to the shortest distance $|r-r_n|$ at which the radius touches the sphere of another atom, so that the problem is still spherically symmetrical, we can still use a solution of type (1). For larger distances than this, however, the problem ceases to be spherically symmetrical, and (1) is no longer a solution. We must then seek a different type of solution which will hold in the region between the spheres. It is known that a general solution of the whole problem is provided by a series of plane waves,

$$\sum_{\mathbf{k}} v(\mathbf{k}) \exp(i\mathbf{k}\cdot r), \quad (3)$$

where only certain discrete wave vectors $\mathbf{k}$ are to be used. These vectors are to be defined as follows. We start with a certain vector $\mathbf{k}_0$, which is arbitrary. Then we may add to this any one of the infinite number of vectors $\mathbf{K}_i$ of the reciprocal lattice.[1] The series (3) is then a solution of the wave equation everywhere, if the $v(\mathbf{k})$'s satisfy the difference equations

$$(\mathbf{k}_0+\mathbf{K}_i)^2 v(\mathbf{k}_0+\mathbf{K}_i) + \sum_{\mathbf{K}_j} W(\mathbf{K}_j) v(\mathbf{k}_0+\mathbf{K}_i+\mathbf{K}_j)$$
$$= E v(\mathbf{k}_0+\mathbf{K}_i). \quad (4)$$

Here, as elsewhere in this paper, it is assumed that atomic units are used (energies measured in units of the Rydberg energy, distances in terms of the radius of the Bohr hydrogen orbit, so that the energy of a free electron whose wave function is $\exp(i\mathbf{k}\cdot r)$ is k^2). The matrix component $W(\mathbf{K}_i)$ is the matrix component of the potential energy between the wave functions in question, normalized in such a way that $W(0)$ is the average potential energy through the cell,

---

[1] For references to this and other points, the reader may consult Mott and Jones, *Properties of Metals and Alloys* (Oxford, 1936); Fröhlich, *Elektronentheorie der Metalle* (Berlin, 1936), as well as the older reviews, by Sommerfeld and Bethe, in the *Handbuch der Physik*, second edition, Vol. 24 (1933), and by J. C. Slater, Rev. Mod. Phys. 6, 209 (1933). Numerous references to special papers can be found in the books and articles mentioned above.

or through the crystal. That is, $W(\mathbf{K}_j)$ is the integral of the potential energy, times

$$\exp\ (i(-\mathbf{k}_0-\mathbf{K}_i+\mathbf{k}_0+\mathbf{K}_i+\mathbf{K}_j)\cdot r) = \exp\ (i\mathbf{K}_j\cdot r),$$

throughout the cell, divided by the volume of the cell. If the volume of the cell is Ω, we then have

$$W(\mathbf{K}_j) = \frac{1}{\Omega} \sum_n \exp\ (i\mathbf{K}_j\cdot r_n) F_n(\mathbf{K}_j), \qquad (5)$$

where the summation is over the atoms of a single cell, and where

$$F_n(\mathbf{K}_j) = \int U_n(|r-r_n|) \exp\ (i\mathbf{K}_j\cdot|r-r_n|) d\tau, \quad (6)$$

where the integral is over the volume of the nth sphere. By expanding the exponential, it can be at once shown that

$$F_n(\mathbf{K}_j) = 4\pi \int_0^{R_n} r^2 U_n(r) \frac{\sin\ (|\mathbf{K}_j|r)}{|\mathbf{K}_j|r} dr. \quad (7)$$

It has been customary to discuss electron diffraction on the assumption that the matrix component $W(\mathbf{K}_j)$ was the one responsible for the process in which a wave of wave number $\mathbf{k}_0+\mathbf{K}_i$ in the crystal changed over to a wave of wave number $\mathbf{k}_0+\mathbf{K}_i+\mathbf{K}_j$, by Bragg reflection from the planes normal to $\mathbf{K}_j$. The Eq. (5) then expresses this quantity in a way analogous to the x-ray structure factor, and (7) gives the form factor of the nth atom, analogous to the x-ray form factor. The equations (4) are then analogous to the equations in the dynamical theory of x-ray diffraction,[2] and are the ones which must be solved if we wish to set up the whole solution for a diffracted beam.

It might be asked, since (3) gives a complete solution of our present problem, why is it necessary to go further? The answer is that the series (3) converges very slowly. The wave function in the neighborhood of a nucleus corresponds to a rapidly moving electron, and it changes phase in very short distances, corresponding to short wave-lengths. Thus in the series (3), we must have appreciable coefficients of the terms even of very high $\mathbf{k}$ values, such

that k^2 for these terms is comparable with the energy of the x-ray terms of the atom. Attempts to solve the difference Eq. (4) directly, made by the writer and Dr. Millman, as well as similar attempts made by others, have convinced us that the use of this series is impractical for obtaining wave functions and energy levels of low energy electrons, valuable though it is for the proof of general theorems and for high energy electrons. In spite of the objections to the use of (3) for practical purposes, still the whole wave function can be expanded in such a series of plane waves, and in particular the part of the function outside the atomic spheres can be so expanded. We shall then assume that the wave function is expanded in series (3) outside the spheres, and in the series (1) inside the spheres. We shall do this in the following way. We set up separate unperturbed functions, each equal to a plane wave outside the spheres, and to a series of type (1) inside the spheres, joining continuously on the surface of the spheres. Then we write the whole solution as a linear combination of such unperturbed functions, determining the coefficients essentially by perturbation theory. But now we may hope that the series represented by this linear combination will converge much more rapidly than the series (3). For the lack of convergence of (3), as we have mentioned, arises from the difficulty of expanding the wave function near the nucleus in plane waves. In our method, the wave function near the nucleus is automatically taken care of, and only the outer part, which really does not depart much from a plane wave anyway, is left to be expanded. Each of our functions can be regarded as an expansion in terms of plane waves, containing all the terms necessary to describe the function near the nucleus, but with correct phase relations so that it reduces to a single plane wave outside the spheres. We shall now proceed with the mathematical formulation of these waves, and shall set up the matrix components of energy between them and the resulting secular equation for determining the energy.

MATHEMATICAL FORMULATION OF THE PROBLEM

Let ψ_i be a function which equals $\exp\ (i\mathbf{k}_i\cdot r)$ outside the various spheres, and which joins

[2] See for instance M. von Laue, Ergeb. d. Exakt. Naturwiss. 10, 133 (1931); also *Die Interferenzen von Röntgen- und Elektronenstrahlen* (Berlin, 1935).

continuously at the surface of each sphere onto a solution of the central field problem, corresponding to the energy E, within that sphere. By a well-known expansion, the exponential $\exp (i\mathbf{k}_i \cdot r)$ can be expanded in spherical coordinates about any point. In particular we expand about the nucleus of the nth atom, at r_n. Then we have

$$\exp (i\mathbf{k}_i \cdot r) = \exp (i\mathbf{k}_i \cdot r_n) \sum_{l=0}^{\infty} \sum_{m=-l}^{l} (2l+1)i^l$$

$$\times j_l(k_i |r-r_n|) \frac{(l-|m|)!}{(l+|m|)!} P_l^{|m|}(\cos \theta)$$

$$\times P_l^{|m|}(\cos \theta_i) \exp im(\phi-\phi_i). \quad (8)$$

Here $(|r-r_n|)$, θ, ϕ are polar coordinates about r_n as a pole, and θ_i, ϕ_i are polar coordinates giving the direction of the wave normal $\mathbf{k}_i$. The functions $j_l(kr)$ are spherical Bessel functions,[3] satisfying the differential equation

$$-\frac{1}{r^2}\frac{d}{dr}\left(r^2 \frac{dj_l}{dr}\right) + \frac{l(l+1)}{r^2} j_l = k^2 j_l. \quad (9)$$

They are finite or zero at the origin, and are so normalized that

$$\lim_{z \to 0} j_l(z) = \frac{z^l}{1 \cdot 3 \cdot 5 \cdots (2l+1)}. \quad (10)$$

By comparing terms, we can then at once determine the coefficients A_{lm} of the expansion (1) of the function inside the sphere, so as to make the function continuous at the surface of the sphere. We at once find that inside the sphere we have

$$\psi_i = \exp (i\mathbf{k}_i \cdot r_n) \sum_{l=0}^{\infty} \sum_{m=-l}^{l} (2l+1)i^l \frac{j_l(k_i R_n)}{u_{nl}(R_n)}$$

$$\times u_{nl}(|r-r_n|) \frac{(l-|m|)!}{(l+|m|)!} P_l^{|m|}(\cos \theta)$$

$$\times P_l^{|m|}(\cos \theta_i) \exp im(\phi-\phi_i). \quad (11)$$

The value (11) inside the sphere at r_n, together with the expression $\exp (i\mathbf{k}_i \cdot r)$ outside all the spheres, determines the function ψ_i completely.

---

[3] For a collection of formulas and tables regarding these functions, see P. M. Morse, *Vibration and Sound* (New York, 1936), pp. 246, 247, 335.

Having formulated our various unperturbed wave functions, we must set up the perturbation problem between them. We assume that the exact solution of our problem is expressed as a series

$$\sum_i v_i \psi_i, \quad (12)$$

where the v_i's are constants. Then by the general methods of quantum mechanics the series (12) will be a solution of the problem if the equations

$$\sum_i (H-E)_{ij} v_i = 0 \quad (13)$$

are satisfied for all values of i. Here H is the energy operator, E the characteristic energy, and

$$(H-E)_{ij} = \int \psi_i^*(H-E)\psi_j d\tau, \quad (14)$$

the matrix component of the operator $H-E$ between the two states in question. In order to satisfy the Eq. (13), we must as usual have the determinant of coefficients $(H-E)_{ij}$ equal to zero. We now compute these matrix components. We must notice one point at the outset. Though our function ψ_i is everywhere continuous, its first derivative is in general not continuous at the surfaces of the various spheres, where the functions join. We may regard the object of our perturbation problem to be the setting up of a combination of functions which not only is continuous but has a continuous slope. But now the kinetic energy operator demands special treatment for a function with discontinuous slope. Two forms of integral are often seen for computing the kinetic energy. The more common one is $\int \psi_i^*(-\nabla^2)\psi_j d\tau$, but the other and more fundamental one is $\int \text{grad } \psi_i^* \cdot \text{grad } \psi_j d\tau$. Ordinarily one can show by integration by parts that one equals the other, but if the function has anywhere a discontinuous slope, they are no longer equal, but differ by a surface integral over the surface of discontinuity. In this case the second, more fundamental form is the correct one, as it is the one which directly enters the variation principle from which Schrödinger's equation is derived. If there is any doubt about this question, it can be easily shown that using the first formula we must add a surface integral, for a discontinuous first derivative amounts to an infinite second derivative on the surface, and integrates to a finite contribution over the surface. This contribution can be found by a limiting process in which the change of slope occurs in smaller and smaller ranges of variable. We shall use the opposite treatment, however, as being more fundamental, starting with the second integral, but eventually reducing part of our result to a surface integral over the surface of discontinuity.

If U is the potential energy, equal to U_n within the nth sphere, and zero outside the spheres, we then have

$$(H-E)_{ij} = \int (\text{grad } \psi_i^* \cdot \text{grad } \psi_j + (U-E)\psi_i^*\psi_j)d\tau. \quad (15)$$

We shall carry out the integration in two parts: first over the region outside the spheres, then over the spheres. Outside the spheres, $\psi_i = \exp i(\mathbf{k}_i \cdot r)$, $U=0$. Then grad $\psi_i^* \cdot$ grad $\psi_j = (\mathbf{k}_i \cdot \mathbf{k}_j) \exp i(\mathbf{k}_j - \mathbf{k}_i) \cdot r$. To find the integral outside the spheres, we integrate over the whole space, and subtract the integral over the spheres. It is easily shown that the integral over each cell will be equal, so that we shall carry out all our integrations just over a single cell, which is assumed to be of volume Ω. Furthermore, to get agreement with (5), we shall divide our integrals by Ω, so that they will represent averages over the volume. Now the relation between the vectors $\mathbf{k}_i$ and $\mathbf{k}_j$ is such that $\exp i(\mathbf{k}_j - \mathbf{k}_i) \cdot r$ integrates to zero over the cell unless $i=j$. Thus we have

$$\frac{1}{\Omega}\int_{\text{cell}} (\text{grad } \psi_i^* \cdot \psi_j - E\psi_i^*\psi_j)d\tau = (\mathbf{k}_i \cdot \mathbf{k}_j - E)\delta_{ij}, \quad (16)$$

where $\delta_{ij} = 1$ if $i=j$, 0 if $i \neq j$. Within the nth sphere, we have the contribution

$$\frac{1}{\Omega}(\mathbf{k}_i \cdot \mathbf{k}_j - E) \exp i(\mathbf{k}_j - \mathbf{k}_i) \cdot r_n$$

$$\times \int_{\text{sphere}} \exp i(\mathbf{k}_j - \mathbf{k}_i) \cdot (r - r_n)d\tau$$

$$= (\mathbf{k}_i \cdot \mathbf{k}_j - E) \exp i(\mathbf{k}_j - \mathbf{k}_i) \cdot r_n$$

$$\times \frac{4\pi R_n^2}{\Omega} \frac{j_1(|\mathbf{k}_j - \mathbf{k}_i|R_n)}{|\mathbf{k}_j - \mathbf{k}_i|}. \quad (17)$$

The terms (17) are to be subtracted from (16) to get the whole contribution to $(H-E)_{ij}$ from the region outside the spheres.

Next we must find the contributions to $(H-E)_{ij}$ from the interiors of the spheres. In this case it is more convenient to integrate (15) by parts according to Green's theorem, obtaining for the nth sphere

$$\frac{1}{\Omega}\int \psi_i^*(-\nabla^2 + U_n - E)\psi_j d\tau + \int \psi_i^*(\partial\psi_j/\partial n)dS, \quad (18)$$

where n is the outer normal in the surface integral. The volume integral vanishes on account of (2). For the surface integral, we use the form (11) for the functions, differentiate the radial part of ψ_j with respect to r, and integrate over the angles, obtaining

$$\exp i(\mathbf{k}_j - \mathbf{k}_i) \cdot r_n \frac{4\pi R_n^2}{\Omega} \sum_{l=0}^{\infty} (2l+1)P_l(\cos\theta_{ij})$$

$$\times j_l(k_iR_n)j_l(k_jR_n)u_{nl}'(R_n)/u_{nl}(R_n). \quad (19)$$

We must now combine (16), (17), and (19), obtaining

$$(H-E)_{ij} = (\mathbf{k}_i \cdot \mathbf{k}_j - E)\delta_{ij} + \frac{1}{\Omega}\sum_n \exp i(\mathbf{k}_j - \mathbf{k}_i) \cdot r_n F_{nij},$$

where

$$F_{nij} = 4\pi R_n^2 \left\{ -(\mathbf{k}_i \cdot \mathbf{k}_j - E)\frac{j_1(|\mathbf{k}_j - \mathbf{k}_i|R_n)}{|\mathbf{k}_j - \mathbf{k}_i|} + \sum_{l=0}^{\infty}(2l+1)P_l(\cos\theta_{ij})j_l(k_iR_n)j_l(k_jR_n) \times u_{nl}'(R_n)/u_{nl}(R_n) \right\}. \quad (20)$$

The resemblance to Eqs. (5) and (6) is plain; F_{nij} plays the part of a form factor in the present theory, in place of the expression $F_n(K_j)$ of (6) and (7).

Having set up the matrix components $(H-E)_{ij}$ in (20), we must next solve the secular equation $\Delta|(H-E)_{ij}| = 0$. Of course, we cannot solve this exactly, and we must look for methods of approximation. It is a more difficult secular equation than one usually meets. In the first place, the functions are not orthogonal, so that as we see from (20) the energy E appears explicitly in the nondiagonal terms. But worse than this, the energy appears implicitly in the expressions $u_{nl}'(R_n)/u_{nl}(R_n)$, which depend on the energy, and which appear both in diagonal and in nondiagonal terms. The only practical method of handling the determinant under the circumstances would seem to be to compute and plot it as a function of E, and find the intersections with the axis graphically. Rather than using the determinant as it stands, it would be more convenient to use a well-known device, and divide all elements of the ith row by the diagonal term $(H-E)_{ii}$. Then the diagonal terms of the new determinant are unity, and the nondiagonal elements are very large for those particular rows for which $(H-E)_{ii}$ is very small, while they are small in other cases. To a first approximation, then, we can consider only the particular rows for which $(H-E)_{ii}$ is small, and the expansion of the determinant becomes very simple. Further approximations can be made by expanding in power series in the small terms. This method amounts to applying a perturbation theory in which we treat the few states whose unperturbed energy is near the energy we are interested in by the perturbation method for degenerate systems, and treat more distant states by the power series method. It should make it possible to get a satisfactory approximation to the whole shape of the curve, and to find its zeros, to a fair approximation, though with considerable labor. The determinant plotted as a function of E will have many intersections with the axis, and may be expected to have roughly the form of a tangent curve, but of course with many local variations. A separate calculation, of course, must be made for each value of the momentum $\mathbf{k}_0$ (that is, at each point of the first or reduced Brillouin zone in $\mathbf{k}$ space). At certain points in this zone there will be symmetry properties which will allow us at once to factor the determinant, so that as

with other methods of approximation it will be easier to get the solution in directions having simple symmetry properties than in arbitrary directions.

In conclusion, we may suggest the cases where this method is likely to be particularly useful. These will obviously be the cases where one term of our series is itself a fairly good approximation, so that the correction terms are small. That is, they are the cases where the real wave function outside the spheres is very close to a single plane wave. Such cases are known to exist for the conduction levels of the alkali metals.[4] The method of Wigner and Seitz, as applied by the author to this case, is satisfactory for the conduction levels themselves, but has been shown by Shockley[5] to become very bad for levels even a few volts above the occupied levels. This is natural, for that method assumes an expansion throughout the whole cell in a very few spherical harmonics. But as we see from (8), a whole series of spherical harmonics is needed to expand a plane wave, and the higher terms become important for rather low energies, so that if we break off the series after a few terms, as the earlier method does, the results will be very inaccurate except for very low energies. The present method, however, with its infinite series of spherical harmonics, would not have this difficulty. It is not unlikely that if it were applied to the case of the alkalies, it would show that the excited levels for some distance up are much more like free electrons than the calculations mentioned in reference 4 would indicate, so that it would form a good approximation for this case. It is to be hoped, however, that the present method of approximation will have a wider range of application than this, for it should in principle suffice for finding any energy levels, and the reasons we have suggested in proposing it lead one to hope that it will be practical in its actual application.

[4] For application to sodium, see J. C. Slater, Phys. Rev. 45, 794 (1934).
[5] W. Shockley, Phys. Rev. 51, 379 (1937).

Reprinted from THE PHYSICAL REVIEW, Vol. 126, No. 2, 517–527, April 15, 1962
Printed in U. S. A.

Energy Bands in Iron via the Augmented Plane Wave Method*

J. H. WOOD

Solid-State and Molecular Theory Group, Massachusetts Institute of Technology, Cambridge, Massachusetts

(Received November 27, 1961)

Results of numerical calculations of the band structure of body-centered cubic and face-centered cubic iron are reported; the calculations have been carried out according to the augmented plane wave (APW) method of Slater. A total of 55 points in the 1/48 of the Brillouin zone has been examined in the bcc case; this provides sufficient information for construction of a density-of-states curve which is presented. For the fcc structure, calculations have been performed at 17 points of high symmetry; no density-of-states curve is calculated.

The potential used is that of Manning and consists of the argon core plus 7 valence electrons. The lattice constants are taken as $a = 3.647 \times 10^{-8}$ cm for the fcc lattice and $a = 2.861 \times 10^{-8}$ cm for the bcc lattice. Fortunately, the latter constant is one of the three used by Stern in a modified tight-binding calculation of the cohesive energy and band structure of iron. Rather good agreement is found between the present calculation and Stern's.

The APW method seems a promising one inasmuch as the convergence in terms of number of plane waves is reached in about 40 plane waves (this for a point in the Brillouin zone having *no* symmetry). Moreover, the method is one which is quite adaptable to a digital computer and has been programmed for the Whirlwind computer (by Saffren) and for the IBM 704 and 709 computers.

INTRODUCTION

THE energy bands of solids have long been of interest although it has been only in recent years, with the advent of the large scale digital computer, that it has proved possible to obtain solutions to this problem in which one can have confidence and so assess the limits of validity of the one-electron approach. Reviews of the energy band formalism and the results (both early and postwar) have been given by Slater, Reitz, and Callaway.[1-3]

Here, we report on calculations of the energy band structure of body-centered cubic and face-centered cubic iron. As in the other band calculations on iron, these calculations take no direct account of the magnetization; thus, the one-electron potential is taken to be independent of the spin-orientation of the electron for whose wave function we are solving. The calculations were carried out using the augmented plane wave (APW) method developed by Slater in 1937.[4]

The APW method was first applied to copper by Chodorow.[5] A variant of the method, due to Saffren and Slater,[6] was used by Howarth in a calculation on copper.[7] At the time of Howarth's work it appeared that the earlier version was one which could not be accommodated on a computer of the size then available. Later work by Saffren[8] proved this assumption false and he

then set up this 1937-APW method on the MIT Whirlwind computer. The author subsequently adapted the method to the IBM 704 and 709 computers, where, of course, size is no longer a problem. Calculations performed by Burdick[9] on copper with the restrictions Chodorow assumed in his calculation give results identical to Chodorow's. Moreover, excellent agreement (to 5 figures) exists among the Whirlwind and 704–709 results.

The work on iron was initiated on Whirlwind, using Saffren's programs. The particular choice of iron was made because of general interest in the transition metals and also in order to determine the usefulness of the APW method in a problem involving $3d$ electrons where we might expect convergence difficulties.

THE APW METHOD

The theory of the 1937 augmented plane wave method has been developed by Slater.[4] The motivating assumption of the method is that the crystal potential for a valence electron in a metal can be chosen to have the "muffin-tin" form. That is, around each nucleus of the lattice one takes an appropriate spherically symmetric potential, delimited by a sphere of radius R_s. In the region between such spheres, one chooses the potential to be constant. This potential is now the one used in the one-electron Schrödinger equation and this together with the imposition of the usual periodic boundary conditions determines, in principle, the solutions of the problem. In view of the choice of potential, one now expands the unknown one-electron wave functions in terms of a particular set of trial functions ψ_i consisting of plane waves in the constant potential region and a general spherical solution inside the spheres. If we choose a single plane wave $e^{i\mathbf{k}\cdot\mathbf{r}}$ in the region of constant potential, then the other portion of this trial function (around the sphere at location r_n)

* Part of a thesis submitted in partial fulfillment of the requirements for the PhD degree in Physics at the Massachusetts Institute of Technology. This work was supported in part by the Office of Naval Research, and in part by the U. S. Army, Navy, and Air Force.

[1] J. C. Slater, *Handbuch der Physik*, edited by S. Flügge (Springer-Verlag, Berlin, 1956), Vol. XIX, p. 1.
[2] J. R. Reitz, *Solid-State Physics*, edited by F. Seitz and D. Turnbull (Academic Press, Inc., New York, 1955), Vol. 1, p. 1.
[3] J. Callaway, *Solid-State Physics*, edited by F. Seitz and D. Turnbull (Academic Press, Inc., New York, 1958), Vol. 7, p. 100.
[4] J. C. Slater, Phys. Rev. **51**, 846 (1937).
[5] M. I. Chodorow, Ph.D. thesis, Department of Physics, Massachusetts Institute of Technology, 1939 (unpublished); Phys. Rev. **55**, 675 (1939).
[6] M. M. Saffren and J. C. Slater, Phys. Rev. **92**, 1126 (1953).
[7] J. D. Howarth, Phys. Rev. **99**, 469 (1955).
[8] M. M. Saffren, Bull. Am. Phys. Soc. **5**, 298 (1960). See also M. M. Saffren, *ibid.* **5**, 281 (1960).

[9] G. A. Burdick, Ph.D. thesis, Department of Physics, Massachusetts Institute of Technology, 1961 (unpublished); Phys. Rev. Letters **7**, 156 (1961).

157

will be[4]

$$\psi_i = \exp(i\mathbf{k} \cdot \mathbf{r}_n) \sum_{l=0}^{\infty} \sum_{m=-l}^{+l} (2l+1)i^l \frac{j_l(kR_n)}{u_l(R_n;E)}$$

$$\times u_l(|\mathbf{r}-\mathbf{r}_n|;E) \frac{(l-|m|)!}{(l+|m|)!} P_l^{|m|}(\cos\theta)$$

$$\times P_l^{|m|}(\cos\theta') \exp[im(\phi-\phi')].$$

θ' and ϕ' refer to the direction of $\mathbf{k}$ where we take the origin of the coordinate system at $\mathbf{r}_n$. The j_l are spherical Bessel functions. Here, the coefficients in the spherical expansion are so chosen that the plane-wave portion matches on continuously in *value* to this expansion. The $u_l(r;E)$ are solutions of the radial wave equation

$$-\frac{1}{r^2}\frac{d}{dr}\left(r^2\frac{du_l}{dr}\right)+\left(\frac{l(l+1)}{r^2}+V(r)\right)u_l=Eu_l, \quad (1)$$

where $V(r)$ is the spherically symmetric potential. Such a function consisting of the plane wave plus the spherical solution is referred to as an augmented plane wave (APW); the solution of the energy band problem can then be regarded as one of determining the coefficients for the expansion of the true one-electron wave function $\Psi_k(r)$ in terms of a set of APW's, ψ_i,

$$\Psi_k(r)=\sum_i v_i\psi_i.$$

The index i on ψ_i is a multiple index; each APW is k dependent through its plane-wave portion and carries an implicit energy dependence through the $u_l(r;E)$ appearing in the spherical sum. The solution of the energy band problem

$$H\Psi_k=E\Psi_k, \quad (2)$$

in terms of APW's is then resolved into the solution of a secular equation. This is, we must find the zeroes of $\det\{(H-E)_{ij}\}$, where $(H-E)$ is the matrix whose elements are

$$(H-E)_{ij}=\int \psi_i^*(H-E)\psi_j d\tau. \quad (3)$$

Thus, the energy appears in the nondiagonal terms both explicitly, and implicitly by way of the radial solutions. The entire determinant is a complicated function of the energy; numerical evaluation of this determinant as a function of the energy allows one to determine the zeroes in energy and thus the approximate eigenvalues of the problem.

The form of $(H-E)_{ij}$ is given by Slater[4] for one atom per unit cell as

$$(H-E)_{ij}=(\mathbf{k}_i\cdot\mathbf{k}_j-E)\delta_{ij}+(1/\Omega)F_{ij},$$

where

$$F_{ij}=4\pi R_s^2\left[-(\mathbf{k}_i\cdot\mathbf{k}_j-E)\frac{j_1(|\mathbf{k}_j-\mathbf{k}_i|R_s)}{|\mathbf{k}_j-\mathbf{k}_i|}\right.$$

$$+\sum_{l=0}^{\infty} (2l+1)P_l(\cos\theta_{ij})j_l(k_iR_s)j_l(k_jR_s)$$

$$\left.\times\frac{u_l'(R_s;E)}{u_l(R_s;E)}\right]. \quad (4)$$

Here Ω is the volume of the unit cell, R_s is the radius of the sphere, the j_l's are spherical Bessel functions, the P_l's are Legendre polynomials, and the u_l's are the solutions of Eq. (1) for the energy E.

METHOD OF COMPUTATION

Having selected a point $\mathbf{k}$ in the first Brillouin zone at which we wish to solve Eq. (2), we must now select the APW's ψ_i from which the matrix of $(H-E)$ is to be constructed.

First we take account of Bloch's theorem which tells us that the wave vector $\mathbf{k}_i$ to be associated with ψ_i is drawn from the set $\{\mathbf{k}+\mathbf{K}_i\}$, the $\mathbf{K}_i$ being the infinite set of the reciprocal lattice vectors. Furthermore, for reasons which will be discussed, it was desirable to initially restrict this set such that no member could be obtained from some other member by an operation of the group of the wave vector[10] $\mathbf{k}$. Computer programs were written to generate this reduced set of $\{\mathbf{k}+\mathbf{K}_i\}$ for the bcc and fcc lattices; the Whirlwind programs being written by Saffren[8] and IBM programs by the author.

Next, in order to conserve computation time, it is useful to take account of the general result that Ψ_k and the ψ_i APW's out of which it is composed, must transform according to one of the irreducible representations of the group of the wave vector.[10] This can be accomplished by the use of group projection operators[11]; employing these operators permits one to obtain all the functions (derived from the various ψ_i) which transform according to a chosen irreducible representation. From the αth irreducible representation of dimension n_α one can form n_α^2 projection operators ρ_{ij}^α. These have the general form[11] (for a unitary representation)

$$\rho_{ij}^\alpha=\sum_R \Gamma_\alpha(R)_{ij}^*R. \quad (5)$$

$\Gamma_\alpha(R)_{ij}^*$ is the complex conjugate of the ij matrix element in the matrix representing the operation R in the αth irreducible representation and the sum is over all the operations R in the group. One may apply such a projection operator to any function f and obtain a new

[10] L. P. Bouckaert, R. Smoluchowski, and E. Wigner, Phys. Rev. **50**, 58 (1936).

[11] G. F. Koster, Technical Report No. 8, Solid State and Molecular Theory Group, Massachusetts Institute of Technology, 1956 (unpublished); V. Heine, *Group Theory in Quantum Mechanics* (Pergamon Press, New York, 1960).

function $f_{ij}{}^\alpha$:

$$\rho_{ij}{}^\alpha f = f_{ij}{}^\alpha. \qquad (6)$$

$f_{ij}{}^\alpha$ now will have definite transformation properties under the group and in particular if R is any operation in the group.[11]

$$Rf_{ij}{}^\alpha = \sum_k \Gamma_\alpha(R)_{ki} f_{kj}{}^\alpha. \qquad (7)$$

Thus all such symmetrized functions, derived from f, which bear the same second index transform among themselves and are, in fact, partners in a basis for this αth irreducible representation. The transformation coefficients for any one of these partners $f_{ij}{}^\alpha$ are taken from the ith column of the matrix $\Gamma_\alpha(R)$.

Now if f and g are any two functions and O is an operator which transforms according to the identity representation of the group, then the following holds true (G is the order of the group and n_α is the dimensionality of the αth irreducible representation):

$$\langle \rho_{ij}{}^\alpha f | O | \rho_{kl}{}^\beta g \rangle = (G/n_\alpha) \delta_{\alpha\beta} \delta_{ik} \langle f | O | \rho_{jl}{}^\alpha g \rangle, \qquad (8)$$

so that there are no matrix elements between partners in the same irreducible representation and no elements between different irreducible representations. Furthermore, the value of the matrix element (8) is the same for all rows so that one need solve only the secular equation among basis functions transforming according to the same column in the irreducible representation. The n_α identical solutions of the secular equation merely reflect the degeneracy of the problem—as the first index of the projection operators is changed, we obtain the n_α partners defined by our eigenvectors.

If f and g are taken to be APW's ψ_i and ψ_j and O is the operator $(H-E)$, then we have the relation (to within a constant):

$$(H-E)_{ij}{}^\alpha = \sum_R \frac{G}{n_\alpha} [\Gamma_{ji}(R)]^* \langle \psi_i | H-E | R\psi_j \rangle,$$

where

$$\langle \psi_i | H-E | R\psi_j \rangle = (\mathbf{k}_i \cdot R\mathbf{k}_j - E)$$

$$\times [\Omega \delta_{ij} - 4\pi R_s{}^2 j_1(|R\mathbf{k}_j - \mathbf{k}_i| R_s)/|R\mathbf{k}_j - \mathbf{k}_i|]$$

$$+ 4\pi R_s{}^2 \sum_{l=0}^{\infty} (2l+1) P_l\left(\frac{\mathbf{k}_i \cdot R\mathbf{k}_j}{|\mathbf{k}_i||\mathbf{k}_j|}\right)$$

$$\times j_l(k_i R_s) j_l(k_j R_s) \frac{u_l'(R_s; E)}{u_l(R_s; E)}. \qquad (10)$$

Computer programs for automatically forming the matrix elements (10) have been written for Whirlwind by Saffern[8] and for the IBM machines by the author.[12] The $\mathbf{k}_i$ and $\mathbf{k}_j$ occuring here are members of the previously mentioned reduced set $\{\mathbf{k}+\mathbf{K}_i\}$ appropriate to

[12] J. H. Wood, Quarterly Progress Report No. 36, Solid State and Molecular Theory Group, Massachusetts Institute of Technology, 1960 (unpublished).

TABLE I. Listing of one-electron potential in rydberg units used in calculations reported here. Values of r are in atomic units. In the bcc case this potential is cut off at radius 2.341 and the constant potential between spheres is taken at 0.816 ry. In the fcc case, cutoff is taken at radius 2.437 and the constant is taken as 0.776 ry. These constants are spherical averages of the tabulated potential between the inscribed spheres of the above radii and the Wigner-Seitz spheres, the latter having the radii 2.662 for the bcc case and 2.693 for the fcc case.

r	$V(r)$	r	$V(r)$
0.005	10173.0	0.840	10.30
0.010	4977.5	0.880	9.240
0.015	3247.3	0.920	8.322
0.020	2384.6	0.960	7.523
0.025	1870.0	1.000	6.824
0.030	1528.1	1.040	6.211
0.035	1285.3	1.080	5.669
0.040	1104.4	1.120	5.193
0.045	964.53	1.160	4.773
0.050	853.28	1.200	4.400
0.055	762.80	1.240	4.068
0.060	687.83	1.280	3.770
0.065	624.78	1.320	3.501
0.070	571.06	1.360	3.258
0.075	524.72	1.400	3.039
0.080	484.40	1.440	2.839
0.085	448.96	1.480	2.657
0.090	417.66	1.520	2.492
0.095	389.78	1.560	2.341
0.100	364.82	1.600	2.202
		1.640	2.075
0.110	322.02	1.680	1.958
0.120	286.74	1.720	1.850
0.130	257.24	1.760	1.750
0.140	232.24	1.800	1.658
0.150	210.87	1.840	1.573
0.160	192.46	1.880	1.494
0.170	176.44	1.920	1.421
0.180	162.37	1.960	1.354
0.190	150.01	2.000	1.292
0.200	139.12	2.040	1.234
		2.080	1.181
0.220	121.29	2.120	1.132
0.240	106.02	2.160	1.086
0.260	93.642	2.200	1.045
0.280	83.582	2.240	1.006
0.300	75.023	2.280	0.9715
0.320	67.741	2.320	0.9392
		2.360	0.9093
0.360	55.986	2.400	0.8812
0.400	46.915	2.440	0.8545
0.440	39.716	2.480	0.8277
0.480	33.890	2.520	0.8032
0.520	29.112	2.560	0.7783
0.560	25.146	2.600	0.7558
0.600	21.835	2.640	0.7347
0.640	19.048	2.680	0.7135
0.680	16.697	2.720	0.6932
0.720	14.701	2.760	0.6736
0.760	13.00	2.800	0.6546
0.800	11.54	2.840	0.6362

the particular $\mathbf{k}$. We see here the reason for using the reduced set—all other members are now automatically generated by the operations R forming the group of k. The input to the programs consists of specification of the irreducible representation α, a list of wave vectors $\{\mathbf{k}+\mathbf{K}_i\}$ for a particular point $\mathbf{k}$, and along with each wave vector the appropriate (second) projection operator index. In addition, one includes a list of energies E for which the determinant of the matrix $(H-E)_{ij}$ is

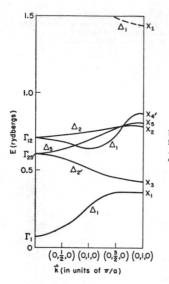

FIG. 1. Energy bands in fcc iron from $\Gamma(0,0,0)$ to $X(0,2,0)$ along [010] direction.

TABLE II. Summary of lattice parameter values used in various calculations.

Manning bcc	5.40 a.u.
Stern bcc	5.404 a.u.
Suffczynski bcc	5.405 a.u.
Callaway bcc	not given
Wood bcc	5.406 a.u.
Manning and Greene fcc	6.86 a.u.
Wood fcc	6.892 a.u.

In the APW calculations reported here, the sphere radius R_s (see text) values were:

bcc	2.341 a.u.
fcc	2.437 a.u.

to be evaluated. Determination of the group of the wave vector [which determines the set R to be used in Eq. (10)], formation of the quantities $u_l'(R_s)/u_l(R_s)$ from the spherical portion of the potential for each energy and generation of the Bessel and Legendre functions then proceeds automatically, and finally the determinant of the matrix for each energy is evaluated. Once the list of energies has been exhausted, an inverse interpolation procedure is performed to determine the energy zeroes of the determinant. The programs have been constructed for fcc and bcc lattices of one atom per unit cell; A. C. Switendick of these laboratories has written IBM programs for the more complex NaCl structure.[13]

RESULTS OF COMPUTATIONS

The calculations reported here were performed using the potential listed in Table I; this potential is that which Manning[14] and Greene and Manning[15] used in their cellular calculations on iron. The valence electrons in metallic iron are the $3d$ and $4s$ electrons, the ground configuration of atomic iron being $3d^6 4s^2$. The choice of this potential was made partly to compare the APW and cellular calculations and partly because the potential was one which had been subjected to a form of self-consistency check. For details of the construction of this potential the reader is referred to Manning's paper. Essentially, the potential is derived from an argon core (from the calculation of Manning and

Goldberg[16]) plus one $4s$-type and six $3d$-type valence electrons. The $3d$ charge was composed of a sum of 6 different radial distributions, each weighted to reflect the concentration of levels described by density-of-states curves for transition metals then available. Manning's criterion for self-consistency was that the width of the d band at the end of the cellular calculation check the width given by the previous approximation. This potential was derived from Manning's bcc calculation and was taken over directly for the Greene and Manning fcc cellular calculations, no modifications being made for the different structure and interatomic distance.

Comparison of the results reported here with those of Manning and Manning and Greene shows that the agreement is not good. Consequently, one might well argue that the self-consistency procedure of Manning (or some more elaborate method) should be carried to conclusion for the APW calculations. This has not been done although it does not appear that such a job is

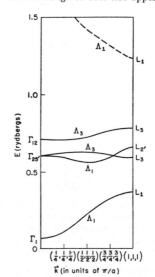

FIG. 2. Energy bands in fcc iron from $\Gamma(0,0,0)$ to $L(1,1,1)$ along [111] direction.

[13] A. C. Switendick, Quarterly Progress Report, No. 40, Solid State and Molecular Theory Group, Massachusetts Institute of Technology, 1961 (unpublished).
[14] M. F. Manning, Phys. Rev. 63, 190 (1943).
[15] J. B. Greene and M. F. Manning, Phys. Rev. 63, 203 (1943).

[16] M. F. Manning and L. Goldberg, Phys. Rev. 53, 662 (1938).

TABLE III. Energies of states in fcc structure. All values are in rydberg units and are with reference to a *zero* constant potential between spheres. To convert energy levels so that they are with reference to the tabulated potential, *subtract* 0.776 ry from each. The symbols preceding the coordinates of the points refer to fcc Brillouin zone lables. The symbols preceding the energies are irreducible representation labels as defined by Bouckaert, Smoluchowski, and Wigner. The latter portion of the table lists some higher states which fall outside the first 6 bands.

4k	Band 1		Band 2		Band 3		Band 4		Band 5		Band 6	
Γ 0,0,0	1	0.069	25'	0.606	25'	0.606	25'	0.606	12	0.712	12	0.712
Δ 0,2,0	1	0.125	2'	0.583	5	0.630	5	0.630	1	0.686	2	0.723
Δ 0,4,0	1	0.267	2'	0.516	1	0.639	5	0.692	5	0.692	2	0.748
Δ 0,6,0	1	0.356	2'	0.456	1	0.722	5	0.769	5	0.769	2	0.775
X 0,8,0	1	0.355	3	0.430	2	0.786	5	0.807	5	0.807	4'	0.871
Λ 1,1,1	1	0.112	1	0.594	3	0.622	3	0.622	3	0.709	3	0.709
Λ 2,2,2	1	0.225	1	0.563	3	0.624	3	0.624	3	0.722	3	0.722
Λ 3,3,3	1	0.342	1	0.590	3	0.609	3	0.609	3	0.769	3	0.769
L 4,4,4	1	0.371	3	0.595	3	0.595	2'	0.658	3	0.787	3	0.787
Σ $\frac{1}{2},\frac{1}{2},0$	1	0.132	3	0.583	2	0.626	1	0.627	4	0.694	1	0.719
Σ 3,3,0	1	0.295	3	0.543	1	0.603	4	0.667	2	0.673	1	0.795
Σ $\frac{3}{2},\frac{3}{2},0$	1	0.451	1	0.520	3	0.546	4	0.670	2	0.733	1	0.958
K 6,6,0	1	0.421	1	0.468	3	0.618	4	0.721	2	0.780	3	1.168
W 4,8,0	2'	0.435	3	0.532	3	0.532	1	0.695	1'	0.808	3	1.299
Γ	15	2.491										
L	1	1.228										
W	1	1.527	2'	1.447								
X	1	1.445										
K	1	1.260	1	1.470								

insuperable with the digital computers now available. In addition to the potential, the specification of the problem requires a value of the lattice constant and a value of the sphere radius R_s. This information is given in Table II along with the values used by Stern,[17] Callaway,[18] Suffczynski,[19] and Manning[14,15] in their calculations.

The results of the calculations are listed in Tables III and IV and in Figs. 1 through 9. The **k** points for which

bcc calculations were made were determined by a cubic grid in k space of dimensions $(\frac{1}{4}\times\frac{1}{4}\times\frac{1}{4})$. The fcc calculations were carried out for a lesser number of points. Our units for measurement of k are indicated in the tables.

The curves are drawn using the information given in the tables and the compatibility relations as outlined by Bouckaert, Smoluchowski, and Wigner.[10] The labeling of the irreducible representations of the wave functions associated with the various $E(\mathbf{k})$ is that of these authors. It is, of course, possible to draw many more such curves, using the information in the tables; we have presented the curves along the directions of high symmetry plus one bcc case (Fig. 9) in which we show the band structure along a line lying in the plane

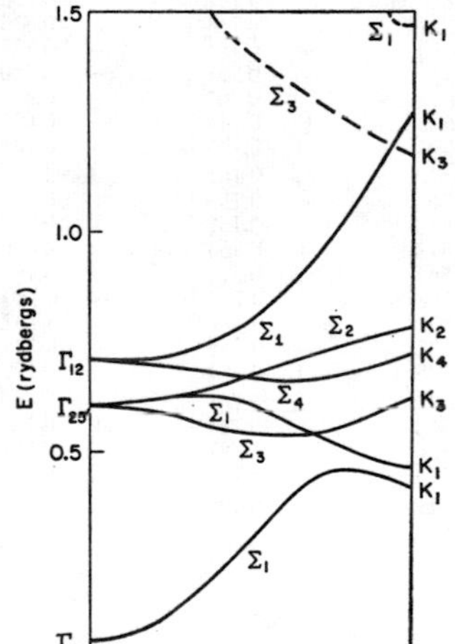

FIG. 3. Energy bands in fcc iron from $\Gamma'(0,0,0)$ to $K(\frac{3}{2},\frac{3}{2},0)$ along [110] direction.

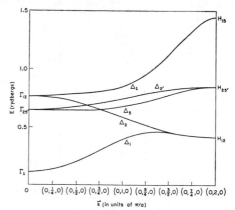

FIG. 4. Energy bands in bcc iron from $\Gamma'(0,0,0)$ to $H(0,2,0)$ along [010] direction.

[17] F. Stern, Phys. Rev. **116**, 1399 (1959).
[18] J. Callaway, Phys. Rev. **99**, 500 (1955).
[19] M. Suffczynski, Acta. Phys. Polon. **16**, 161 (1957).

TABLE IV. Energies of states in bcc structure. All values are in rydberg units and are with reference to a *zero* constant potential between spheres. To convert energy levels so that they are with reference to the tabulated potential, *subtract* 0.816 ry from each. The symbols preceding the coordinates of the points refer to bcc Brillouin zone labels. The symbols preceding the energies are irreducible representation labels as defined by Bouckaert, Smoluchowski, and Wigner. (A plus or minus sign indicates the behavior of the associated wave function upon reflection in the symmetry plane in which **k** lies.) The latter portion of the table lists some higher states, which fall outside the first 6 bands.

4k	Band 1	Band 2	Band 3	Band 4	Band 5	Band 6
Γ 0,0,0	1 0.108	25′ 0.640	25′ 0.640	25′ 0.640	12 0.762	12 0.762
Δ 0,1,0	1 0.132	5 0.644	5 0.644	2′ 0.654	2 0.756	1 0.771
Δ 0,2,0	1 0.199	5 0.643	5 0.643	2′ 0.676	2 0.716	1 0.786
Δ 0,3,0	1 0.297	2 0.650	5 0.651	5 0.651	2′ 0.702	1 0.808
Δ 0,4,0	1 0.396	2 0.581	5 0.674	5 0.674	2′ 0.741	1 0.849
Δ 0,5,0	1 0.450	2 0.517	5 0.715	5 0.715	2′ 0.782	1 0.948
Δ 0,6,0	1 0.449	2 0.464	5 0.771	5 0.771	2′ 0.817	1 1.118
Δ 0,7,0	1 0.424	2 0.425	5 0.824	5 0.824	2′ 0.841	1 1.318
H 0,8,0	12 0.413	12 0.413	25′ 0.850	25′ 0.850	25′ 0.850	15 1.435
Σ 1,1,0	1 0.154	2 0.631	1 0.642	3 0.676	1 0.757	4 0.773
1,2,0	+ 0.208	− 0.614	+ 0.627	− 0.700	+ 0.723	+ 0.777
1,3,0	+ 0.303	+ 0.612	− 0.616	+ 0.694	− 0.737	+ 0.800
1,4,0	+ 0.398	+ 0.570	− 0.634	+ 0.696	− 0.777	+ 0.847
1,5,0	+ 0.454	+ 0.515	− 0.672	+ 0.709	− 0.815	+ 0.961
1,6,0	+ 0.455	+ 0.468	− 0.725	+ 0.747	− 0.843	+ 1.142
G 1,7,0	1 0.442	4 0.439	3 0.788	1 0.804	2 0.861	4 1.332
Σ 2,2,0	1 0.275	2 0.594	1 0.618	3 0.751	1 0.753	4 0.773
2,3,0	+ 0.341	− 0.581	+ 0.608	+ 0.738	− 0.787	+ 0.789
2,4,0	+ 0.407	− 0.586	+ 0.592	+ 0.733	+ 0.826	+ 0.850
2,5,0	+ 0.448	+ 0.551	− 0.616	+ 0.713	− 0.853	+ 0.988
G 2,6,0	1 0.467	4 0.507	3 0.669	1 0.722	2 0.867	4 1.143
Σ 3,3,0	1 0.383	2 0.560	1 0.656	1 0.767	4 0.784	3 0.835
3,4,0	+ 0.403	− 0.553	+ 0.667	+ 0.761	+ 0.833	− 0.861
G 3,5,0	1 0.429	3 0.579	4 0.618	1 0.737	2 0.874	4 0.947
N 4,4,0	1 0.399	2 0.545	1′ 0.748	1 0.765	4 0.787	3 0.877
Λ 1,1,1	1 0.177	3 0.626	3 0.626	1 0.694	3 0.763	3 0.763
1,2,1	+ 0.229	+ 0.605	− 0.608	+ 0.727	− 0.731	+ 0.773
1,3,1	+ 0.320	− 0.590	+ 0.607	− 0.708	+ 0.767	+ 0.800
1,4,1	+ 0.410	− 0.557	+ 0.623	− 0.703	+ 0.790	+ 0.862
1,5,1	+ 0.466	− 0.513	+ 0.639	− 0.727	+ 0.813	+ 0.989
1,6,1	+ 0.469	− 0.473	+ 0.676	− 0.775	+ 0.832	+ 1.174
F 1,7,1	3 0.450	3 0.450	1 0.737	3 0.834	3 0.834	3 1.378
2,2,1	+ 0.286	− 0.582	+ 0.594	+ 0.748	− 0.767	+ 0.775
2,3,1	0.361	0.571	0.593	0.744	0.786	0.830
2,4,1	0.426	0.559	0.600	0.737	0.806	0.906
2,5,1	0.467	0.544	0.599	0.738	0.830	1.036
2,6,1	+ 0.477	− 0.507	+ 0.620	+ 0.754	− 0.835	− 1.187
3,3,1	+ 0.395	− 0.550	+ 0.620	+ 0.761	− 0.780	+ 0.876
3,4,1	0.418	0.549	0.645	0.761	0.801	0.936
3,5,1	+ 0.441	+ 0.563	− 0.605	+ 0.744	− 0.605	− 1.018
D 4,4,1	1 0.418	4 0.544	3 0.694	1 0.774	2 0.788	3 0.951
Λ 2,2,2	1 0.350	3 0.570	3 0.570	3 0.767	3 0.767	1 0.834
2,3,2	+ 0.409	− 0.551	+ 0.564	− 0.756	+ 0.781	+ 0.893
2,4,2	+ 0.458	− 0.537	+ 0.583	− 0.751	+ 0.792	+ 0.979
2,5,2	+ 0.500	− 0.527	+ 0.573	− 0.760	+ 0.800	+ 1.118
F 2,6,2	3 0.520	3 0.520	1 0.567	3 0.794	3 0.794	3 1.294
3,3,2	+ 0.451	− 0.539	+ 0.568	+ 0.767	− 0.780	+ 0.963
3,4,2	0.467	0.538	0.597	0.771	0.792	1.047
3,5,2	+ 0.482	+ 0.542	− 0.581	+ 0.765	− 0.794	− 1.139
D 4,4,2	1 0.465	4 0.537	3 0.625	1 0.780	2 0.790	3 1.083
Λ 3,3,3	1 0.518	3 0.538	3 0.538	3 0.785	3 0.785	1 1.057
3,4,3	+ 0.506	− 0.535	+ 0.562	− 0.780	+ 0.785	+ 1.154
F 3,5,3	1 0.508	3 0.556	3 0.556	3 0.787	3 0.787	3 1.282
D 4,4,3	1 0.517	4 0.535	3 0.574	1 0.788	2 0.793	3 1.232
P 4,4,4	4 0.541	4 0.541	4 0.541	3 0.791	3 0.791	4 1.393
Γ	15 3.09					
H	12 1.91	1 2.25				
P	1 1.53					
N	1 1.34	4′ 1.97				

ΓPH, which line has only the symmetry of the plane.

The hatches along the abscissa indicate the points at which calculations were performed. The figures of the respective Brillouin zones may be found in many places; in particular, see reference 3, p. 117.

It can be seen from the figures that the interaction of what are commonly referred to as *s* and *d* bands is

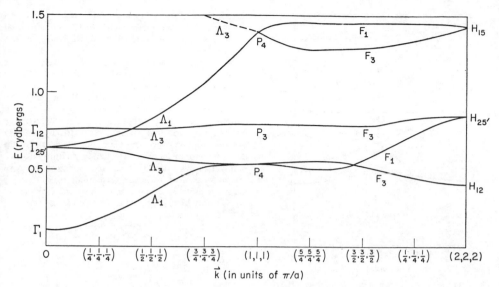

FIG. 5. Energy bands in bcc iron from $\Gamma(0,0,0)$ to $H(2,2,2)$ along [111] direction.

taken automatically into account by virtue of using all angular momenta in the spherical expansion and all wave vectors allowed by Bloch's theorem in the plane-wave portion of the trial functions. Use of the appropriate projection operators ensures that the functions attached to the various $E(\mathbf{k})$ transform appropriately and include all proper combinations of the spherical harmonics. [For some irreducible representations of some $\mathbf{k}$, it is known[20] that certain angular momenta l cannot provide a basis; in these cases, the application of the projection operators results omission of terms of these l from the expressions (10).]

The dashed curves in the diagrams are sketched in by guesswork. They connect the higher energy levels at points of high symmetry for which calculations were performed—calculations at these higher energies have not yet been carried out for the points of lower symmetry so the dashed curves are only approximate.

The density-of-states curve for the bcc phase was compiled from the results of the calculations, which determine the energy at 1024 points in the complete Brillouin zone, weighting each point both according to degeneracy and symmetry. Figure 10 is a histogram constructed using steps $\Delta E = 0.05$ ry. Figure 11 is a smooth curve chosen to fit two histograms constructed using $\Delta E = 0.02$ ry; only the d band is shown here. Figure 12 indicates the number of states per atom which are available at any energy and again we assumed each state is doubly occupied. No density-of-states curve has been calculated for the fcc structure because of the

comparatively small number of points at which calculations were performed. More extensive calculations for the fcc case were not performed because the potential used was determined by Manning for the bcc case only; this potential was merely inserted into the fcc structure with no changes to take account of the

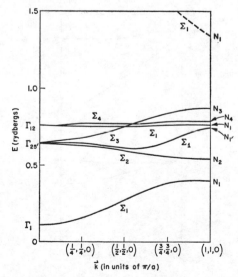

FIG. 6. Energy bands in bcc iron from $\Gamma(0,0,0)$ to $N(1,1,0)$ along [110] direction.

[20] D. G. Bell, Revs. Modern Phys. 26, 106 (1954).

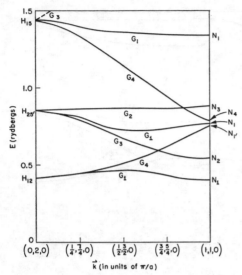

FIG. 7. Energy bands in bcc iron from $H(0,2,0)$ to $N(1,1,0)$ along line $k_x + k_y = 2$.

change in lattice constant and number of nearest neighbors. For these reasons and in view of limited computer availability, we felt the bulk of effort should go into elucidating the bcc case.

The location of the Fermi level ($E_F = 0.770$ ry) as defined here is obtained by filling each available state with one electron of each spin and thus might be re-

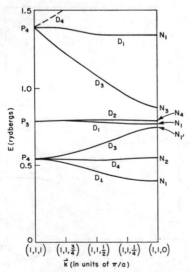

FIG. 8. Energy bands in bcc iron from $P(1,1,1)$ to $N(1,1,0)$ along line $k_x = k_y = 1$.

ferred to as a "nonmagnetic" Fermi level. If we call the energy location corresponding to H_{12} the bottom of the d band, then the *occupied* width of this band is 0.36 ry or 4.9 ev.

This density-of-states curve is qualitatively similar to the curves previously deduced for the transition series metals. The general features of the curve agree with those in Belding's publication[21] although the extent of the curve along the energy axis is roughly double that of hers. In both curves one observes the familiar two principal maxima separated by a fairly deep minimum. However, this minimum does not dip down to zero and separate the band structure into two nonoverlapping regions of allowed energies; here, we are in agreement with the predictions of Callaway's investigations[22] of d bands in cubic lattices. While we do not have a density-of-states curve for the fcc case,

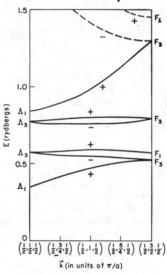

FIG. 9. Energy bands in bcc iron from $\Lambda(\frac{1}{2},\frac{1}{2},\frac{1}{2})$ to $F(\frac{1}{2},\frac{3}{2},\frac{1}{2})$ along a line in the $k_x = k_z$ plane. This indicates how one may map out the behavior of $E(\mathbf{k})$ throughout the zone, using the information in Table IV.

it is clear from the $E(\mathbf{k})$ curves for this structure that again no separation is obtained.

Cheng, Wei, and Beck[23] have calculated, from their measurements of electronic specific heats of transition metal alloys, a density-of-states curve for the transition series assuming a rigid band model. Our curve is in qualitative disagreement with theirs; they obtain an extremely high value of the density of states to the left

[21] Ellinor F. Belding, Phil. Mag. 4, 1145 (1959).
[22] J. Callaway, Phys. Rev. 115, 386 (1959); 120, 731 (1960); 121, 1351 (1961).
[23] C. H. Cheng, C. T. Wei, and P. A. Beck, Phys. Rev. 120, 426 (1960).

of the iron peak, somewhere between Cr and Mn, which we do not find at all. This may be due to a breakdown of the rigid band model and thus it would be useful to have a series of calculations for the transition metals to test this hypothesis.

If we take our density-of-states curve and arbitrarily promote a total charge per atom of one electron of down spin from below $E=0.77=E_F$ and move it up into the unoccupied region above, thus giving us 2 Bohr magnetons per atom to account for the saturation magnetization, then we find that the Fermi level for spin-down electrons is located at $E=0.69$ ry [at which $N(E)$ is 0.77 electron/atom/ev] and that for spin-up electrons is located at $E=0.83$ ry [at which $N(E)$ is 1.68 electrons/atom/ev]. These two Fermi levels must match, of course, which means we should slide the density-of-states curve for up spin 0.14 ry to the left. Recalling that the curve as drawn is for *double* occupancy of each state, we see that we have at this new Fermi level $0.77/2+1.68/2=1.22$ electrons per atom

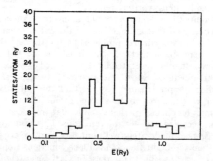

FIG. 10. Density-of-states curve for bcc iron. Histogram constructed using $\Delta E=0.05$ ry.

per ev. Cheng, Wei, and Beck give a value of about 2.0 electrons/atom ev. The bandwidth, defined in the sense used earlier, is now 0.42 ry or 5.7 ev for the spin-up electrons and 0.28 ry or 3.8 ev for spin-down electrons. The bandwidths as measured from the respective $E(\Gamma_1)$ are 9.8 ev and 7.9 ev, respectively. Tomboulian and Bedo[24] estimate, from the valence band emission spectra, that the bandwidth is 8.0 ev.

If this description of the magnetic state, in which we have identical density of states curves for each spin shifted away from one another (presumably by exchange interactions), is taken, then the new composite density-of-states curve for the d band that is obtained is sketched in Fig. 13. Comparing with the original case, we see that the major peak has been reduced in height, the minimum has been "sharpened" though not reduced and the left-hand peak has increased somewhat in height. While this description, in which we have arbitrarily lowered the energies of all spin-up electrons

[24] D. H. Tomboulian and D. E. Bedo, Phys. Rev. **121**, 146 (1961).

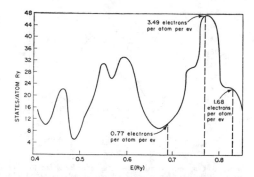

FIG. 11. Smoothed density of states for d band of bcc iron.

by the same 0.14 ry is oversimplified, it does seem likely that a band calculation in which the spin-up and spin-down electrons were handled separately might considerably change the structure of the conventional density-of-states curve.

A level-by-level comparison of the bcc calculation with other bcc iron calculations is given in Table V. One would not expect agreement among the calculations, since different potentials were used and various approximations were introduced. However, the agreement among the present results and those of Stern is much better than one might expect. Stern's value of the width of the occupied portion of the d band is 0.33 ry as compared with our value of 0.36 ry for the nonmagnetic state. Stern's description of his density-of-states curve is one that agrees with ours.

It is reassuring that it is possible to use two quite different methods of solution of the energy band problem and yet obtain comparable results. It has been only in the last ten or fifteen years that we have been in a position to compare different calculations, simply because we can have confidence that each calculation represents an accurate solution of the problem pre-

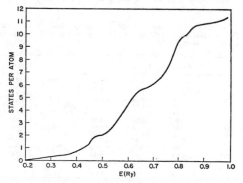

FIG. 12. Number of states per atom available at a given energy for bcc iron.

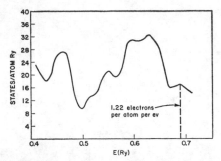

Fig. 13. Composite density-of-states curve for d band of bcc iron in which bands for spin-up electrons have been shifted 0.14 ry downward from those for spin-down electrons.

sented. These accurate solutions have been made possible through the great improvement of computing machines; it is no longer necessary to make drastic approximations in order to fit the problem to the machine.

We regard the energy levels quoted here as accurate to 0.003 ry. Table VI indicates the convergence of the levels in terms of the length of the largest wave vector entering the APW determinant. The general conclusion is that it is adequate to go out to fourth-nearest neighbors in reciprocal space for construction of the wave vectors $\mathbf{k}+\mathbf{K}_j$. Of course, for a point of no symmetry this implies a large (of the order of 40×40) secular equation but aside from computer time requirements, this imposes no difficulty.

Insofar as the cutoff on l goes, we have uniformly used all angular momentum up to $l=12$ in these calculations. Increasing this number up to $l=19$ affects the eigenvalues in the seventh decimal place. Examination of a few states at Γ indicates that cutting off at $l=8$ is perfectly satisfactory. However, in this method, it is necessary to include angular momenta beyond $l=2$ even though one normally speaks only of s, p, and d bands.

The possibility of extending up to high angular momenta and large wave vectors in construction of the APW determinant with little difficulty is an extremely useful feature of the APW method. We need calculate only three l-dependent functions, viz., the Legendre polynomials, the spherical Bessel functions, and the logarithmic derivatives u_l'/u_l in the assumed potential, all of which are relatively easy to calculate. No complicated auxiliary functions are necessary in the method.

CONCLUSIONS

The APW method has proved to be a powerful method for solving the one-electron Schrödinger equation for a metal. It is not restricted to points of high symmetry in the Brillouin zone and thus it is possible to make a thorough investigation throughout the zone without the necessity of relying on interpolation procedures. There is no necessity for solving for the core-state wave functions[25] as in the orthogonalized plane-wave method. The method is one which is peculiarly adaptable to a digital computer so that the calculational burden is almost entirely removed.

A quite general question still remains to be answered, however, and that is the choice of the one-electron potential for a particular problem. In the framework of the energy-band method, this must be the self-consistent potential generated by the occupied one-electron Bloch functions. Most energy-band calculations, including the present one, assume that this potential is not greatly different from what one would obtain using atomic functions (perhaps somewhat modified) for these occupied one-electron functions. This assumption has worked moderately well, but now that we are in a position to obtain the actual Bloch functions from all $\mathbf{k}$ it appears feasible to use these in a self-consistent field method. This would put us in an excellent position to assess the limits of the energy-band method.

TABLE V. Comparison of bcc Fe energy band calculations. The energies are taken relative to the respective $E(H_{12})$ and are in rydberg units.[a]

	Stern	Wood	Callaway	Suffczynski[b]	Manning
Γ_{25}'	+0.09	+0.23	+0.03	+0.08	−0.10
Γ_{12}	+0.32	+0.35	+0.05	+0.16	+0.00
H_{12}	0	0	0	0	0
H_{25}'	+0.58	+0.44	+0.07	+0.21	+0.52
P_4	−0.11	+0.13		+0.10	+0.04
P_1	+0.37	+0.38		+0.16	+0.38
N_1	−0.01	−0.01	−0.03	+0.04	−0.12
N_2	+0.02	+0.04	+0.03	+0.03	−0.10
N_1	+0.13	+0.35	+0.06	+0.16	+0.37
N_4	+0.37	+0.38	+0.08	+0.15	+0.38
N_3	+0.68	+0.47	+0.04	+0.21	+0.52
Over-all d band width	0.68	0.47	0.12	0.21	0.62

[a] Energies estimated from graphs in case of other authors.
[b] Calculation in which second-nearest neighbors were used.

TABLE VI. Energies of two sample bcc levels as a function of the square of the length of the wave vector of the last APW included in the secular equation. [In our units, the first-nearest neighbors in $\mathbf{k}$ space are of the type (2,2,0).]

$|\mathbf{k}|^2$	E	$|\mathbf{k}|^2$	E	$|\mathbf{k}|^2$	E
Point $\mathbf{k}=(2,5,1)/4$					
13.9	0.7584	19.9	0.7394	26.9	0.7367
14.9	0.7554	20.9	0.7387	27.9	0.7356
15.9	0.7495	21.9	0.7386	28.9	0.7352
16.9	0.7407	23.9	0.7385	30.9	0.7351
17.9	0.7403	24.9	0.7382	31.9	0.7351
18.9	0.7396	25.9	0.7368	32.9	0.7351
Point $\mathbf{k}=(2,3,0)/4$; odd representation					
16.8	0.7994	26.8	0.7895	34.8	0.7880
17.8	0.7954	28.8	0.7889	36.8	0.7878
19.8	0.7913	29.8	0.7883	37.8	0.7878
20.8	0.7912	31.8	0.7881	38.8	0.7876
23.8	0.7907	32.8	0.7880	42.8	0.7876
25.8	0.7898				

[25] M. M. Saffren, Ph.D. Thesis, Department of Physics, Massachusetts Institute of Technology (1959) (unpublished).

The potential used in the present calculations has led to results which seem to be in fair agreement with experiment; calculation of more **k** points and a consequent refinement of the density-of-states curves might be indicated, although we feel this is hardly worthwhile until we have a better potential. We have compared bandwidth and electronic specific heat and found reasonable agreement. The experimental controversy with regard to the number of 3d electrons in iron seems to have been satisfactorily resolved by recent experiments of Batterman *et al.*[26]; it appears that no *qualitative* change of the conventional energy-band picture is necessary to explain the experimental results.

Perhaps one obvious feature of the calculations should be mentioned. These calculations, as well as Stern's, have produced a valence band whose occupied width is considerable; we cannot very well consider the d bands to be "narrow bands." This has come about because both in our calculations and in Stern's, the form of the radial d function has not been assumed *a priori* as atomic, but has in fact been calculated for the case under consideration and the changes have been considerable enough to widen the bands beyond what one might expect on the basis of a simple tight-binding argument.

In conclusion, we are now in a position to map out accurately the one-electron wave functions and energy levels throughout the entire Brillouin zone and thus it should be possible to answer quantitatively the questions as to what Fermi surfaces may look like, how the total electronic charge density behaves as a function of position, how much hyperfine interaction we might expect from an energy-band picture, etc. By and large, most of the past effort has been directed at the behavior of the one-electron energies but the previous questions are equally important ones.

Notes added in proof. Recent reports of calculations

on energy bands in copper carried out by Segall,[27] using the Chodorow potential, show excellent agreement with Burdick's calculations.[9] Segall has used the Green's function method of Kohn and Rostocker, as described by Ham and Segall.[28] We, thus, have good cross checks among Chodorow's hand calculations,[5] the calculations of Burdick, and the calculations of Segall.

Wohlfarth and Cornwell[29] have recently presented a density of states curve for bcc iron which exhibits sharp peaks which are known to be demanded.[30] Our curves do not show these peaks; the peaks have been smoothed out by the numerical methods used in constructing the curves. The presence of the peaks could be extremely important, as Wohlfarth and Cornwell point out, and may explain (among other things) the sharp peak observed by Cheng, Wei, and Beck.[23]

ACKNOWLEDGMENTS

The writer thanks Professor J. C. Slater, who suggested the problem, for his continued interest and support. He is also indebted to members of the Solid-State and Molecular Theory Group at the Massachusetts Institute of Technology for many discussions. Especial thanks are due to M. M. Saffren for use of computer programs and for many discussions which were invaluable.

He also thanks the staff of the MIT Computation Center for advice, help, and use of the Whirlwind and IBM computation systems. A portion of the calculations was performed at the computing installation of the Lincoln Laboratory of the Massachusetts Institute of Technology and the writer is grateful for the extension of their facilities.

[26] B. W. Batterman, D. R. Chipman, and J. J. DeMarco, Phys. Rev. **122**, 68 (1961).

[27] B. Segall, Phys. Rev. Letters **7**, 154 (1961); Phys. Rev. **125**, 109 (1962).
[28] F. S. Ham and B. Segall, Phys. Rev. **124**, 1786 (1961).
[29] E. P. Wohlfarth and J. F. Cornwell, Phys. Rev. Letters **7**, 342 (1961).
[30] L. Van Hove, Phys. Rev. **89**, 1189 (1953); J. C. Phillips, Phys. Rev. **104**, 1263 (1956).

Reprinted from THE PHYSICAL REVIEW, Vol. 129, No. 1, 138–150, 1 January, 1963
Printed in U. S. A.

Energy Band Structure of Copper*

GLENN A. BURDICK†‡

Massachusetts Institute of Technology Cambridge, Massachusetts

(Received 28 June 1962)

The $E(k)$ values were computed for the equivalent of 2048 points in the Brillouin zone and for energies ranging from the bottom of the 4s-band to approximately 2 Ry above the Fermi energy. From these calculations the Fermi energy, Fermi surface, and density of states were determined. Comparison of results with experiment shows not only qualitative but in most cases quantitative agreement. Agreement with recent independent theoretical work by Segall suggests an accurate solution of Schrödinger's equation for the potential used has been obtained.

INTRODUCTION

THE energy bands, Fermi surface, and density of states for copper have been determined by the augmented plane wave (APW) method. Since early 1954 the Solid-State and Molecular Theory Group (SSMTG) at the Massachusetts Institute of Technology has been engaged in programming the APW method for the digital computer.[1] This method was first proposed by Slater in 1937[2–4] and the results of the work described herein together with that of Chodorow on copper,[5] Saffren on sodium,[1] Wood on iron,[1,6] and Allen on potassium[1] give strong support to its being a very practical and accurate way of determining energy bands. The results for copper, in particular, demonstrate that energy-band calculations can agree quantitatively with experiment.

Copper has been the subject of considerable theoretical as well as experimental investigations. However, until quite recently there did not exist sufficient facilities, such as the APW digital computer program used in this work, to allow calculations to be made except at points of high symmetry in the Brillouin zone. As far as the author knows this work represents the most complete energy-band calculation made to date. One of the first calculations for copper was made by Krutter in 1935.[7] He used an extension of the Wigner-Seitz cellular method and concluded that the bands were quite free electron-like and obtained no overlapping of the "s" and "d" bands. Others using the cellular method with somewhat different potentials were Fuchs,[8,9] Tibbs,[10] and Howarth.[11] Chodorow's work in

1939[5,12] was the first application of the APW method. Fukuchi[13] used the orthogonalized plane wave method for copper in 1956. More recently Segall[14,15] has employed the Green's function method on copper. In the past, theoretical works on solids have been primarily restricted to intercomparisons of energy eigenvalues, their separations, their ordering, and similar general features of band structure; the reasons being that the $E(\mathbf{k})$ could be determined for only a few $\mathbf{k}$ of high symmetry. Furthermore, results obtained from theory could be compared to experiment in only the most general way (e.g., comparing d bandwidths with widths of x-ray emission spectra). In 1939, Rudberg and Slater[16] extended existing cellular method calculations to obtain an approximate density of states curve for copper. Beeman and Friedman[17] used this curve to make a qualitative comparison with their x-ray emission and absorption data for the K shell. They found quite good comparisons considering the necessarily sketchy data which could be used in determining the density of states. This will be discussed in greater detail later. The primary concern over past energy-band calculations (not only copper) was their inability to agree amongst themselves and the fact there had been only the most moderate success in being able to agree with experiment. Recent work in the SSMTG together with the work recently reported by Segall[14] and the work reported here seem to indicate that past difficulties lie in faulty potentials and/or computational errors and not in the energy-band theory itself.[18]

In the past, when $E(\mathbf{k})$ obtained in different studies have disagreed, it was not known whether the dis-

* This paper is a condensed version of the author's doctorate thesis submitted to the Massachusetts Institute of Technology in August 1961.

† Work performed while a National Science Foundation Fellow.

‡ Present Address: Sperry Microwave Electronics Company, Clearwater, Florida.

[1] Quarterly Progress Reports, Solid-State and Molecular Theory Group, April 15, 1954 to date (unpublished), contributions from D. J. Howarth, M. M. Saffren, J. H. Wood, and others; see: M. M. Saffren beginning with QPR, July, 1955 for work on sodium; L. C. Allen beginning with QPR, July, 1957 for work on potassium.

[2] J. C. Slater, Phys. Rev. 51, 846 (1937).

[3] J. C. Slater, Phys. Rev. 92, 603 (1953).

[4] M. M. Saffren and J. C. Slater, Phys. Rev. 92, 1126 (1953).

[5] M. I. Chodorow, Ph.D. Thesis, M.I.T., 1939 (unpublished).

[6] J. H. Wood, Phys. Rev. 117, 714 (1960); 126, 517 (1962).

[7] H. M. Krutter, Phys. Rev. 48, 664 (1935)

[8] K. Fuchs, Proc. Roy. Soc. (London) A151, 585 (1935).

[9] K. Fuchs, Proc. Roy. Soc. (London) A153, 622 (1936).

[10] S. R. Tibbs, Proc. Cambridge Phil. Soc. 34, 89 (1938).

[11] D. J. Howarth, Proc. Roy. Soc. (London) A220, 513 (1953).

[12] M. I. Chodorow, Phys. Rev. 55, 675 (1939).

[13] M. Fukuchi, Progr. Theoret. Phys. (Kyoto) 16, 222 (1956).

[14] B. Segall, American Physical Society, annual meeting, New York, February 1–4, 1961 and meeting held in Washington, D. C., April 24–27, 1961; B. Segall and E. O. Kreiger, Bull. Am. Phys. Soc. 6, 10 (1961). B. Segall, Phys. Rev. 125, 109 (1962).

[15] B. Segall, General Electric Research Laboratory, Report No. 61-RL-(2785G), July, 1961 (unpublished).

[16] E. Rudberg and J. C. Slater, Phys. Rev. 50, 150 (1936).

[17] W. W. Beeman and H. Friedman, Phys. Rev. 56, 392 (1939).

[18] A joint paper by J. H. Wood, Jean Hanus, and the author discussing the dependence of energy bands on potential is presently being prepared for publication.

crepancies were due to differences in the crystal potential or to inaccuracies of either or both of the methods employed. Thanks to Segall's cooperation, pertinent information on this is now available. The extremely close agreement between his detailed calculations and the author's independent calculations using a different technique indicate that both techniques yield accurate solutions to the periodic potential problem. The very close agreement of these results and their agreement with experiment give us confidence that band structure studies like the present ones will be very useful in the understanding of many of the aspects of the electronic properties of solids.

As pointed out later, it has been possible to make a straightforward determination of the Fermi energy, Fermi surface, and density of states due to the large number of $E(\mathbf{k})$ values calculated. Segall did not calculate $E(\mathbf{k})$ at a sufficient number of general points to allow a determination of the density of states. However, he was able to calculate pertinent parameters of the Fermi surface by making use of two quite good approximations, the greatest inaccuracy being in his approximation of the volume inside the Fermi surface which he estimates to be in the range of 3–5%. The current work substantiates this estimate.

THEORY

Digital Computer Program

The digital computer program used to make the calculations in this report was provided by J. H. Wood who adapted M. M. Saffren's Whirlwind computer program to the IBM 704 and the IBM 709 computers. The program uses the Noumerov[19] method to integrate the radial wave equation and evaluates the Legendre polynominals and spherical Bessel functions in the standard manner by utilizing the various recurrence relations. Since the program has been thoroughly tested by Wood and utilized by several members of SSMTG no detailed description as to the specifics of the program will be given. Perhaps the strongest support for its accuracy lies in the very close agreement of the results obtained by this program as compared to independent calculations by Chodorow[5] and Segall.[14,15]

APW Method

The APW method is due to Slater[2] and was modified slightly by Slater and Saffren.[3,4] The method as originally proposed by Slater is the one used in this work. For the sake of completeness a brief account of the method is now given. It is felt that a comprehensive treatment is unwarranted since such a treatment can be found in several works.[2–5,20,21]

[19] For a detailed account of this method, see G. W. Pratt, Phys. Rev. 88, 1217 (1952).
[20] D. J. Howarth, Phys. Rev. 99, 469 (1955).
[21] M. M. Saffren, Ph.D. thesis, M.I.T., 1959 (unpublished).

A necessary requirement for any method to yield good solutions to the electron in a periodic potential problem is that rapid convergence be obtained when the wave function is expanded in terms of the basis set being used. This criterion is obtained in the current method by expanding the wave function in terms of "atomic-like" functions within spheres centered about each nucleus and in terms of plane waves in the region between spheres. It is here assumed that the potential is spherically symmetric within the spheres and constant in the region between spheres. It is further assumed (although this assumption is unnecessary) that there is only one atom per Wigner-Seitz cell. As is well known, we need concern ourselves only with those space coordinates $\mathbf{r}$ restricted to the first Wigner-Seitz cell and with those wave vectors $\mathbf{k}$ restricted to the first Brillouin zone of reciprocal space since the wave functions must be of the form

$$\Psi_{\mathbf{k}}(\mathbf{r}) = e^{i\mathbf{k}\cdot\mathbf{r}} w_k(\mathbf{r}), \tag{1}$$

where

$$\Psi_{\mathbf{k}}(\mathbf{r}+\mathbf{R}_j) = e^{i\mathbf{k}\cdot(\mathbf{r}+\mathbf{R}_j)} w_k(\mathbf{r}) = e^{i\mathbf{k}\cdot\mathbf{R}_j}\Psi_{\mathbf{k}}(\mathbf{r}), \tag{2}$$

$\mathbf{R}_j$ being a lattice vector.

Choose a coordinate system whose origin is at the center of the first Wigner-Seitz cell and coincident with a copper nucleus. Let R represent one-half of the nearest-neighbor distance. Then for $|\mathbf{r}| \leq R$, the potential, say, $U(\mathbf{r})$ is spherically symmetric and the wave function can be put in the form

$$\Psi = \sum_{l=0}^{\infty} \sum_{m=-l}^{l} A_{lm} P_l^{|m|}(\cos\theta) e^{im\phi} u_l(r). \tag{3}$$

Here $u_l(r)$ satisfies the equation

$$-\frac{1}{2}\frac{d}{dr}\left(r^2\frac{du_l}{dr}\right) + \frac{l(l+1)}{r^2} + U(r)u_l = Eu_l, \tag{4}$$

and is to be regular at the origin (unlike the atomic case, being regular at infinity is not required). In the remaining region of the Wigner-Seitz cell the potential is assumed constant and any function of the form $e^{i\mathbf{k}\cdot\mathbf{r}}$ satisfies the Schrödinger equation. Now we use the well-known expansion for $e^{i\mathbf{k}\cdot\mathbf{r}}$ and obtain

$$e^{i\mathbf{k}\cdot\mathbf{r}} = \sum_{l=0}^{\infty} \sum_{m=-l}^{l} (2l+1)i^l j_l(kr)\frac{(l-|m|)!}{(l+|m|)!}P_l^{|m|}(\cos\theta)$$
$$\times P_l^{|m|}(\cos\theta_k)e^{im(\phi-\phi_k)}. \tag{5}$$

Here r, θ, ϕ are polar coordinates about the origin and θ_k, ϕ_k are polar coordinates giving the direction of the wave vector $\mathbf{k}$. The functions $j_l(kr)$ are spherical Bessel functions and satisfy the differential equation

$$-\frac{1}{r^2}\frac{d}{dr}\left(r^2\frac{dj_l}{dr}\right) + \frac{l(l+1)}{r^2}j_l = k^2 j_l. \tag{6}$$

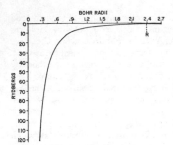

FIG. 1. Cu potential used for calculating wave functions.

The $P_l^{|m|}$ are the associated Legendre polynomials. In the reduced zone scheme which we have chosen, Ψ_k is a periodic but multiple-valued function of $\mathbf{k}$. Thus, if $\mathbf{k}_i = \mathbf{k} + \mathbf{K}_i$, where $\mathbf{k}$ is a wave vector restricted to the first Brillouin zone and $\mathbf{K}_i$ is a reciprocal lattice vector, then

$$\Psi_{ki} = \Psi_k. \tag{7}$$

In line with this, the natural choice of a basis set for expansion of a wave function with wave vector $\mathbf{k}$ is the set G_j, where G_j is given by Eq. (3) for $r \leq R$ and is $e^{i\mathbf{k}_i \cdot \mathbf{r}}$ for $r \geq R$. This G_j is made continuous at $r = R$ by comparing coefficients in Eqs. (3) and (5). We find that

$$A_{lm}{}^i = (2l+1)i^l \frac{j_l(k_iR)}{u_l(R)} \frac{(l-|m|)!}{(l+|m|)!} P_l^{|m|}(\cos\theta_i)e^{im\phi_i}. \tag{8}$$

Note, however, that the first derivative will not in general be continuous. See reference 2 for discussion of this aspect of problem. Expanding Ψ_k in terms of this basis set, we obtain

$$\Psi_k = \sum_i a_i G_i,$$

TABLE I. Chodorow's potential energy for copper[a,b] (values are in atomic units).

r	$2Z_p(r)$	r	$2Z_p(r)$	r	$2Z_p(r)$
0.000	58.000	0.280	25.462	*1.02*	*6.567*
0.005	57.500	0.300	24.264	1.10	5.963
0.010	56.206	*0.340*	*22.186*	*1.18*	*5.429*
0.015	54.966	0.350	21.723	1.20	5.310
0.020	53.797	*0.380*	*20.470*	*1.26*	*4.983*
0.025	52.688	0.400	19.660	1.30	4.778
0.030	51.644	*0.420*	*18.851*	*1.34*	*4.573*
0.035	50.656	0.450	17.678	1.40	4.284
0.040	49.720	*0.460*	*17.308*	*1.42*	*4.197*
0.050	47.970	0.500	15.965	*1.58*	*3.594*
0.060	46.358	*0.540*	*14.772*	1.60	3.533
0.070	44.849	0.550	14.488	*1.74*	*3.183*
0.080	43.420	*0.580*	*13.625*	1.80	3.066
0.090	42.060	0.600	13.128	*1.90*	*2.874*
0.100	40.755	*0.620*	*12.631*	2.00	2.724
0.120	38.333	*0.660*	*11.680*	2.06	2.635
0.140	36.140	0.700	10.874	2.20	2.468
0.160	34.157	*0.780*	*9.408*	*2.22*	*2.446*
0.180	32.359	0.800	9.099	*2.38*	*2.293*
0.200	30.741	*0.860*	*8.252*	2.40	2.277
0.220	29.276	0.900	7.782	2.41	2.270
0.240	27.917	*0.940*	*7.312*	2.60	2.441
0.260	26.662	1.00	6.749	2.80	2.629

[a] Potential $= -2Z_p(r)/r$.
[b] Interpolated values are italicized.

where i ranges over all reciprocal lattice vectors. Applying the variational principle, we obtain the condition

$$\sum_j (H-E)_{ij}A_j = 0, \tag{9}$$

where

$$(H-E)_{ij} = \int \Psi_i^*(H-E)\Psi_j dT, \tag{10}$$

which can be shown to be

$$(H-E)_{ij} = (\mathbf{k}_i \cdot \mathbf{k}_j - E)\left\{ \delta_{ij} + \frac{4\pi R^2}{\Omega} \frac{j_1(|\mathbf{k}_j - \mathbf{k}_i|R)}{|\mathbf{k}_j - \mathbf{k}_i|} \right.$$
$$\left. + \sum_{l=0}^{\infty} (2l+1)P_l(\cos\theta_{ij}) j_l(k_iR) j_l(k_jR) \frac{u_l'(R)}{u_l(R)} \right\}. \tag{11}$$

The problem then is to solve

$$\det|(H-E)_{ij}| = 0. \tag{12}$$

The quantities $(H-E)_{ij}$ are implicit, as well as explicit, functions of the energy since the quantities $u_l'(R)/u_l(R)$ are implicit functions of the energy. For those $\mathbf{k}$ possessing symmetry the determinant will factor, resulting in considerable simplification for its solution.

Potential

The potential used for determining the energy eigenvalues for copper was derived by Chodorow.[5] This potential was arrived at by the addition of two potentials. The first potential is that potential which yields Hartree-Fock wave functions for $3d$ electrons when used in the Hartree equation; that is to say

$$V(r) = (\nabla^2\Psi/\Psi) + E, \tag{13}$$

where Ψ represents the Hartree-Fock wave function for $3d$ electrons in Cu$^+$. The second potential represents the Coulomb contribution of the $4s$ electrons. For this potential Chodorow used $4s$ wave functions determined from a previous cellular calculation due to Krutter.

It was necessary for the author to estimate the potential at certain points not given in Chodorow's numerical table. Chodorow's original potential plus the interpolated values are given in Table I. The sphere radius was taken to be half the nearest-neighbor dis-

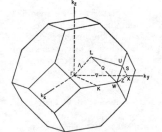

FIG. 2. The Brillouin zone for the face-centered cubic lattice.

TABLE II. Points of the first Brillouin zone for the fcc lattice.

BSW label	Order of the group of k	No. of like vectors	Wave vector k	BSW label	Order of the group of k	No. of like vectors	Wave vector k	BSW label	Order of the group of k	No. of like vectors	Wave vector k
Γ	48	1	000	Σ	4	12	440		2	24	441
Δ	8	6	010		2	24	450		1	48	451
Δ	8	6	020		2	24	460		1	48	461
Δ	8	6	030		2	24	470	Q	2	24	471
Δ	8	6	040	W	8	6	480		2	24	551
Δ	8	6	050	Σ	4	12	550		1	24	561
Δ	8	6	060		2	24	560	Λ	6	8	222
Δ	8	6	070		2	8	570		2	24	232
X	16	3	080	K	4	4	660		2	24	242
Σ	4	12	110	Λ	6	8	111		2	24	252
	2	24	120		2	24	121		2	24	262
	2	24	130		2	24	131		2	24	272
	2	24	140		2	24	141	U	4	8	282
	2	24	150		2	24	151		2	24	332
	2	24	160		2	24	161		1	48	342
	2	24	170		2	24	171		1	48	352
Z	4	12	180	S	4	12	181		1	48	362
Σ	4	12	220		2	24	221		1	24	372
	2	24	230		1	48	231		2	24	442
	2	24	240		1	48	241		1	48	452
	2	24	250		1	48	251	Q	2	24	462
	2	24	260		1	48	261		2	12	552
	2	24	270		1	48	271	Λ	6	8	333
Z	4	12	280		2	24	281		2	24	343
Σ	4	12	330		2	24	331		2	24	353
	2	24	340		1	48	341		2	12	363
	2	24	350		1	48	351		2	24	443
	2	24	360		1	48	361	Q	2	24	453
	2	24	370		1	48	371	L	12	4	444
Z	4	12	380		2	16	381				

tance or, what amounts to the same thing, the radius of the inscribed sphere in the Wigner-Seitz cell. A plot of the potential used is given in Fig. 1.

Face-Centered Cubic Lattice

The first Brillouin zone for the fcc lattice is shown in Fig. 2 and the various points of symmetry are labeled.[22] For the purpose of labeling points in the first Brillouin zone the factor $\pi/4a$ will frequently be dropped. Thus the wave vector $\mathbf{k} = (\pi/4a)(0,8,0)$ (which is the point labeled X in Fig. 2) will be written simply as $(0,8,0)$ or even as 080 when there is no chance for confusion. The reason for this particular choice will become apparent somewhat later. The coordinates of the symmetry points as shown in Fig. 2 are

$$\Gamma = 000; \quad \Delta = 0x0 \quad \text{where } 0 < x < 8$$
$$X = 080; \quad \Sigma = xx0 \quad \text{where } 0 < x < 6$$
$$L = 444; \quad \Lambda = xxx \quad \text{where } 0 < x < 4$$
$$W = 480; \quad Q = 444 + 0x\bar{x} \quad \text{where } 0 < x < 4$$
$$K = 660; \quad Z = x80 \quad \text{where } 0 < x < 4$$
$$U = 282;$$
$$S = (2+x, 8, 2-x) \quad \text{where } 0 < x < 2.$$

A bar over a number in the above list is to be interpreted as a minus sign.

For the purpose of doing a complete determination of the energy band structure such that a reliable density of states curve and the topology of the Fermi surface could be obtained, the first Brillouin zone was partitioned into 2048 cubical volume elements. The energy eigenvalues were then computed for those $\mathbf{k}$ located at the center of each volume element. It is only necessary to compute the eigenvalues for those $\mathbf{k}$ lying in one forty-eighth of the Brillouin zone. From these, by the use of symmetry properties, the eigenvalues can be obtained for all 2048 points. The volume enclosed by the surfaces ΓLK, ΓKWX, ΓXUL, $LKWU$, and WXU (see Fig. 2) constitutes an appropriate one forty-eighth of the zone and 89 of the 2048 points used and the number of "like" points (or vectors) in the zone are listed in Table II. Thus, there is only one point "like" gamma, there are six points "like" 010. Here, $\mathbf{k}$ is said to be "like" $\mathbf{k}$ if

$$E_n(\mathbf{k}') = E_n(\mathbf{k}) \tag{14}$$

for all n, where n is an integer which labels the various energy bands. We shall use the usual convention and order the energies in such a way that

$$E_n(\mathbf{k}) \le E_{n+1}(\mathbf{k}), \tag{15}$$

the equality holding only in the event of degeneracy. The order of the group of the wave vector and the BSW label for symmetry points are also listed in Table II.

TABLE III. The $E(\mathbf{k})$ vs $\mathbf{k}$ are listed. The first column gives the BSW symbol (where appropriate); the second column specifies $\mathbf{k}$ (see text); the third and alternate columns specifies the irreducible representation appropriate for that eigenvalue; the fourth and alternate columns give the energy eigenvalues in rydbergs. In order to obtain the correct energy for a given $\mathbf{k}$ the value of the constant potential between spheres (-0.939 Ry) must be added to the listed value. Thus, the first energy listed under "Band 1" corresponds to Γ_1 and is $(-0.104-0.939)=-1.043$ Ry. The italicized values were obtained by graphical interpolation.

	k	Band 1	Band 2	Band 3	Band 4	Band 5	Band 6
Γ	000	1 -0.10	25′ 0.299	25′ 0.299	25′ 0.299	12 0.357	12 0.357
Δ	010	1 *-0.09*	2′ 0.294	5 0.301	5 0.301	1 0.353	2 0.358
Δ	020	1 *-0.05*	2′ 0.282	5 0.309	5 0.309	1 0.341	2 0.361
Δ	030	1 *$+0.01$*	2′ 0.265	5 0.323	5 0.323	1 0.329	2 0.365
Δ	040	1 *0.08*	2′ 0.243	1 0.328	5 0.342	5 0.342	2 0.371
Δ	050	1 0.148	2′ 0.224	5 0.365	5 0.365	1 0.372	2 0.379
Δ	060	1 0.166	2′ 0.210	5 0.388	5 0.388	2 0.390	1 0.483
Δ	070	1 0.164	2′ 0.201	5 0.405	5 0.405	2 0.394	1 0.621
X	080	1 0.163	3 0.200	2 0.399	5 0.412	5 0.412	4′ 0.704
Σ	110	1 *-0.08*	3 0.291	2 0.303	1 0.303	4 0.352	1 0.356
	120	+ -0.02	− 0.28	+ 0.30	− 0.31	+ 0.34	+ 0.35
	130	+ 0.05	− 0.264	+ 0.31	− 0.323	+ 0.33	+ 0.36
	140	+ 0.11	− 0.245	+ 0.310	− 0.342	+ 0.35	+ 0.37
	150	+ 0.157	− 0.227	+ 0.327	− 0.365	+ 0.37	+ 0.41
	160	+ 0.173	− 0.213	+ 0.358	− 0.388	+ 0.38	+ 0.515
	170	+ 0.171	− 0.204	+ 0.38	+ 0.39	− 0.405	+ 0.651
Z	180	1 0.168	4 0.203	3 0.393	1 0.393	2 0.412	3 0.736
Σ	220	1 *0.00*	3 0.275	1 0.308	2 0.315	4 0.339	1 0.364
	230	+ *0.07*	− 0.264	+ 0.30	− 0.325	+ 0.33	+ 0.38
	240	+ 0.133	− 0.250	+ 0.294	+ 0.348	− 0.343	+ 0.41
	250	+ 0.183	− 0.236	+ 0.295	+ 0.364	− 0.365	+ 0.47
	260	+ 0.193	− 0.224	+ 0.317	+ 0.378	− 0.388	+ 0.579
	270	+ 0.188	− 0.217	+ 0.340	+ 0.38	− 0.405	+ 0.721
Z	280	1 0.185	4 0.216	3 0.351	1 0.380	2 0.412	3 0.815
Σ	330	1 0.11	3 0.262	1 0.298	2 0.333	4 0.330	1 0.411
	340	+ 0.174	− 0.257	+ 0.283	− 0.346	+ 0.335	+ 0.46
	350	+ 0.215	− 0.250	+ 0.270	− 0.366	+ 0.351	+ 0.537
	360	+ 0.219	− 0.243	+ 0.280	− 0.388	+ 0.361	+ 0.658
	370	+ 0.210	− 0.237	+ 0.298	− 0.404	+ 0.362	+ 0.80
Z	380	1 0.205	4 0.237	3 0.307	2 0.412	1 0.363	3 0.921
Σ	440	1 0.212	3 0.264	1 0.272	4 0.332	2 0.355	1 0.523
	450	+ *0.22*	− 0.267	+ *0.26*	+ *0.34*	− 0.370	+ 0.619
	460	+ 0.23	+ 0.25	− 0.268	+ 0.35	− 0.388	+ 0.751
	470	+ 0.22	+ 0.26	− 0.267	+ 0.352	− 0.404	+ 0.721
W	480	2′ 0.216	3 0.268	3 0.268	1 0.354	1′ 0.412	3 1.044
Σ	550	1 0.23	1 0.25	3 0.286	4 0.345	2 0.377	1 0.727
	560	+ 0.22	+ 0.24	− 0.298	+ 0.354	− 0.391	+ 0.863
	570	+ 0.21	+ 0.23	− 0.304	+ 0.360	− 0.404	− 0.941
K	660	1 0.205	1 0.228	3 0.327	4 0.367	2 0.396	3 0.906
Λ	111	1 -0.065	3 0.305	1 0.289	3 0.353	3 0.305	3 0.353
	121	+ *$+0.00$*	+ 0.27	− 0.309	+ 0.30	− 0.35	+ 0.34
	131	+ *0.06*	+ 0.266	− 0.318	+ 0.31	− 0.36	+ 0.34
	141	+ 0.11	+ 0.248	− 0.333	+ 0.305	− 0.37	+ 0.373
	151	+ 0.165	+ 0.232	− 0.348	+ 0.318	− 0.390	+ 0.43
	161	+ 0.179	+ 0.21	− 0.367	+ 0.348	− 0.40	+ 0.538
	171	+ 0.17	+ 0.20	− 0.38	+ 0.372	− 0.40	+ 0.676
S	181	1 0.17	1 0.206	3 0.381	4 0.389	2 0.408	3 0.765
	221	1 *0.03*	+ 0.27	+ 0.30	− 0.31	0.34	+ 0.36
	231	*0.09*	0.26	0.30	0.31	0.35	0.379
	241	0.139	0.258	0.297	0.329	0.370	0.411
	251	0.185	0.243	0.296	0.342	0.388	0.47
	261	0.19	0.230	0.315	0.360	0.400	0.59
	271	0.195	0.222	0.337	0.372	0.401	0.740
	281	+ 0.191	+ 0.218	− 0.345	+ 0.375	− 0.405	
	331	+ *0.12*	+ 0.27	+ 0.29	− 0.316	0.35	+ 0.40
	341	0.171	0.273	0.287	0.322	0.362	0.47
	351	0.206	0.260	0.280	0.336	0.381	0.542
	361	0.219	0.244	0.287	0.351	0.393	0.668
	371	0.215	0.239	0.299	0.359	0.401	0.823
	381	+ 0.21	+ 0.23	− 0.304	+ 0.36	− 0.404	+ 1.026
	441	+ 0.198	+ 0.27	+ 0.28	− 0.322	+ 0.366	+ 0.523
	451	0.219	0.261	0.288	0.331	0.380	0.623
	461	0.236	0.242	0.283	0.343	0.391	0.755
Q	471	− 0.226	+ 0.252	− 0.276	+ 0.352	+ 0.401	− 0.897
	551	+ 0.22	+ 0.25	+ 0.29	− 0.335	− 0.385	+ 0.727
	561	0.222	0.243	0.299	0.347	0.393	0.832
Λ	222	1 0.05	1 0.281	3 0.309	3 0.309	3 0.359	3 0.359
	232	+ *0.11*	+ 0.28	− 0.309	+ 0.30	− 0.374	+ 0.36
	242	+ 0.150	+ 0.27	− 0.315	+ 0.29	− 0.389	+ 0.41
	252	+ 0.188	+ 0.258	− 0.326	+ 0.296	− 0.399	+ 0.507

TABLE III (continued).

	k	Band 1	Band 2	Band 3	Band 4	Band 5	Band 6
	262	+ 0.70	+ 0.241	− 0.342	+ 0.30	− 0.403	+ 0.63
	272	+ 0.20	+ 0.23	− 0.357	+ 0.321	− 0.400	+ 0.790
U	282	1 0.20	1 0.228	3 0.327	4 0.367	2 0.396	3 0.904
	332	+ 0.132	+ 0.30	− 0.305	+ 0.30		+ 0.398
	342	0.165	0.291	0.306	0.314	0.383	+ 0.46
	352	0.193	0.272	0.306	0.320	0.396	0.550
	362	0.212	0.253	0.302	0.332	0.400	0.691
	372	0.222	0.242	0.299	0.347	0.393	0.832
	442	+ 0.180	+ 0.285	− 0.307	+ 0.330	− 0.384	+ 0.522
	452	0.197	0.272	0.315	0.321	0.392	0.623
Q	462	+ 0.216	− 0.256	+ 0.329	− 0.303	+ 0.395	− 0.728
	552	+ 0.204	− 0.320	+ 0.265	− 0.396	+ 0.315	+ 0.686
Λ	333	1 0.147	3 0.301	3 0.301	1 0.366	3 0.386	3 0.386
	343	+ 0.165	− 0.233	+ 0.294	+ 0.360	− 0.350	
	353	+ 0.183	+ 0.281	− 0.308	+ 0.337	− 0.401	
	363	+ 0.204	+ 0.265	− 0.320	+ 0.315	− 0.396	+ 0.686
	443	+ 0.168	+ 0.293	− 0.300	+ 0.377	− 0.396	+ 0.516
Q	453	+ 0.179	− 0.284	+ 0.305	− 0.353	+ 0.400	− 0.587
L		1 0.164	3 0.297	3 0.297	3 0.401	3 0.401	2' 0.510

E(k) for the excited bands

	k	Band 7	Band 8	Band 9	Band 10	Band 11	Band 12
Γ	000	2' 2.271	15 2.36	15 2.36	25' 2.634	25' 2.634	25' 2.634
Δ	010	5 2.300	5 2.300	2' 2.233	1 2.352	1 2.867	2' 2.719
Δ	020	5 2.134	5 2.134	2' 2.152	1 2.247	1 2.623	2' 2.887
Δ	030	5 1.974	5 1.974	2' 2.075	1 2.126	1 2.344	
Δ	040	5 1.830	5 1.830	1 1.931	2' 2.015	1 2.168	
Δ	050	1 1.672	5 1.708	5 1.708	2' 1.970	1 2.097	
Δ	060	1 1.417	5 1.614	5 1.614	2' 1.940	1 2.063	
Δ	070		5 1.554	5 1.554	2' 1.923		
X	080	1 1.091	5' 1.54	5' 1.54	3 1.915	1 2.042	
Σ	110	3 2.117	1 2.162	3 2.368	4 2.445	2 2.657	1 2.683
	120	− 1.97	+ 2.005	+ 2.378			
	130	− 1.845	+ 1.863	− 2.225			
	140	− 1.723	+ 1.736	+ 1.959	− 2.142	+ 2.265	
	150	− 1.616	+ 1.63	+ 1.69	− 2.081		
	160	+ 1.428	− 1.533	+ 1.550	− 2.037		
	170	+ 1.209	+ 1.497	− 1.480	− 2.02		
Z	180	1 1.096	4 1.460	1 1.478	4 2.006	1 2.126	2 3.51
Σ	220	3 1.823	1 1.850	3 2.449	1 2.50	4 2.54	2 2.695
	230	− 1.690	+ 1.713	− 2.428	− 2.840		
	240	− 1.569	+ 1.593	+ 1.98			
	250	− 1.467	+ 1.550	+ 1.718			
	260	− 1.388	+ 1.42	+ 1.46			
	270	+ 1.233	− 1.340	+ 1.38			
Z	280	1 1.113	1 1.371	4 1.30	1 2.318	4 2.32	1 3.498
Σ	330	3 1.551	1 1.579	1 2.321	4 2.334	3 2.592	4 2.722
	340	− 1.427	+ 1.469				
	350	− 1.327	+ 1.385	+ 1.770			
	360	− 1.248	+ 1.33	+ 1.513			
	370	− 1.196	+ 1.27	+ 1.29			
Z	380	1 1.145	4 1.180	1 1.27	4 2.41	1 2.61	
Σ	440	3 1.305	1 1.370	4 2.082	1 2.173	3 2.805	2 2.889
	450	− 1.200					
	460	− 1.116	+ 1.241	+ 1.588	+ 2.37		
	470	− 1.064	+ 1.209	+ 1.354			
W	480	3 1.044	2' 1.184	1 1.212	3 2.672	2' 2.709	
Σ	550	3 1.08	4 1.862				
	560	− 1.02	+ 1.181	+ 1.666			
	570	+ 1.026	+ 1.14	+ 1.444			
K	660	1 0.998	1 1.125	4 1.688	1 2.009	1 2.693	
Λ	111	1 1.968	1 2.300	3 2.332	3 2.332	1 2.750	3 2.769
	121	+ 1.814					
	131	+ 1.674	− 2.02				
	141	+ 1.554	+ 1.95	− 1.858			
	151	+ 1.457	+ 1.694	− 1.739	+ 2.02		
	161	+ 1.38	+ 1.440	− 1.650	+ 1.99		
	171	+ 1.217	+ 1.332	− 1.591	+ 1.97		
S	181	1 1.103	1 1.315	4 1.574	1 1.972	1 2.258	
	221	+ 1.656	+ 2.02				
	231	1.515	1.900				
	241	1.42	1.78	2.02			
	251	1.302	1.66	1.74			

TABLE III (Continued).

	k		Band 7		Band 8		Band 9		Band 10		Band 11		Band 12
	261		1.226		1.47		1.606						
	271		1.19		1.27		1.557						
	281	+	1.10	+	1.18	+	1.541						
	331	+	1.379	+	1.771								
	341		1.262		1.657								
	351		1.168		1.58		1.78						
	361		1.096		1.50		1.54						
	371		1.05		1.29		1.457						
	381	+	1.15	+	1.444								
	441	+	1.147	+	1.548								
	451		1.06		1.464		1.852						
	461		0.984		1.42		1.598						
Q	471	+	0.958	−	1.361	+	1.370						
	551	+	0.963	+	1.382	−	1.870						
	561		0.923										
Λ	222	1	1.496	1	2.241	3	2.248	3	2.248	3	2.676	3	2.676
	232	+	1.354										
	242	+	1.240	−	1.947	+	2.02						
	252	+	1.144	+	1.754	−	1.834						
	262	+	1.06	+	1.501	−	1.752						
	272	+	1.023	+	1.275	−	1.702	+	2.02				
U	282	1	0.998	1	1.145	4	1.688	1	2.009	1	2.693		
	332	+	1.220	+	1.98								
	342		1.105		1.876								
	352		1.02		1.78		1.82						
	362		0.946		1.555		1.725						
	372		0.923		1.327		1.683						
	442	+	0.993	+	1.777								
	452		0.914		1.70		1.886						
Q	462			−	1.626	+	1.646	−	2.305	+	2.602		
	552	+	0.875	+	1.615	−	1.913						
Λ	333	1	1.085	1	2.163	3	2.198	3	2.198	3	2.504	3	2.504
	343			+	2.09	−	2.09		2.16		3.285		
	353	+	0.898	+	1.863	−	1.98						
	363	+	0.874			−	1.913						
	443	+	0.886	+	2.02								
Q	453	+	0.854	−	1.916	+	1.958	−	2.196	−	2.709	+	3.000
L	444	1	0.845	2′	2.130	3	2.441	3	2.441	1	2.804		

Some additional $E(\mathbf{k})$ of high energy

	k		Band 13		Band 14		Band 15		Band 16		Band 17
Δ	010	5	2.758	5	2.758						
Δ	020	5	2.937	5	2.937						
Σ	110	3	2.898	4	2.95						
Σ	220	1	3.054	3	3.184	1	3.413	3	3.446	1	3.70
Σ	330	2	2.771								
Λ	111	3	2.769	3	2.769	3	2.980	3	2.980		
Λ	222	1	2.775								
Λ	333	1	2.804								
Q	453	+	3.519	−	3.518						

Note that there are three points "like" $X(080)$ whereas there are six such points shown in Fig. 2 (viz., the center of each of the square faces). The reason for this is that each of these six points is shared with an adjoining Brillouin zone and, therefore, only three belong to the first zone. In general, the number of "like" points can be obtained by dividing 48 (the order of the cubic group) by the order of the group of the wave vector. This rule is valid for all points except those on the hexagonal faces, the reason for this being that these surfaces are arbitrary to a certain extent (see reference 22). Of course, the sum of all the entries under "No. of like vectors" should be 2048, which it is.

Parameters of the Calculation

Slater's atomic units (a.u.) have been used throughout unless otherwise stated. Thus, the unit of energy is the rydberg and the unit of dimension is the Bohr radius:

$$1 \text{ rydberg (Ry)} = 13.605 \text{ eV},$$
$$1 \text{ Bohr radius} = \hbar^2/me^2 = 0.529171 \text{ Å}. \tag{16}$$

The lattice constant for copper was taken to be

$$a = 3.6147 \text{ Å} = 6.83087 \text{ a.u.} \tag{17}$$

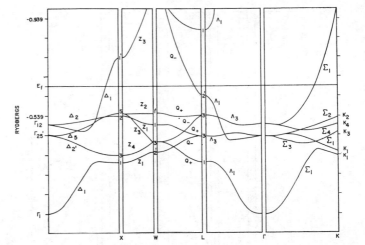

FIG. 3. Energy bands for copper using Chodorow's potential.

This is the value measured by Frohnmeyer and Glocker[23] in 1953.

The "sphere radius" R was taken to be half the nearest-neighbor distance. Hence,

$$R = \sqrt{2}(a/4) = 2.4151 \text{ a.u.} \qquad (18)$$

The quantity π/a is now easily determined and is

$$\pi/a = 0.459911 \text{ a.u.} \qquad (19)$$

Energy Eigenvalues

The energy versus $\mathbf{k}$, $E(\mathbf{k})$, was computed for the equivalent of 2048 points of the Brillouin zone. These calculations were carried out for the six bands "at" and immediately below the Fermi energy (the band "at" the Fermi energy being the conduction band and is half "full") and for energies up to 2 Ry above the Fermi energy. For certain points of high symmetry the calculations were made for still higher energies. The results of these calculations are tabulated in Table III. A plot of the energy bands is shown in Figs. 3 and 4. Figure 3 gives the detailed structure for energies near the Fermi energy, whereas Fig. 4 is a plot on a condensed energy scale in order to show the excited bands. The bands are labeled in a manner consistent with Eq. (15) where the band containing the state arising from the $4s$ electrons located at $\mathbf{k} = (0,0,0)$ (which is the Γ_1 state) is defined as the first band. The bands are then numbered consecutively as one increases in energy for fixed $\mathbf{k}$.

The critical consideration at this point is one of convergence. For our purposes, we say that convergence has been obtained if a given energy eigenvalue is un-

[22] L. P. Bouchaert, R. Smoluchowski, and E. Wigner, Phys. Rev. **50**, 58 (1936); hereafter referred to as BSW.
[23] G. Frohnmeyer and R. Glocker, Acta Cryst. **6**, 19 (1953).

affected when an arbitrary increase is made in the number of l values and/or the number of $\mathbf{k}_i$ used in the expression of the APW's and the wave function, respectively; "unaffected" means that the eigenvalue did not change within the accuracy being sought. From previous work in the SSMTG it has been shown that convergence is attained if one uses the first five l values $(=0, 1, 2, 3, 4)$ and all $\mathbf{k}_i$ for which $k_i^2 \leq 40\pi^2/a^2$. Under these conditions an accuracy to better than 0.01 Ry can be expected. This is in accord with what the author has found. Doubling the number of l and k values used, either separately or simultaneously, never changed the eigenvalues by more than 0.005 Ry.

The Fermi Energy

Periodic boundary conditions have been used. This restricts the allowable $\mathbf{k}$ values to a uniformly distributed discrete set in reciprocal space, containing N allowable $\mathbf{k}$ values in each Brillouin zone where N represents the number of unit cells in the solid being considered. Each $\mathbf{k}$ state can accommodate two electrons, one with spin up the other with spin down. Now, recall that the nth energy band can be defined as the set of all energies $E_n(\mathbf{k})$ obtained as $\mathbf{k}$ ranges over all permissible values in the nth Brillouin zone. In the reduced zone scheme this amounts to fixing n (that is the particular branch of energy values) and allowing $\mathbf{k}$ to range over all permissible values of the first Brillouin zone. Hence, a given energy band can accommodate two electrons from each atom in the solid.

In the case of copper, the bands arising from the $1s$, $2s$, $2p$, $3s$, and $3p$ levels of the atom lie considerably below the conduction band and, consequently, will be completely occupied. This being the case, we need consider only the bands arising from the $4s$ and $3d$ atomic states. Hence, the computed bands must ac-

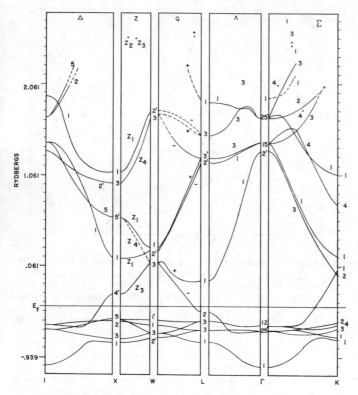

Fig. 4. Energy bands for copper using Chodorow's potential—high-energy region.

commodate eleven electrons from each atom; ten $3d$ electrons and one $4s$ electron.

The procedure used to determine the Fermi energy is the following. The 89 energies listed for each band in Table III, in reality, represent 2048 energies as dis-cussed earlier. The number of times that an energy corresponding to a given **k** is to be counted is given in Table II under the heading "No. of like vectors." Taking this into account, we start with the lowest energy and label it number one, the next lowest and label it

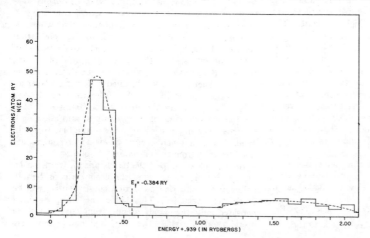

Fig. 5. Histogram for the density of states.

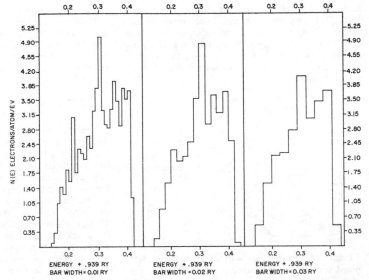

FIG. 6. Fine structure of "d-hump."

number two, and so on until we have exhausted the list of energies. Assuming that each such energy is the average for all $E(\mathbf{k})$ from the same volume element, the first (5.5) $(2048) = 11\ 264$ energies will be occupied and all higher energies will be unoccupied. It therefore follows that the Fermi energy, in this approximation, lies somewhere between energy number 11 264 and energy number 11 265.

It so happens that both energies have the same value of -0.384 Ry. We thus have

$$\text{Fermi energy} = E_f = -0.384 \ \text{Ry.} \qquad (20)$$

The Density of States

The density of states is defined as the number of energy states per unit volume per unit energy range. Thus the number of states per unit volume of the crystal having energies in the range E to $E + dE$ is given by

$$N(E) = n(E) dE, \qquad (21)$$

where $n(E)$ is the density of states.

The $n(E)$ curve was obtained in the following way. A ΔE was chosen, then the energy scale was partitioned into intervals by the points $E + n(\Delta E)$ for $n = 0, 1, 2, 3, \cdots$. The number of computed energy values lying within the first interval was determined, then a bar with height proportional to this number was plotted in the interval. The process was then repeated for the second interval and so on, until all energy values were exhausted. The value of ΔE was then increased and the entire process repeated. This was done until the histogram did not change its form appreciably from one ΔE to the next. A smooth curve was then drawn using

the final histogram as a guide. The curve was made to pass through the midpoint of the top of each bar except for regions where such a procedure gave unrealistically rapid fluctuations.

The "stable" histogram was one which had a $\Delta E = 0.09$ Ry. This histogram and the resulting density of states curve are shown in Fig. 5. A much smaller ΔE can be used over the region of the "d hump" where the eigenvalues are heavily concentrated. Figure 6 shows a series of histograms for this region which suggest that considerable fine structure is present in the "d hump."

The Fermi Surface

The Fermi surface is given implicitly by the equation

$$E(k) = E_f = -0.38 \ \text{Ry.}$$

This equation was solved graphically by plotting $E(\mathbf{k})$ versus $\mathbf{k}$ in various directions. It was then an easy matter to establish those points $\mathbf{k}_f$ on the Fermi surface

FIG. 7. (100) cross-section of the Fermi surface.

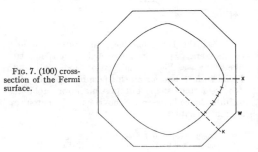

from the intersection of the line $E=E_f$ with the $E(\mathbf{k})$ curve. This procedure was carried out for enough $\mathbf{k}_f$ to enable a fairly accurate determination of the E_f contours of constant energy in three planes; the $\langle 100 \rangle$ plane, the $\langle 110 \rangle$ plane, and the plane containing the hexagonal face. These contours for E_f are shown in Figs. 7, 8, and 9, respectively.

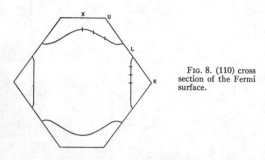

FIG. 8. (110) cross section of the Fermi surface.

Points on the contours which were actually determined are marked by small circles, or by short straight lines. The possible errors involved have been indicated by the length of the lines.

The striking features of the Fermi surface (as have been pointed out earlier[24,25]) are:

(1) The "belly" region deviates quite significantly from being spherical. It is somewhat protruded ("egg shaped") in the $\langle 100 \rangle$ direction and contracted in the $\langle 110 \rangle$ direction.

(2) The Fermi surface touches the edge of the zone over a relatively large region at the center of the eight hexagonal faces. The portion of the surface extending in these directions (the $\langle 111 \rangle$ directions) are referred to as the "necks" in the literature.

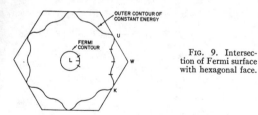

FIG. 9. Intersection of Fermi surface with hexagonal face.

(3) On the hexagonal face, the outer contour of constant energy presents a very striking "cookie cutter" like shape (see Fig. 9). Calculations indicate that the Fermi surface contour on this face may also be of the "cookie-cutter" shape but possible error prohibits a definite choice between a "cookie-cutter" contour and a circular contour.

The Fermi surface, as computed, here was compared with Morse's experimentally determined Fermi surface and found to be in excellent agreement.[25] More recent experiments by Bohm and Esterling[26] indicate a Fermi surface which is (within stated possible errors) identical to the author's in the parameters available for comparison.

DISCUSSION OF RESULTS AND COMPARISON WITH EXPERIMENTS

As stated earlier, Segall calculated the $E(\mathbf{k})$ for copper using the Green's function method. He used Chodorow's potential (as well as a modified Chodorow potential) and calculated the $E(\mathbf{k})$ only along various symmetry lines and at points in the (110) plane. The author's corresponding values agree with Segall's within 0.01 Ry in practically all cases. Although the potentials used by Segall and the author were both essentially Chodorow's original one, there were slight differences. To check the effect of these differences, Segall used exactly the author's potential to calculate the $E(\mathbf{k})$ at a few points of high symmetry.[27] Table IV compares these points with the authors.

TABLE IV. Comparison of APW and Green's function solutions of Schrödinger's equation (energy in rydbergs).

Point	APW (Burdick)	Green's function (Segall)
X_1	-0.776	-0.771
X_3	-0.739	-0.738
X_4'	-0.234	-0.233
L_1	-0.775	-0.773
L_3	-0.642	-0.644

The remarkable agreement illustrated by Table IV strongly suggests that an accurate solution of Schrödinger's equation for the potential used has been achieved by both parties. In every case where both parties calculated a particular physical quantity using Chodorow's potential, they were in close agreement. For example, Segall reports an E_f of -0.385 ± 0.010 Ry; the author's is -0.384 Ry. The fact that the author's Fermi energy and Fermi surface are in such good agreement with Segall's indicates that the approximations made by Segall are quite good. Segall did not compute a sufficient number of $E(\mathbf{k})$ to make a straightforward determination of E_f or the density of states possible.

Density of States vs Soft X-Ray Absorption and Emission

The absorption of x rays incident on a metal will pass through various maxima as the frequency is increased. These maxima will correspond to lifting electrons from

[24] B. Segall, Phys. Rev. Letters **7**, 154 (1961).
[25] Glenn A. Burdick, Phys. Rev. Letters **7**, 156 (1961).

[26] H. V. Bohm and V. J. Esterling, Bull. Am. Phys. Soc. **6**, 438 (1961); H. V. Bohm (private communication).
[27] B. Segall (private communication).

the various low-lying bands up to the first unoccupied states which occur in the conduction band. Thus, as the frequency of the incident x-rays is increased, we pass through the absorption edge and on into the fine structure of the absorption. The sudden increase in absorption at the "edge" is because at this frequency the x-ray photons have just enough energy to "lift" electrons from one of the low-lying bands up to the Fermi energy; since the electron energies in these lower bands are nearly independent of **k** (these bands are said to be flat), all electrons in the band suddenly become available to the absorption process, thus resulting in a sudden increase (the absorption edge) in the absorption of x rays. The photon energy at which the absorption edge occurs should therefore be the energy separation of the band in question and the Fermi energy. That is, the absorption edge gives the Fermi energy relative to that band which gives rise to the "edge." This identification of the absorption edge will allow us to compare features of our calculated density of states curve with the fine structure of the absorption vs photon energy curve. To make these comparisons we shall assume that the transition probability for the bands in question is a slowly

TABLE V. Energy in eV.

	Beeman and Friedman	Burdick	Rudberg and Slater
E_D	−3.4	−3.4	−3.6
E_C	−1.9	−1.9	−2.1
$E_{F'}$	−0.2	...	...
E_M	4.0		3.4
E_A	14.7	14.5	12.2
E_G	19.4	20.9	17.2
E_B	24.1	...	21.7

varying function of the energy. If this is the case, the fine structure of the absorption curve should reproduce the general features of our density of states curve in the region just above the Fermi energy.

The x-ray emission in metals occurs when some of the states in the low-lying bands have been vacated by some mechanism. Once vacant states are available in these bands then electrons in the conduction band can drop into the available "holes" thus giving rise to x-ray emission. A study of the emission spectra should therefore give us information about the density of states just below the Fermi energy. In particular, the emission spectra should confirm the general shape of the large "hump" in our density of states curve if this "hump" is really there; of course, it is again assumed that the transition probability is approximately constant in this region.

Beeman and Friedman (17) made x-ray absorption and emission measurements on copper and, as stated in the introduction, compared their results with a density of states curve obtained by Rudberg and Slater.[16] We now compare our density of states with Beeman's work.

Figures 10(a), 10(b), and 10(c) show Beeman's absorption curve, Slater's density of states, and the author's density of states, respectively. Beeman and Friedman attempted to correlate certain points of their absorption and emission curves for the K shell with points on Rudberg and Slater's density of states. "Corresponding" points for the three have been labeled with the same letter in the respective figures. The points in Figs. 10(a) and 10(b) were located from data given in reference 17. The energy scales have been shifted to make the points labeled F (Fermi energy) have the same energy; this energy has been arbitrarily set equal to zero. The energies of the various points relative to the Fermi energy are tabulated in Table V for the three cases.

The most striking difference in the two density-of-states curves is the "camel" hump which appears in Fig. 10(b) but not in Fig. 10(c). The x-ray emission

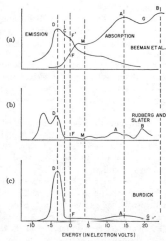

FIG. 10(a). K-band absorption and emission spectra for copper (from Beeman *et al.*). (b) Rudberg and Slater's density of states for copper. (c) Burdick's density of states for copper.

curves measured for various bands indicate that the shape of this portion of the density of states is more nearly like that of Fig. 10(c). Perhaps a point of greater surprise should be the general likeness of Figs. 10(b) and 10(c) in view of the limited data available at the time Rudberg and Slater did their work. The two curves are in remarkable agreement with respect to E_D and E_C. Furthermore, the shape and height of the density of states in the immediate neighborhood of E_F are in agreement. The two curves were brought to the same vertical scale by requiring the areas under the curves for $E \leq E_F$ to be the same.

The minimum at M in Fig. 10(a) is missing in Fig. 10(c). A possible explanation for this minimum is the following. The energy-band plot of Fig. 3 indicates that the wave functions are mostly p like (e.g., this is the symmetry of L_2') in the neighborhood of the Fermi energy, changing to mostly s like (e.g., L_1) about 4 eV above the Fermi energy. Recalling that we are considering transitions from a state of s-like symmetry (K shell) we should expect a large reduction in transition probability about 4 eV above the Fermi energy. Thus, the dip at M is probably due not to a decrease in the density of states but mainly to a fairly large decrease in transition probability. It is interesting to note that the energy of L_1 minus the Fermi energy is 4.0 eV agreeing surprisingly well with $E_M - E_F$ of Beeman and Friedman's work which is also 4.0 eV. If the minimum is due primarily to the decrease in transition probability (as the above would suggest) then we should observe maxima at this point in case of L_2 or M_2 absorption which has p symmetry. The above interpretation of the minimum at M would also provide a possible explanation for the high energy satellite observed in the $M_{2,3}$ emission spectrum as determined by Bedo and Tomboulian.[28] In their measurements, a secondary maximum in the emission occurs 7.4 eV above the principal maximum (see Table 1, p. 466, reference 28). If we say that the principal maximum corresponds to D in Fig. 14 (which it certainly must) then, the second maximum occurs 4.0 eV ($=7.4-3.4$) or at precisely the point where we said that the eigenfunctions become mostly s like.

Bedo and Tomboulian's work would indicate that the "d hump" in our density of states should occur about 5.0 eV below the Fermi energy. This value does not agree nearly so well with the theoretical value as does Beeman and Friedman's value.

The emission curve in Fig. 10 is in remarkable agreement with the author's density of states. The emission intensity is comparatively constant in the interval E_C to E_F corresponding to a "flat" density of states in this interval. A sharp drop in emission occurs at E_F agreeing very well with the sudden decrease in the percentage of levels occupied as one goes above the Fermi energy. (There will be a number of higher levels occupied as a result of "kicking" the K electrons up to higher levels, or out of the metal, in order to obtain the necessary vacant states in the K shell. This contributes to the long high-energy tail of the emission curve.) One might think that the emission intensity at D should be much larger than it is and if the transition probability were constant it certainly would be. We must remember, however, that the levels in the vicinity of D are mostly of "d"-like symmetry and, therefore, there will be a strong quenching of the "d hump" in the K-emission spectra.

[28] D. E. Bedo and D. H. Tomboulian Phys. Rev. 113, 464 (1959).

Optical Data

Roberts[29] has measured the absorption of electromagnetic radiation in the optical region by reflectivity measurements. He measures a minimum in the absorption at $0.65\,\mu$ and a diffuse relative maximum at approximately $0.50\,\mu$. These values correspond to energies of 1.9 and 2.5 eV, respectively; the half maximum corresponds to an energy of 2.2 eV and is the value referred to in the literature as the "well-known" interband transition of copper. Now, the 1.9 eV should correspond to the author's value of $E_F - E_C$ which was computed to be 1.9 eV. The 2.5 eV should correspond to $E_F - E_D$ which was computed to be 3.4 eV.

It is interesting to note that Segall[15] attributed the 2.2-eV value to transitions from the d state around L_3 to the p state at the Fermi energy. He obtained a value of 2.6 eV using his modified potential and a value of 2.1 eV using Chodorow's potential. The author's corresponding value is 2.2 eV. The fact that the latter value agrees precisely with that obtained from the density of states and that obtained by Roberts is fortuitous. This is to say, there is no reason for them to be in more than qualitative agreement.

SUMMARY

A thorough energy band calculation has been carried out for copper using Chodorow's potential for d electrons and Slater's APW method. The computations were done on a high-speed digital computer using a program due to Wood.

The $E(k)$ values were computed for the equivalent of 2048 points in the Brillouin zone and for energies ranging from the bottom of the $4s$ band to approximately 2 Ry above the Fermi energy. From these calculations the Fermi energy, Fermi surface, and density of states were determined. Comparison of results with experiment has shown not only qualitative but in most cases quantitative agreement. Agreement with independent theoretical work by Segall suggests that an accurate solution of Schrödinger's equation using Chodorow's potential has been obtained.

ACKNOWLEDGMENTS

It is with pleasure that the author acknowledges his indebtedness to Dr. M. I. Chodorow for the potential used, Dr. J. H. Wood for the computer program and various discussions, Professor G. F. Koster for various discussions, and Professor J. C. Slater under whose direction this work was carried out. He further expresses his appreciation to Dr. B. Segall for his free exchange of unpublished data and to Mrs. Azzie Thomas for her preparation of the manuscript.

[29] S. Roberts, Phys. Rev. 118, 1509 (1960).

ERRATA – Figure 1

The L_6^+ state shown with an energy of 0.05 Ry should have had an energy of approximately 0.25 Ry, placing it between the two L_6^- states, when both the spin-orbit and the mass-velocity and $\vec{\epsilon} \cdot \vec{p}$ corrections are included.

RELATIVISTIC EFFECTS IN THE BAND STRUCTURE OF PbTe*

L. E. Johnson, J. B. Conklin, and G. W. Pratt, Jr.

Materials Theory Group, Department of Electrical Engineering,
Massachusetts Institute of Technology, Cambridge, Massachusetts

(Received 16 October 1963; revised manuscript received 12 November 1963)

The purpose of this Letter is to point out that relativistic interactions have a drastic effect on the energy band structrue of PbTe and are of major importance in understanding the energy gaps and effective masses. These interactions are commonly derived by converting the 4-component Dirac equation into a second-order equation and then reducing this to a two-component form. When this is done, as in the Pauli approximation, two other terms appear besides the spin-orbit interaction, namely, the mass-velocity energy correction and a term of the form $(i\mu_0/2mc)\vec{\epsilon} \cdot \vec{p}$, where $\vec{\epsilon}$ is the electric field seen by an electron and $\vec{p}$ is its momentum. If the spatial components of the vector potential are assumed to be zero, the one-electron Hamiltonian is[1]

$$\mathcal{H} = -(\hbar^2/2m)\nabla^2 - e\varphi - (1/2mc^2)(E + e\varphi)^2$$
$$- (i\mu_0/2mc)\vec{\epsilon} \cdot \vec{p} + (\mu_0/2mc)\vec{\sigma} \cdot (\vec{\epsilon} \times \vec{p}).$$

We show in this Letter that the mass-velocity

term $(-1/2mc^2)(E+e\varphi)^2$ and the term $-(i\mu_0/2mc)$ $\times\vec{\epsilon}\cdot\vec{p}$ have a very marked effect on the (111) band edge of PbTe.

The mass-velocity and $\vec{\epsilon}\cdot\vec{p}$ terms will be largest when an electron is near the nucleus. Since the atomic orbitals behave as r^l for small r, s functions will have the largest energy shifts. Even in the hydrogen atom these corrections to the 2s energy are several times larger than the spin-orbit splitting of the 2p level. In a solid the one-electron wave functions do not have a definite orbital angular momentum and it is common for a Bloch function to start at the center of the Brillouin zone predominately of one l character and at a zone edge to have a different l character. That is, regarded as a function of k, the Bloch function associated with a particular band has a different admixture of $s, p, d, \cdots$ character at different points of the zone. Thus if the Bloch function were p-like at $k=0$ and s-like at an edge, these relativistic corrections could substantially change the band shape at the edge but only slightly at the center. Therefore, these corrections are k dependent and will affect both energy gaps and effective masses.

This reasoning has led us to include the mass-velocity and $\vec{\epsilon}\cdot\vec{p}$ terms in an augmented plane-wave (APW) investigation of the band structure of PbTe. The results obtained so far are so striking that we feel they should be presented here in advance of a full discussion. We wish to stress that it is the relativistic effects that we are concerned with here and for that reason we leave aside the quantitative nature of the bands. In brief, the APW scheme has been carried out for PbTe for several ionicities and the results given here are for zero ionicity. The bands were first found using a crystal potential constructed from atomic potentials for the Pb and Te atoms kindly supplied by Herman. These "unperturbed" band energies are given in the left-hand column of Fig. 1 at the (111) zone edge where experiment indicates the top of the valence band and bottom of the conduction band to be.

The valence-conduction band gap for the "unperturbed" bands is between L_2' and L_3' and is seen to be about 1.51 eV. The effect of the spin-orbit interaction was taken into account not by first-order perturbation theory but by setting up the 12×12 secular equation arising from the L_3, L_2', L_3', and L_1 bands and finding the eigenstates and energies. These energies are shown in the middle column of Fig. 1. The spin-orbit

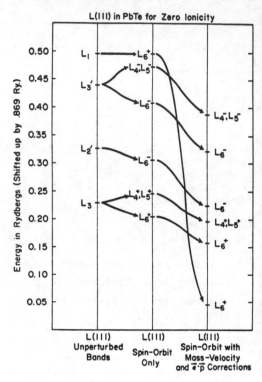

FIG. 1. Results at the (111) zone edge for PbTe with zero ionicity.

splitting of the "unperturbed" bands is apparent and now the gap occurs between the two L_6^- states and is 1.37 eV.

Regarding these spin-orbit states as a new basis set, the 12×12 energy matrix due to the mass-velocity and $\vec{\epsilon}\cdot\vec{p}$ corrections was set up and the corresponding secular equation solved resulting in the energies shown in the right-hand column of Fig. 1. The drastic change in the band energies is evident. The upper L_6^+ in the middle column is s-like about the Pb and will experience the greatest relativistic shift since these effects are a rapidly increasing function of atomic number. This is indeed the case as shown in Fig. 1 where the L_6^+ state shifts from the highest to the lowest lying level. Away from L the L_6 bands become Λ_6 and cannot cross so that this depression of the L_6^+ state does not make PbTe a metal. Now the gap lies between the L_4^+, L_5^+ level and the L_6^- level and it has dropped from 1.37 eV to 0.40 eV in much closer agreement with experiment which indicates a value of about 0.3 eV. Furthermore, the lowest three bands belonging to the valence set all have even parity while the three upper bands all have odd parity. Therefore, an optical transition would be allowed at L across the gap and this also satisfies the conditions required by the $\vec{k} \cdot \vec{p}$ perturbation method for small effective masses both for holes and electrons at L. This agreement with experiment is seen to be entirely due to including these relativistic corrections.

It is interesting to compare these results obtained for the solid with the relativistic shifts for the isolated Pb and Te atoms which have been found by Herman and Skillman.[2] They are shown in Fig. 2. A tight-binding analysis of the PbTe case shows that at L the p functions of Pb do mix with the s functions of Te but not with the Te p orbitals. However, at $k = 0$ symmetry forbids s-p mixing. Any s-p mixing will be very important at L because of the much larger corrections to the s energies. Let us assume, however, that the conduction band at L is given only in terms of the $6p$ functions of Pb and the valence band only in terms of the $5p$ functions of Te. Then the atomic results shown in Fig. 2 would indicate a decrease in the energy gap at L of 0.42 eV since the relativistic effects depress the Pb-$6p$ energy more than the Te-$5p$ energy. This very qualitative argument shows that the free atom results indicate the presence of the gap change for the solid. The much larger gap change obtained in the APW calculation is presumably due to s-p mixing. The relativistic effects evaluated in this paper and the free atom relativistic results of reference 2 have not been found by including these interactions in a self-consistent field calculation. However, Waber[3] has done this for the free Pb and Te atoms by self-consistently solving the Dirac equation. His results are very close to those of Herman and Skillman indicating that self-consistent corrections are not of great importance.

It is quite clear from these results that the mass-velocity and $\vec{\epsilon} \cdot \vec{p}$ terms will be absolutely essential in many band calculations and will lead to major corrections. Without them the band energies and effective masses at the point L in PbTe would be meaningless. Furthermore, it can be expected that these terms will lead to substantial shifts in s-like impurity levels as already indicated by Appel.[4]

The authors wish to thank the staff of Massachusetts Institute of Technology Cooperative Computing Laboratory for their cooperation in the preparation of these numerical results.

After this Letter was submitted, it came to our attention that Herman, Kuglin, Cuff, and Kortum have been considering independently the problem of relativistic effects on energy band structures and were submitting a Letter[5] discussing their treatment.

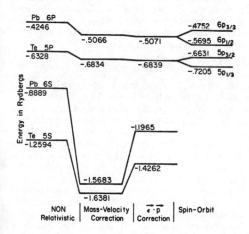

FIG. 2. The energy levels of the atomic $5s$ and $5p$ functions of Te and $6s$ and $6p$ levels of Pb as taken from the work of Herman and Skillman, reference 2.

*Work supported by U. S. Army Research Office, Durham, North Carolina.

[1]See the discussion in Chap. I, Sec. 12, and in particular, Eq. (12.11), of H. A. Bethe and E. E. Salpeter, Quantum Mechanics of One- and Two-Electron Atoms (Academic Press, Inc., New York, 1957).

[2]F. Herman and S. Skillman, Atomic Structure Calculations (Prentice-Hall, Inc., Englewood Cliffs, New Jersey, 1963).

[3]J. Waber (private communication).

[4]J. Appel, Bull. Am. Phys. Soc. 8, 256 (1963).

[5]F. Herman, C. D. Kuglin, K. F. Cuff, and R. L. Kortum, following Letter [Phys. Rev. Letters 11, 541 (1963)].

PHYSICAL REVIEW   VOLUME 133, NUMBER 5A   2 MARCH 1964

Energy Bands for Solid Argon*

L. F. Mattheiss†

Solid-State and Molecular Theory Group, Massachusetts Institute of Technology, Cambridge, Massachusetts

(Received 11 October 1963)

Energy bands have been calculated for solid argon using the augmented plane-wave method. The crystal potential used in this calculation has been approximated by a superposition of atomic potentials and involves the Slater free-electron exchange approximation. In order to estimate the error introduced by this approximation, a quantitative comparison has been made between the Hartree-Fock and free-electron exchange potentials for atomic argon. The results indicate that the free-electron exchange approximation is most accurate for the less tightly bound valence electrons, though errors of the order of 0.1 Ry remain. The present energy bands are found to be in qualitative agreement with the earlier results of Knox and Bassani, though there are important quantitative differences. The present calculation yields a band gap of 13.3 eV, which is in fair agreement with the experimentally observed value of 14.3 eV.

I. INTRODUCTION

THE energy bands for solid argon have been calculated recently by Knox and Bassani[1] using a perturbation approximation to the orthogonalized-plane-wave (OPW) method developed by Bassani and Celli.[2] The 3s and 3p levels were calculated using the tight binding approximation, and the OPW method was modified to take into account the variation of these core levels with wave vector. It seemed desirable to carry out a similar calculation using the augmented-plane-wave (APW) method[3,4] in order to determine whether or not this method was practical when narrow valence bands and nearly free-electron conduction bands were involved.

It turns out that the APW method is capable of handling without difficulty both the tightly bound valence band and the excited conduction band states. The general features of the 3s and 3p valence bands obtained by the APW method are very similar to those calculated by Knox and Bassani using the tight binding approximation. However, the corresponding positions of these bands on an absolute energy scale (relative to electron at rest at infinity) differ significantly in the two calculations. In the case of the conduction bands, there are again differences in the absolute energies of the various states, but more important, there are differences in the relative ordering of states. These discrepancies cannot be attributed to a difference in potential since checks were made with the same potential which was used by Knox and Bassani, and similar differences were obtained.

The general method for constructing the crystal potential which has been used in the present calculation is described in Sec. II. Exchange has been introduced by means of Slater's free-electron exchange approximation.[5]

Section III contains a quantitative discussion of this approximation in its application to the argon atom. It is found that the free-electron exchange approximation does not always overestimate exchange, as is frequently emphasized in the literature.[6,7] It is shown that the changes in the one-electron energies of the various electrons in going from the Hartree-Fock to the free-electron exchange approximation can be estimated quite accurately by means of first-order perturbation theory. This provides one with a reasonable estimate of the accuracy with which a given potential will represent the relative positions of the different bands on an absolute energy scale, at least in the case of narrow non-overlapping bands. This information is particularly important in the vicinity of the Fermi surface and in the interpretation of such phenomena as optical absorption. The results of the present APW calculations for solid argon are presented in Sec. IV, while Sec. V contains a brief discussion of these results and the accuracy of the free-electron exchange approximation.

II. CRYSTAL POTENTIAL

Solid argon is face-centered cubic, with a lattice constant of 10.03 au (5.31 Å).[8] In the APW method, the crystal potential is usually approximated by a so-called "muffin-tin" potential. Each atom is surrounded by a sphere, inside of which the potential is spherically symmetric. Between spheres, the potential is assumed to be constant. This constant is usually chosen to be the average value of the potential in the region between the sphere and the boundaries of the Wigner-Seitz cell. In the present calculation, the radius of the inscribed sphere was chosen so that the spheres surrounding neighboring atoms just touched at the cell boundaries.

The crystal potential for solid argon has been approximated by a superposition of spherically sym-

* This work was supported by the National Science Foundation.
† Presently employed at Bell Telephone Laboratories, Incorporated, Murray Hill, New Jersey.
[1] R. S. Knox and F. Bassani, Phys. Rev. 124, 652 (1961).
[2] F. Bassani and V. Celli, Phys. Chem. Solids 20, 64 (1961).
[3] J. C. Slater, Phys. Rev. 51, 846 (1937).
[4] J. H. Wood, Phys. Rev. 126, 517 (1962).
[5] J. C. Slater, *Quantum Theory of Atomic Structure* (McGraw-Hill Book Company, Inc., New York, 1960).
[6] J. Callaway, *Solid-State Physics*, edited by F. Seitz and D. Turnbull (Academic Press, Inc., New York, 1958), Vol. 7, p. 100.
[7] J. E. Robinson, F. Bassani, R. S. Knox, and J. R. Schrieffer, Phys. Rev. Letters 9, 215 (1962).
[8] E. R. Dobbs and G. O. Jones, in *Reports on Progress in Physics*, edited by A. C. Stickland (The Physical Society, London, 1957), Vol. 20, p. 516.

TABLE I. The crystal potential for face-centered cubic argon. The radial distance r is in atomic units and $V(r)$ is in rydbergs. The average potential in the region between the APW sphere and the Wigner-Seitz cell is -0.3697 rydberg.

r	$-V(r)$	r	$-V(r)$
0.01	3502.9162	0.46	29.9888
0.02	1701.5038	0.50	26.0148
0.03	1101.5748	0.54	22.7465
0.04	802.5071	0.58	20.0256
0.05	623.9115	0.62	17.7405
0.06	505.5518	0.66	15.8101
0.07	421.5774	0.70	14.1721
0.08	359.0582	0.80	11.0417
0.09	310.8172	0.90	8.8422
0.10	272.5569	1.00	7.2112
0.12	215.9745	1.10	5.9544
0.14	176.4496	1.20	4.9645
0.16	147.5126	1.30	4.1747
0.18	125.5360	1.40	3.5391
0.20	108.3462	1.50	3.0238
0.22	94.5796	1.60	2.6030
0.24	83.3456	1 70	2.2569
0.26	74.0382	1.80	1.9701
0.28	66.2300	1.90	1.7307
0.30	59.6094	2.00	1.5291
0.34	49.0545	2.50	0.8828
0.38	41.0828	3.00	0.5568
0.42	34.8983	3.50	0.3966

metric atomic potentials, calculated from self-consistent field Hartree-Fock solutions for the argon atom by Watson and Freeman.[9] Exchange has been treated by means of Slater's free-electron exchange approximation. In discussing the manner in which the crystal potential has been approximated, it is convenient to consider the Coulomb and exchange contributions separately.

The total Coulomb potential at a given lattice site (which is taken to be at the origin of coordinates) has been represented by the neutral atom Coulomb potential for argon, plus contributions from neighboring Coulomb potentials. The effects of neighboring Coulomb potentials have been introduced by expanding them about the origin, using Löwdin's alpha-function expansion.[10] To obtain a spherically symmetric crystal Coulomb potential, it is necessary to include only the $l=0$ term from this expansion in spherical harmonics. In the case of argon, the large lattice spacing required only the inclusion of the effects from nearest-neighboring Coulomb potentials.

An analogous method has been used to calculate an approximation to the crystal exchange potential. According to Slater's free-electron exchange approximation,[5]

$$V^{\text{fe}}(\mathbf{r}) = -6[3\rho(\mathbf{r})/8\pi]^{1/3}. \quad (1)$$

In the atomic case, $\rho(\mathbf{r})$ represents the charge density of the occupied states. We have approximated the crystal charge density by a superposition of atomic charge densities, again using Löwdin's alpha-function

expansion, and again keeping only the spherically symmetric terms. Then, Eq. (1) was applied, using for $\rho(\mathbf{r})$, the total charge density. As before, the large lattice spacing for argon required only the effects of nearest neighbors to be included in this calculation.

Clearly, such methods for constructing the Coulomb and exchange potentials are not too important in argon, where the occupied atomic functions are well localized and neither the Coulomb potentials nor the charge densities overlap appreciably. However, this approach has been found to yield reasonable results when applied to the elements of the iron-transition series, which follow argon in the periodic table. The crystal potential for argon used in the present calculations is tabulated in Table I. This potential differs only slightly from the corresponding atomic potential, the largest difference being approximately 0.04 Ry near the APW sphere radius.

In view of the statements that the free-electron exchange approximation overestimates the exchange effect, especially in the low-density tails of atomic functions,[7] it seems worthwhile to examine this situation in more detail here. If this were the case, the method for constructing the exchange potential which is described here would only exaggerate this effect. The results of such an investigation are presented in Sec. III.

III. COMPARISON OF HARTREE-FOCK AND FREE-ELECTRON EXCHANGE POTENTIALS

A comparison of the Hartree-Fock and various approximate averaged exchange potentials for an atomic system has been carried out previously by Herman, Callaway, and Acton for germanium.[11] Since they used self-consistent field solutions for germanium computed without exchange, it was felt that some of their results might be misleading due to inaccurate wave functions. We shall make a similar comparison for the argon atom using accurate solutions to the Hartree-Fock equations. We shall limit this discussion to a comparison of the Hartree-Fock and free-electron exchange potentials.

For an atom with closed shells, the Hartree-Fock exchange potential for an electron in a state with quantum numbers n, l can be written:

$$V_{nl}^{\text{HF}}(r) = -\left[\sum_{n'l'} \sum_{k} c^{k}(l0; l'0) \right.$$
$$\left. \times \left(\frac{2l'+1}{2l+1} \right)^{1/2} \frac{P_{n'l'}(r)}{P_{nl}(r)} \frac{2}{r} Y_{k}(n'l', nl|r) \right]. \quad (2)$$

The sum is over all closed shells of the atom, the coefficients $c^{k}(l0; l'0)$ are tabulated integrals over spherical harmonics, the functions $P_{nl}(r)$ are the radial wave

[9] R. E. Watson and A. J. Freeman, Phys. Rev. 123, 521 (1961).
[10] P. O. Löwdin, Advan. Phys. 5, 1 (1956).

[11] F. Herman, J. Callaway, and F. S. Acton, Phys. Rev. 95, 371 (1954).

TABLE II. A comparison of $P_{nl}{}^2(r)V_{nl}{}^{\mathrm{HF}}(r)$ and $P_{nl}{}^2(r)^{\mathrm{fe}}(r)$ as a function of r for atomic argon. r is in atomic units.

r	$-P_{1s}{}^2V_{1s}{}^{\mathrm{HF}}$	$-P_{1s}{}^2V^{\mathrm{fe}}$	$-P_{2s}{}^2V_{2s}{}^{\mathrm{HF}}$	$-P_{2s}{}^2V^{\mathrm{fe}}$	$-P_{3s}{}^2V_{3s}{}^{\mathrm{HF}}$	$-P_{3s}{}^2V^{\mathrm{fe}}$	$-P_{2p}{}^2V_{2p}{}^{\mathrm{HF}}$	$-P_{2p}{}^2V^{\mathrm{fe}}$	$-P_{3p}{}^2V_{3p}{}^{\mathrm{HF}}$	$-P_{3p}{}^2V^{\mathrm{fe}}$
0.02	150.290	157.508	9.120	12.310	0.819	1.199	0.088	0.134	0.0064	0.0108
0.04	258.737	243.887	13.915	17.009	1.226	1.639	0.802	1.205	0.065	0.095
0.06	246.303	214.555	10.421	11.678	0.892	1.096	2.351	3.466	0.158	0.270
0.08	186.170	151.636	4.941	4.993	0.404	0.440	4.474	6.340	0.288	0.485
0.10	125.757	96.795	1.161	0.992	0.085	0.070	6.908	9.221	0.423	0.691
0.20	10.991	7.785	11.316	10.597	0.857	1.099	18.645	19.986	0.910	1.277
0.40	0.0922	0.0254	18.028	14.855	0.540	0.531	13.384	12.015	1.957	1.860
0.60	0.0015	0.00009	4.782	3.280	0.085	0.174	3.385	2.572	0.078	0.172
0.80			0.876	0.568	1.010	1.031	0.669	0.494	0.606	0.719
1.00			0.152	0.103	1.780	1.666	0.128	0.103	1.088	1.179
1.40			0.0059	0.0027	1.639	1.378	0.0057	0.0037	1.193	1.189
1.80			0.00041	0.00008	0.821	0.600	0.00041	0.00015	0.744	0.679
2.20					0.324	0.202			0.365	0.304
2.60					0.115	0.060			0.165	0.120
3.00					0.040	0.017			0.070	0.045

functions, and $Y_k(n'l',nl/r)$ represent the functions

$$Y_k(n'l',\,nl\,|\,r) = \frac{1}{r^k}\int_0^r P_{n'l'}(r')P_{nl}(r')r'^k dr'$$

$$+ r^{k+1}\int_r^\infty \frac{P_{n'l'}(r')P_{nl}(r')}{r'^{k+1}}dr'. \quad (3)$$

For purposes of comparing the Hartree-Fock and free-electron exchange potentials, it is convenient to calculate $P_{nl}{}^2(r)V_{nl}{}^{\mathrm{HF}}(r)$ and $P_{nl}{}^2(r)V^{\mathrm{fe}}(r)$. The results of such calculations for atomic argon are given in Table II. From these results, it is clear that the free-electron exchange approximation *underestimates* exchange at large values of the radial distance r for all occupied atomic states. An earlier calculation by Hartree[12] on Cu+ produced similar results. Hartree plotted the various Hartree-Fock exchange potentials as a function of the radial distance r. According to his figures, the free-electron exchange approximation underestimates exchange for all occupied states at a radial distance of 2 au.

It is interesting to take the difference between the Hartree-Fock and free-electron exchange potentials, use this as a perturbation, and apply first-order perturbation theory to determine the first-order corrections to the one-electron energy levels. This involves either the evaluation of the $F^k(nl;n'l')$ and $G^k(nl;n'l')$ integrals,[5]

in addition to the integrals

$$\int_0^\infty P_{nl}{}^2(r)V^{\mathrm{fe}}(r)dr, \quad (4)$$

or the direct integration of the differences between $P_{nl}{}^2(r)V_{nl}{}^{\mathrm{HF}}(r)$ and $P_{nl}{}^2(r)V^{\mathrm{fe}}(r)$. The results of such calculations for argon are given in Table III.

A good estimate of the accuracy of using perturbation theory can be obtained by direct integration of the radial Schrödinger equation, using the potential obtained from the Hartree-Fock solutions and the free-electron exchange approximation. This would represent the first iteration in going from Hartree-Fock to self-consistent solutions involving the free-electron exchange approximation, usually designated Hartree-Fock-Slater solutions. These energies are also given in Table III. For comparison, the eigenvalues for the self-consistent Hartree-Fock-Slater solutions, as obtained by Herman and Skillman,[13] are also included. The differences between the Hartree-Fock eigenvalues and those obtained from the first iteration compare well with the perturbation theory results. Comparison with the Hartree-Fock-Slater eigenvalues indicates that there are still significant adjustments in the eigenvalues before self-consistency is achieved, though these changes are not large for the less tightly bound electrons.

TABLE III. The eigenvalues $\epsilon_{nl}{}^{(a)}$ and $\epsilon_{nl}{}^{(c)}$ are the self-consistent Hartree-Fock and Hartree-Fock-Slater one-electron energies, respectively, for atomic argon (in Ry). The energies $\epsilon_{nl}{}^{(b)}$ represent eigenvalues for the radial Schrödinger equation involving a potential computed from the Hartree-Fock charge density and the free-electron exchange approximation.

nl	$\epsilon_{nl}{}^{(a)}$	$\epsilon_{nl}{}^{(b)}$	$\epsilon_{nl}{}^{(c)}$	$\epsilon_{nl}{}^{(b)} - \epsilon_{nl}{}^{(a)}$	$\int_0^\infty P_{nl}{}^2[V^{\mathrm{fe}} - V^{\mathrm{HF}}]dr$
$1s$	-237.21	-234.15	-232.44	3.06	3.19
$2s$	-24.64	-23.55	-22.79	1.09	1.01
$2p$	-19.14	-19.04	-18.13	0.10	0.12
$3s$	-2.55	-2.34	-2.05	0.21	0.23
$3p$	-1.18	-1.25	-1.01	-0.07	-0.05

[12] D. R. Hartree, Phys. Rev. 109, 840 (1958).
[13] F. Herman (private communication).

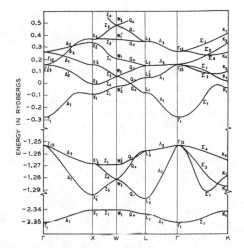

FIG. 1. Energy bands for face-centered cubic argon. Calculations were carried out only at the points Γ, X, W, L, and K of the Brillouin zone. The connecting lines represent reasonable guesses to the actual shapes of the bands. Energies are given in Ry. Note the change in scale between the valence 3s and 3p bands and the conduction bands.

The results of Table III indicate that the free-electron exchange potential, averaged over all r, underestimates exchange for the 1s, 2s, and 2p levels, and overestimates it slightly for the 3p level. However, the 3p eigenvalue also rises above the Hartree-Fock value by the time self-consistency is achieved.

IV. RESULTS

The results of the APW calculations for solid argon are listed in Table IV and sketched in Fig. 1. Convergence tests indicate that these results are accurate to approximately 0.001 Ry for the potential under consideration. Actual calculations were carried out only at the points Γ, X, W, L, and K in Brillouin zone. The notation is that of Bouckaert, Smoluchowski, and Wigner.[14] The lines connecting these points represent reasonable guesses to the actual shapes of the various bands, consistent with the compatibility relations.

The calculated widths of the 3s and 3p valence bands compare favorably with those reported earlier by Knox and Bassani.[1] However, the present bands are located at higher energies. From the results of Table III, it is seen that the present 3s and 3p bands lie in the immediate vicinity of the corresponding atomic levels obtained from the free-electron exchange calculations.

The APW results for the conduction bands differ significantly from those of Knox and Bassani. The two calculations agree only in predicting that the bottom of

[14] L. P. Bouckaert, R. Smoluchowski, and E. Wigner, Phys. Rev. 50, 58 (1936).

the conduction band lies at Γ, and has the symmetry Γ₁. The APW results indicate that the 3d band lies in the middle of the 4s–4p conduction band, and that the lowest states at the edges of the Brillouin zone are predominantly "d" like rather than "s" or "p" like, as predicted by Knox and Bassani. Again, the energy range of the conduction bands differs considerably from that of Knox and Bassani.

V. DISCUSSION

The present calculations predict an energy gap of 13.3 eV from the top of the 3p valence band (Γ_{15}) to the bottom of the conduction band (Γ_1). This value compares well with the experimental value of 14.3 eV measured by Baldini,[15] and the value of 12.4 eV obtained in the calculations by Knox and Bassani.

These results indicate that quite reasonable energy bands can be obtained using the free-electron exchange approximation. Despite the fact that this approximation causes changes in the one-electron atomic energy levels from the Hartree-Fock values (and a corresponding shift in the energies of the resultant bands), it appears likely that this shift in energy can be estimated reasonably well by first-order perturbation theory. This will give at least a rough estimate of the inaccuracy in the relative positions of the different bands.

The source of the discrepancies between the present results and the earlier calculations by Knox and Bassani is uncertain. The fact that their 3s and 3p bands are lower in energy is probably due to the fact that they used the Hartree-Fock eigenvalues to position these

TABLE IV. Energies of various states for solid argon at the center and boundaries of the first Brillouin zone. All values are in Ry and are relative to zero potential in the vacuum outside the boundaries of the crystal.

State	3s band	3p band	Conduction bands		
Γ_1	−2.351		−0.274		
$\Gamma_{25'}$			0.158		
Γ_{12}			0.265		
Γ_{15}		−1.253	1.439		
X_1	−2.341		−0.085	0.603	0.881
X_2			0.339		
X_3			−0.002		
$X_{4'}$		−1.294	0.157		
X_5			0.367		
$X_{5'}$		−1.268	0.530	1.582	
W_1	−2.341		0.204	0.518	
$W_{1'}$			0.364		
$W_{2'}$		−1.269	−0.028	0.620	1.126
W_3		−1.281	0.058	0.481	1.052
L_1	−2.344		−0.077	0.503	
$L_{2'}$		−1.297	0.044		
L_3			0.144	0.345	
$L_{3'}$		−1.258	1.517		
K_1	−2.342	−1.278	−0.038	0.014	0.410
K_2			0.334		
K_3		−1.287	0.101	0.470	
K_4		−1.265	0.256	0.683	1.573

[15] G. Baldini, Phys. Rev. 128, 1562 (1962).

bands. This may also have produced the differences in the ordering of the conduction band states. These latter differences could also be due to limitations in the perturbation approximation to the orthogonalized-plane-wave method which was used by Knox and Bassani.

One interesting observation regarding the conduction bands for argon is the similarity between these bands and those obtained for face-centered cubic iron by Wood[4] and for copper by Burdick[16] and also by Segall.[17] Aside from minor changes in the ordering of states in the $4s$–$4p$ bands (which can be explained by differences in lattice spacing), the bands are remarkably similar. This may lend some support to the rigid band approximation, a proposal which has enjoyed fair success in explaining several aspects of the electronic properties of the transition metals and their alloys.

VI. ACKNOWLEDGMENTS

The author wishes to thank Professor John C. Slater for his encouragement, interest, and support of this work. The author is indebted to J. H. Wood for introducing him to the APW method and the use of his programs. He has benefitted from many useful discussions with A. C. Switendick. He wishes to thank Frank Herman for providing him with a copy of his Hartree-Fock-Slater atomic self-consistent field program.

[16] G. A. Burdick, Phys. Rev. 129, 138 (1963).
[17] B. Segall, Phys. Rev. 125, 109 (1962).

THE FERMI SURFACE OF BERYLLIUM

J. H. TERRELL*

*Department of Physics, Brandeis University, Waltham, Massachusetts
and Solid State and Molecular Theory Group, Massachusetts Institute
of Technology, Cambridge, Massachusetts*

Received 4 January 1964

The purpose of this letter is to report on an ab initio energy band calculation of beryllium which gives a Fermi surface in good agreement with a recent De Haas - Van Alphen experiment [1]. It is hoped that the data presented here will be useful as a guide in interpreting further experimental work on this interesting metal.

We have completed an energy band calculation of hcp beryllium by the augmented plane wave method [2] giving energy eigenvalues (convergence to 0.001 Ry) at forty-five points in $\frac{1}{24}$th of the first Brillouin zone along the major symmetry directions and at points of lower symmetry in the planes ΓKM, Δ UP, ALH**. Two more planes were drawn so that the upper half of the Brillouin zone was divided equally into four sections (fig. 1). Tiny hexagons were chosen so as

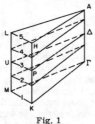

Fig. 1

to fill up the entire zone and graphically interpolated energies were found at the centres of the small hexagons for the equivalent of 1152 points with an estimated error of less than 0.01 Ry. Placing the energies in ascending order and counting up to the 2304th energy value gave a Fermi energy E_F=0.84 ± 0.01 Ry measured from the bottom of the band***.

The crystal potential was approximated by a superposition of spherically symmetric atomic potentials calculated from self-consistent Hartree-Fock solutions of the beryllium atom and corrected for exchange by means of the Slater free electron exchange approximation†. The room temperature lattice parameters a = 4.3192 a.u. and c = 6.7713 a.u. [5] were used where 1 atomic unit = 0.529 × 10⁻⁸ cm.

A density of states curve was constructed which had a shape similar to that of Herring and Hill [6]. The density of states at the Fermi surface gave for the electronic specific heat a value of C_V ~ 0.5 × 10⁻⁴ cal/deg² mole (C_V = 0.54 × 10⁻⁴ cal/deg² mole from experiment [7]). Energy (E) versus wave vector (k) curves were plotted in each of the five planes labeled as shown in fig. 1. The intersections of E with E_F=0.84 Ry in each of the five planes are shown in fig. 2, 3 and 4. The Fermi surface is seen to consist of a hole region in the form of a six cornered coronet connected by tiny necks and an electron region in the form of two cigars each with a triangular midsection which becomes circular as one moves toward the ends. There is also a slight indentation in the midsection.

Table 1 presents distances in reciprocal space from theory and experiment labeled according to Watts [1]. The error in the theoretical values ap-

Table 1

Distances labeled according to Watts	Theory (1/a.u.)	Experiment (1/a.u.)
ab	0.190	0.180
ef	0.93	0.96
cd	0.185	0.183
kl	0.23	0.23
on	0.01	0.02
mn	0.58	0.57
ml	0.59	0.57

* Supported by the National Science Foundation (NSF-G19994) and the U.S. Army Research Office - Durham (ARO-G233).
** The notations are those of Herring [3].
*** For hcp beryllium there are 2 atoms/unit cell and 2 electrons/atom giving 4 electrons for each atom in the Brillouin zone. Since a given energy band can accommodate 2 electrons from each atom in the solid, $\frac{4}{2}$ × (1152) = 2304 energies will lie below the Fermi energy.

† As an example of this procedure see Mattheiss [4].

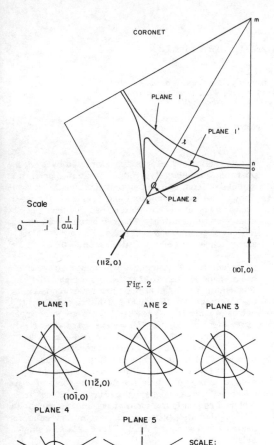

Fig. 2

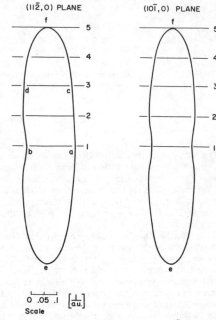

Fig. 4. Cross sections of cigars in planes ‖ to (000.1) direction.

Fig. 3. Cross sections of cigars in planes ⊥ (000.1) direction.

pearing as a result of the uncertainty in the Fermi energy is about ±0.01 [1/a.u.]. The theoretical extremal areas of the Fermi surface for various directions of the magnetic field are presented in table 2 along with the corresponding frequencies in magnetic field (H) of the De Haas - Van Alphen oscillations calculated using the Onsager relation $f = \hbar cA/2\pi e$ where A is the extremal area and the magnetic field is measured in gauss.

The experimental Fermi surface of Watts [1] consisted of a hole region in the form of a coronet

and an electron region in the form of two cigars. The cigars were circular in cross-section with slight "waists" at their midsection. The theoretical Fermi surface is much like that of Watts' experiment. The theoretical midsection of the cigars is triangular and they are slightly shorter in length. The indentation at the midsection as shown in fig. 4 supports Watts' observation that the cigars have "waists" *. The two frequencies with H in the (000.1) direction due to the presence of the "waists" are found to coalesce when H is about 45° away from the (000.1) direction in good agreement with Watts' observation that the frequencies coalesce 47° away.

The contour labeled 1' in fig. 2 was drawn midway between planes 1 and 2 so that the details of the large pieces of the coronet might be seen and extremal areas found. As seen from tables 1 and 2 the agreement with experiment is good except that our necks (assumed to be cylindrical) are too small. If the Fermi energy is lowered slightly (within the error indicated) even better agreement with experiment is obtained except that our cigars are still shorter in length than the experimental ones. The overall agreement with experiment is surprisingly good considering the relatively few points in the

† Further evidence of this is reported by Ginsberg [8].

190

Table 2

Type of orbit	Direction of magnetic field (*H*)	Extremal area $[1/a.u.]^2$	De Haas - Van Alphen frequencies $\times 10^6$	
			Theory (gauss)	Experiment (gauss) Fig. 1 in ref. 1
Coronet				
Circle within coronet	(000.1)	1.07	400	396
Orbit around outside of coronet	(000.1)	1.36	509	---
Large pieces of coronet	(11$\bar{2}$.0)	0.031	11.6	12.5
Large pieces of coronet	(11$\bar{2}$.0)	0.041	14.9	15.0
Large pieces of coronet	(10$\bar{1}$.0)	0.035	13.2	14.9
Necks connecting large pieces	(11$\bar{2}$.0)	0.0001	0.03	0.10
	(11$\bar{2}$.0)	0.0002	0.07	0.25
	(10$\bar{1}$.0)	0.0001	0.04	0.12
Cigars				
	(11$\bar{2}$.0)	0.152	56.7	53
	(10$\bar{1}$.0)	0.140	52.3	53
"waist" (Plane 1)	(000.1)	0.026	9.5	9.8
Plane 2	(000.1)	0.027	10.1	10.1

Brillouin zone which were used and the many approximations inherent in ab initio energy band calculations.

While this paper was being completed an orthogonalised plane wave calculation of beryllium came to our attention [9]. It is quite encouraging that the augmented and orthogonalised plane wave results are in good agreement. The major difference is that the cigars obtained by the orthogonalised plane wave method have definite bulges at their midsection, contrary to present experimental results.

I am indebted to Dr. L. F. Mattheiss of Bell Telephone Laboratories for his vital collaboration in the early phase of this work and for continued encouragement and to Dr. A. J. Freeman for helpful discussions and suggestions. The hospitality of the National Magnet Laboratory, M. I. T. , where part of this work was completed is gratefully acknowledged.

1) B. R. Watts, Physics Letters 3 (1963) 284.
2) J. C. Slater, Phys. Rev. 92 (1953) 603.
   M. M. Saffren and J. C. Slater, Phys. Rev. 92 (1953) 1126.
   J. C. Slater, Phys. Rev. 51 (1937) 846.
   J. H. Wood, Phys. Rev. 126 (1962) 517.
3) C. Herring, J. Franklin Inst. 233 (1942) 525.
4) L. F. Mattheiss, QPR, No. 46, 15 Oct. 1962, S. S. M. T. G., M. I. T.
5) W. B. Pearson, A Handbook of Lattice Spacings and Structures of Metals and Alloys (Pergamon Press, 1958).
6) C. Herring and A. G. Hill, Phys. Rev. 58 (1940) 132.
7) R. Hill and P. Smith, Phil. Mag. 44 (1953) 636.
8) R. Ginsberg, Bull. Am. Phys. Soc. II, 7 (1962) 8, 548.
9) T. L. Loucks and P. H. Cutler, Phys. Rev., to appear.

* * * * *

PHYSICAL REVIEW   VOLUME 134, NUMBER 4A   18 MAY 1964

Energy Bands for the Iron Transition Series*

L. F. MATTHEISS†

Solid-State and Molecular Theory Group, Massachusetts Institute of Technology, Cambridge, Massachusetts

(Received 16 December 1963)

Preliminary energy-band calculations for elements of the iron transition series have been completed using the augmented plane-wave method. The results include plots of energy as a function of wave vector along a line of symmetry for elements crystallizing in the face-centered cubic (Ar, Co, Ni, Cu), body-centered cubic (V, Cr, Fe), and hexagonal close packed (Ti, Zn) structures. These results indicate the presence of systematic trends in the band structures for the various elements and provide some justification for the application of the rigid band model to transition metals and their alloys.

I. INTRODUCTION

ENERGY bands have been calculated for a majority of the elements in the iron transition series using the augmented plane-wave (APW) method.[1,2] While the present results are preliminary in nature and not in any sense complete, they may be of some interest to experimentalists and theoreticians who are concerned with the electronic structure of the transition-series elements. The present results represent energy bands for three different crystal structures, with a variety of lattice constants. Despite the detailed differences that are imposed by symmetry requirements and variations in lattice constants, the results suggest some interesting and rather clear-cut trends in the band structure of these elements as one proceeds through the

transition series. These calculations lend some support to the rigid band model for the transition series. They support the hope that systematic studies of the band structure of the transition-series elements can provide useful qualitative, and perhaps quantitative, information concerning their electronic structure.

As in all calculations involving d electrons, the results are sensitive to the choice of potentials. The crystal potentials used in these calculations were all constructed in an analogous manner, and were approximated by a superposition of atomic potentials. The method involves the use of Hartree-Fock solutions to the corresponding atomic problem[3] and the free-electron-exchange approximation.[4] The details of this method for constructing approximate crystal potentials have been described earlier,[5] though a brief resumé is presented in Sec. II of

* This work was supported by the National Science Foundation.
† Presently employed at Bell Telephone Laboratories, Incorporated, Murray Hill, New Jersey.

[1] J. C. Slater, Phys. Rev. **51**, 846 (1937).
[2] J. H. Wood, Phys. Rev. **126**, 517 (1962).

[3] R. E. Watson, Phys. Rev. **119**, 1934 (1960); R. E. Watson and A. J. Freeman, Phys. Rev. **123**, 521 (1961).
[4] J. C. Slater, Phys. Rev. **81**, 385 (1951).
[5] L. F. Mattheiss, Phys. Rev. **133**, A1399 (1964).

this paper, along with other information pertaining to this present series of calculations. The energy bands along a single line of symmetry in the appropriate Brillouin zone are presented in Sec. III for Ar, Ti, V, Cr, Fe, Co, Ni, Cu, and Zn, while the last section contains a brief discussion of these results.

II. DESCRIPTION OF THE CALCULATIONS

In these calculations, the crystal potential has been approximated by a superposition of atomic potentials. The Coulomb and exchange contributions to the crystal potential are treated separately. An approximate crystal Coulomb potential and charge density in a given atomic cell is obtained by expanding the neutral atom Coulomb potentials and charge densities of neighboring atoms about the origin, using Löwdin's alpha function expansion,[6] keeping only the $l=0$ or spherically symmetric terms in these expansions. Using the free-electron-exchange approximation, the exchange potenial is proportional to the cube root of the superimposed atomic-charge densities.

The potentials obtained by this method are generally rather flat near the boundaries of the atomic cell, at least in the case of metals, so they are readily approximated by a "muffin-tin" type potential, as required by the APW method. The constant value of the potential outside the APW spheres is taken as the average value of the potential in this region. This usually results in a discontinuity in the potential at the sphere radius amounting to a few hundredths of a Rydberg.

In the construction of approximate crystal potentials for transition-series elements, there is frequently some ambiguity in choosing the most reasonable atomic configuration. This sort of difficulty can only be answered satisfactorily by experimental information and/or self-consistent energy-band calculations. For the present, we have been content to study the effect that changing the atomic configuration has on the band structure. In addition, there are magnetic effects which create additional complications in this series of elements. For simplicity, all magnetic effects have been neglected in these calculations, and the crystals have been assumed to be nonmagnetic in character.

The lattice constants which have been used in these calculations have generally been the room-temperature values as tabulated by Pearson.[7] The exceptions are those for Ar and Zn. The lattice constant for Ar is the low-temperature value obtained by Dobbs and Jones.[8] In the case of Zn, Harrison[9] has extrapolated the room-temperature lattice constants to low temperatures since the results are expected to be sensitive to the choice of

TABLE I. In this table, we list the elements of the iron transition series, their structures, the lattice constants used in this series of calculations (in atomic units), and the assumed atomic configurations.

Element	Structure	a(au)	c(au)	Configuration
Ar	fcc	10.0346		$(3s)^2(3p)^6$
K				
Ca				
Sc				
Ti	hcp	5.5755	8.8503	$(3d)^3(4s)^1$
V	bcc	5.7225		$(3d)^4(4s)^1$
Cr	bcc	5.4512		$(3d)^5(4s)^1$
Mn				
Fe	bcc	5.4168		$(3d)^7(4s)^1$
Co	fcc	6.6975		$(3d)^8(4s)^1$
Ni	fcc	6.6590		$(3d)^9(4s)^1$
Cu	fcc	6.8309		$(3d)^{10}(4s)^1$
Zn	hcp	5.0120	9.1453	$(3d)^{10}(4s)^2$

c/a ratio. For purposes of comparison, his values have been used in these calculations. Table I contains a summary of the elements considered in these calculations, their structures, the values of the lattice constants, and the assumed atomic configurations.

III. RESULTS

The principal results of these calculations are presented in Fig. 1. These results represent plots of energy as a function of wave vector along lines of symmetry from the center to a boundary of the appropriate Brillouin zones. For the face-centered cubic structure (Ar, Co, Ni, and Cu), the bands are plotted from Γ along the Δ direction to the point X, using the notation of Bouckaert, Smoluchowski, and Wigner.[10] In the body-centered cubic structure (V, Cr, and Fe), the bands are plotted from Γ along the Δ direction to the point H. Finally, in the hexagonal close-packed structure (Ti and Zn), they start at Γ and proceed along the line T in the $k_z=0$ plane which terminates at the point K, one of the vertices of the hexagon (in the notation of Herring[11]).

The energy is in Rydbergs and the wave vectors for the different elements are drawn to scale for purposes of comparison. The horizontal dashed lines represent rough estimates of the Fermi energy for each element. For simplicity, some of the more highly excited bands have been omitted in some cases, particularly in the face-centered cubic structure, or in other situations, they have been sketched in by dashed lines.

In Fig. 2, it is shown what effect varying the atomic configuration has on the band structure of a typical element, namely vanadium. The bands to the right are the ones shown in Fig. 1 for vanadium; the ones to the left are those obtained from a potential which results from an atomic configuration containing an additional $4s$ electron and one less $3d$ electron. In general, this results in a narrowing of the $3d$ band and a decrease in

[6] P. O. Löwdin, Advan. Phys. 5, 1 (1956).
[7] W. B. Pearson, *A Handbook of Lattice Spacings and Structures of Metals and Alloys* (Pergamon Press, Inc., New York, 1958).
[8] E. R. Dobbs and G. O. Jones, in *Reports on Progress in Physics*, edited by A. C. Stickland (The Physical Society, London, 1957), Vol. 20, p. 516.
[9] W. A. Harrison, Phys. Rev. 126, 497 (1962).
[10] L. P. Bouckaert, R. Smoluchowski, and E. Wigner, Phys. Rev. 50, 58 (1936).
[11] C. Herring, J. Franklin Inst. 233, 525 (1942).

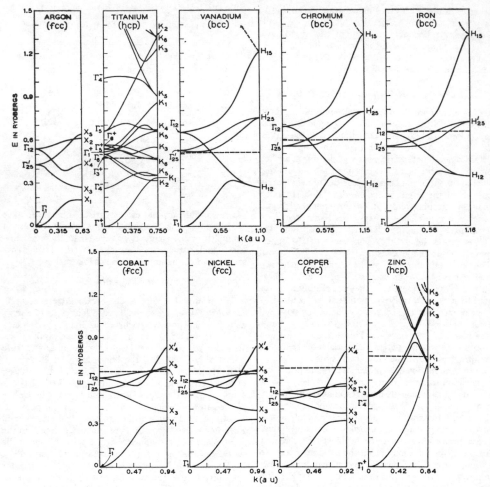

FIG. 1. Energy bands for Ar, Ti, V, Cr, Fe, Co, Ni, Cu, and Zn as a function of wave vector along a line of symmetry in the appropriate Brillouin zone. For the face-centered cubic structure, the bands are plotted from Γ along Δ to the point X. For the body-centered cubic structure, they are plotted from Γ along Δ to the point H. Finally, for the hexagonal close-packed structure, they are plotted from Γ along T to the point K. The energies are in Rydbergs and the wave vectors are in atomic units.

the energy separation between the top of the $3d$ band and the bottom of the $4s$-$4p$ bands.

IV. DISCUSSION

In the simplified picture of the energy bands for the iron transition-series elements, one finds a narrow $3d$ band in the midst of a rather broad $4s$-$4p$ band. The width of the $3d$ band and especially its position relative to the bottom of the $4s$-$4p$ band depend rather critically on the potential. Nevertheless, the results of Fig. 1 exhibit a reasonably smooth variation from element to element, especially for those substances having the

same crystal structure. This seems to lend some support to the rigid band model for the transition-series elements, an approximation which has been of considerable value in understanding the electronic properties of these elements and their alloys.

There is a gradual narrowing of the $3d$ band as one progresses through the series. This effect was discussed by Slater in order to explain the occurrence of ferromagnetism in the latter part of the series.[12] In going from Cu to Zn, the $3d$ band suddenly drops about 0.5 Ry below the bottom of the $4s$-$4p$ bands, and its width

[12] J. C. Slater, Rev. Mod. Phys. **25**, 199 (1953).

decreases to less than 0.1 Ry. As a result, the energy bands for zinc are very free-electron-like. For those elements where the $3d$ band falls in the middle of the $4s$-$4p$ bands, the interactions between states having the same symmetry causes considerable modification to the free-electron bands, though at points of symmetry, the effect is sometimes small. The bands for Ti and Zn demonstrate this effect nicely.

The results of Fig. 2 emphasize the uncertainty which is inherent in any energy-band calculation for a transition-series element. These uncertainties have been pointed out previously in the literature, particularly by Callaway.[13] These difficulties can only be cleared up satisfactorily with the aid of more detailed experimental information regarding the band structure of these elements in addition to self-consistent energy-band calculations.

The results presented here are not complete enough to permit detailed comparisons to be made with experiment or a discussion of the resulting Fermi surfaces. However, there are some striking similarities between the energy bands shown in Fig. 1 and the results obtained by earlier calculations. In particular, there is good qualitative agreement between the Cu results shown in Fig. 1 and the bands calculated by Segall[14] and also by Burdick.[15] Similarly, the results for Fe are in good agreement with the published results of Wood.[2] The agreement for Ar with the results of calculations by Knox and Bassani[16] is good, and has been described previously.[5] In the case of Cr, it is difficult to compare the present results with those of earlier calculations by Asdente and Friedel[17] since they neglect the interactions between the $3d$ band and the $4s$-$4p$ bands. However, the present results do justify, to some extent, the treatment of Cr by Lomer,[18] who used the results of Wood's iron calculations to discuss the energy bands in antiferromagnetic Cr.

In the case of Zn, the ordering of levels is identical with that obtained by Harrison.[9] This ordering differs from that obtained in earlier calculations for hexagonal

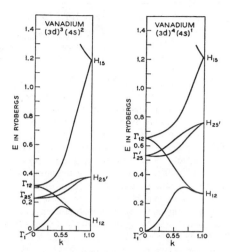

FIG. 2. Energy bands for vanadium along the line Δ obtained from two different potentials. The bands to the left resulted from an atomic configuration of $(3d)^3(4s)^2$ while those to the right involved a $(3d)^4(4s)^1$ configuration.

close-packed metals by Herring and Hill for Be[19] and Falicov for Mg.[20] This change in ordering might be due to the presence of an occupied $3d$ band just below the $4s$-$4p$ bands. The results for Ti agree qualitatively with those obtained by Altmann and Bradley.[21] Finally, the Ni results are in good agreement with those obtained by Hanus.[22]

ACKNOWLEDGMENTS

The author wishes to thank Professor John C. Slater for encouraging and supporting this work. The author is grateful to J. H. Wood and A. C. Switendick for the use of their APW programs and for many useful discussions and comments.

[13] J. Callaway, Phys. Rev. **99**, 500 (1955).
[14] B. Segall, Phys. Rev. **125**, 109 (1962).
[15] G. A. Burdick, Phys. Rev. **129**, 138 (1963).
[16] R. S. Knox and F. Bassani, Phys. Rev. **124**, 652 (1961).
[17] M. Asdente and J. Friedel, Phys. Rev. **124**, 384 (1961).
[18] W. M. Lomer, Proc. Phys. Soc. (London) **80**, 489 (1962).

[19] C. Herring and A. G. Hill, Phys. Rev. **58**, 132 (1940).
[20] L. M. Falicov, Phil. Trans. Roy Soc. A**255**, 55 (1962).
[21] C. J. Bradley, Ph.D. thesis, Oxford University, 1962 (unpublished).
[22] J. G. Hanus, Solid-State and Molecular Theory Group, Massachusetts Institute of Technology, Quarterly Progress Report No. 44, p. 29, 1962 (unpublished).

VOLUME 13, NUMBER 17   PHYSICAL REVIEW LETTERS   26 OCTOBER 1964

ESTIMATE OF THE SPIN-ORBIT PARAMETER ξ_{5d} IN METALLIC TUNGSTEN

L. F. Mattheiss and R. E. Watson

Bell Telephone Laboratories, Murray Hill, New Jersey
(Received 28 September 1964)

In the previous Letter, Walsh and Grimes[1] have presented the results of size-effect experiments on body-centered cubic tungsten which, on the basis of the Lomer model for the Fermi surface of chromium-group metals,[2,3] yield clear evidence for the presence of spin-orbit interactions in metallic tungsten. By comparing the results of nonrelativistic augmented-plane-wave energy-band calculations for tungsten with these experimental results, it has been possible to estimate the $5d$ spin-orbit parameter ξ_{5d} in tungsten to be approximately 0.03 Ry (0.4 eV). Using this value for ξ_{5d}, one can account for the disappearance of the electron lenses along the $\langle 100 \rangle$ axes in tungsten, a result which is consistent with the de Haas–van Alphen measurements of Sparlin and Marcus.[4]

It is difficult to obtain an accurate estimate of the atomic spin-orbit parameter ξ_{5d} from the measured optical spectra[5] for tungsten since intermediate, rather than Russell-Saunders,

coupling is obeyed. Roughly, the possible values range from 0.02 to 0.05 Ry. Herman and Skillman[6] have calculated a first-order perturbation-theory estimate of ξ_{5d} using self-consistent Hartree-Fock-Slater atomic functions and they have obtained a value of 0.03 Ry.

The present estimate for ξ_{5d} is obtained from a simplified spin-orbit calculation involving $5d$ band states along the $\langle 100 \rangle$ or Δ direction in the Brillouin zone. The results of these calculations, as a function of ξ_{5d}, are shown in Fig. 1. In Fig. 1(a), the single and double group notation[7] for the various states is indicated, the former being included in parentheses. The state with Γ_1 symmetry corresponds to the bottom of the $6s$ conduction band; those states with $\Gamma_{25'}$, Γ_{12}, and $H_{25'}$ symmetry represent tungsten $5d$ band states. The computed Fermi energy is indicated by the broken horizontal line. Detailed comparison of the nonrelativistic Fermi surface which results from these calculations with the results of

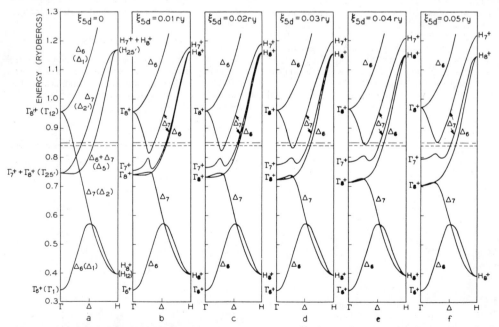

FIG. 1. Results of a simplified spin-orbit calculation along the $\langle 100 \rangle$ or Δ direction for body-centered cubic tungsten as a function of the spin-orbit parameter ξ_{5d}.

de Haas—van Alphen measurements by Sparlin[8] indicates that the s-d energy separation shown in Fig. 1(a) is approximately 0.1 Ry too small. Thus, the state with Γ_1 symmetry should have an energy of approximately 0.24 Ry instead of 0.34 Ry, the $5d$ states remaining fixed. It is estimated that this modification will lower the Fermi energy in the $5d$ bands by about 0.01 Ry. This is indicated by the dashed horizontal line.

The introduction of spin-orbit interactions results in a splitting of the Δ_5 degeneracy and removal of the Δ_7 crossings. To obtain a semi-quantitative estimate of these effects, it is convenient to adopt a simplified model regarding the wave functions for these states. We assume that the wave functions for the energy band states with Δ_2-, $\Delta_{2'}$-, and Δ_5-type symmetry are purely $5d$-like in character. If it is further assumed that these $5d$ functions all have the same radial function $P_{5d}(r)$, then the spin-orbit effects can be described in terms of a single spin-orbit parameter ξ_{5d}. Although it is well known that the d radial functions vary throughout the d bands,[9] it should be a good approximation to assume a fixed radial function in the vicinity of the Fermi energy.

In Fig. 1, the interaction of the three states with Δ_7 symmetry has been studied as a function of ξ_{5d} along the Δ direction. Neglecting off-diagonal matrix elements, it is found that the Δ_5 state is split by $\pm\frac{1}{2}\xi_{5d}$, the Δ_7 and Δ_6 states having the higher and lower energies, respectively. Including the effects of off-diagonal spin-orbit matrix elements between the three Δ_7-type states requires the solution of a three-by-three secular determinant; the results are shown in Figs. 1(b) through 1(f) for ξ_{5d} ranging from 0.01 to 0.05 Ry. In these calculations, the off-diagonal matrix elements between the three Δ_6-type states have been neglected. In the vicinity of the Fermi energy, the effects of the lower and upper Δ_6 states on the central one should be small and cancel to a first approximation.

From the experimental observation by Walsh and Grimes that the spin-orbit splitting between the electron "jack" at Γ and the hole octahedron at H is 5% of the Γ-H distance, we can estimate from Fig. 1 that the spin-orbit parameter ξ_{5d} at the Fermi surface in metallic tungsten is approximately 0.03 Ry. One interesting consequence of a spin-orbit parameter ξ_{5d} equal to approximately 0.03 Ry concerns the existence of electron lenses within the necks joining the electron octahedron at Γ with the balls along Δ. Sparlin and Marcus have not observed de Haas—van Alphen periods in tungsten which can be associated with these lenses.[4] Neglecting the spin-orbit interaction, the presence of necks implies the existence of lenses since the two surfaces must touch in the {100} and {110} planes.[3] Since the lenses are a result of the highest Δ_7 state passing through the Fermi energy, the present calculations suggest that the lenses will disappear in tungsten when ξ_{5d} is between 0.03 and 0.04 Ry. Thus, within the accuracy of the present calculation, the lenses in tungsten are either very small or nonexistent.

---

[1]W. M. Walsh and C. C. Grimes, preceding Letter [Phys. Rev. Letters 13, 523 (1964)].

[2]W. M. Lomer, Proc. Phys. Soc. (London) 80, 489 (1962).

[3]W. M. Lomer, Proc. Phys. Soc. (London) 84, 327 (1964).

[4]D. M. Sparlin and J. A. Marcus, Bull. Am. Phys. Soc. 9, 250 (1964).

[5]C. E. Moore, Atomic Energy Levels, National Bureau of Standards Circular No. 467 (U. S. Government Printing Office, Washington, D. C., 1949), Vol. III.

[6]F. Herman and S. Skillman, Atomic Structure Calculations (Prentice-Hall, Inc., Englewood Cliffs, New Jersey, 1963).

[7]R. J. Elliott, Phys. Rev. 96, 280 (1954).

[8]D. M. Sparlin, thesis, Northwestern University, 1964 (unpublished).

[9]J. H. Wood, Phys. Rev. 117, 714 (1960).

BAND STRUCTURE AND MAGNETISM OF GADOLINIUM METAL

J. O. Dimmock

Lincoln Laboratory,* Massachusetts Institute of Technology, Lexington, Massachusetts

and

A. J. Freeman

National Magnet Laboratory,† Massachusetts Institute of Technology, Cambridge, Massachusetts

(Received 18 November 1964)

The type-$4f$ rare-earth metals have been viewed traditionally as consisting of trivalent atomic cores, including the $4f$ shell, plus three conduction electrons per atom. Previous theoretical work[1] has attempted to explain the available experimental data by assuming that the three conduction electrons occupy essentially free-electron bands perturbed perhaps by a fairly small crystal potential. Much of this theoretical work depends critically on the assumed free-electron nature of the conduction bands. However, it has been difficult to explain by means of the free-electron model the large saturation magnetization[2] of Gd ($7.5\mu_B/$ atom) and especially the large electronic specific heat[3] of the rare-earth metals which indicates a density of states at the Fermi surface some eight times that given by the free-electron model.

This Letter reports briefly some results of a nonrelativistic augmented plane wave[4] (APW) calculation of the electronic energy bands in gadolinium metal. The calculated conduction bands differ markedly from those of the free-electron model, and instead closely resemble those of the transition metals. This is due to the fact that bands originating from atomic $5d$ and $6s$ states overlap and are strongly mixed. The bands near the Fermi surface are of mixed s-d character and yield a density of states about three times that given in the free-electron model. This accounts for the large observed saturation magnetization of Gd metal and may account for the high electronic specific heats of rare-earth metals.

The one-electron potential, used as input for the APW calculation, was obtained from a superposition of spherically symmetric atomic potentials. Results have been calculated for two different atomic starting potentials: The first was determined from free-atom Hartree-Fock-Slater (HFS) wave functions[5] for the configuration Gd^0 $4f^7 6s^2 5d$, while the second was obtained from analytic Hartree-Fock wave functions[6] for the configuration Gd^{+1} $4f^7 6s^2$ plus an atomic $5d$ wave function. The conduction bands obtained using these two potentials were practically identical indicating that they do not depend critically on the potential. We report here the results determined from the HFS potential which was chronologically the first potential used.

Energy eigenvalues were calculated at 45 points in $1/24$ of the first Brillouin zone. The calculated $E(k)$ curves for the conduction bands of gadolinium metal along the major symmetry directions are shown in Fig. 1. The strong deviation of these bands from those of a free-electron or nearly free-electron model can be seen in the high density of relatively flat bands, which are largely of d character. The calculation also yields a very narrow $4f$ band (width ~0.05 eV) about 0.8 Ry below the bottom of the $5d$-$6s$ bands. (This separation, however, was found to depend strongly on the potential used and is consequently not very reliable.) The very narrow width of the $4f$ band indicates that the $4f$ electrons are, as expected, highly localized.

The density of states of the conduction bands was obtained by dividing the Brillouin zone into 192 identical hexagons, each characterized by the energies calculated at its center. A histogram representing the computed den-

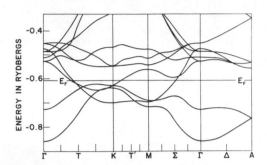

FIG. 1. Calculated $E(k)$ curves for the conduction bands of gadolinium metal along the major symmetry directions.

sity of states $N(E)$ is given in Fig. 2. The density of states for the free-electron model is superimposed for comparison. As seen from this figure the $5d$ bands have a width of about 0.5 Ry, and yield a high density of states. The Fermi energy, for three electrons per atom, is $E_F = 0.25$ measured from the bottom of the band as compared with a value of 0.54 Ry for the free-electron model. At the Fermi energy, the calculated density of states is large, $N(E_F) = 1.8$ electrons per atom per eV compared with the free-electron value of 0.6 eV^{-1}. This is due to the fact that the electron bands in the vicinity of the Fermi surface are of mixed s-d character and are consequently much flatter than would be expected from a free-electron model.

Let us consider the magnetic properties

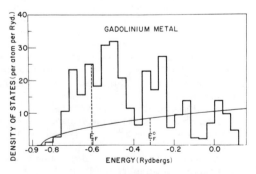

FIG. 2. A histogram representation of the density of states in electrons per atom per Ry. The parabolic curve is the prediction of the free-electron model.

of gadolinium. Saturation magnetization measurements[2] give $7.5\mu_B$ per Gd atom in the metal or $0.5\mu_B$ more than expected for an ^8S ion. It is common to assume that this additional moment arises from a polarization of the conduction electrons. Using our computed density of states and a simple model in which the conduction electrons are polarized by exchange with the localized $4f$ electrons, one may estimate the exchange integral J required to produce this additional moment. For gadolinium the induced moment is given by $\mu = \frac{7}{2}JN(E_F)\mu_B$. For $N(E_F) = 1.8$ eV^{-1} we find $J = 0.08$ eV. This J is about 5 times smaller than that computed[7] between atomic $4f$ and $5d$ electrons but agrees with values of J (0.05-0.10 eV) calculated between a localized $4f$ electron and a plane wave.[8,9] (Orthogonalized plane-wave calculations, on the other hand, give[9] $J = 0.04$-0.07 eV.) From these estimates, we conclude that the "extra" magnetization in Gd can arise very easily from a reasonable exchange between the magnetic $4f$ electrons and the s-d conduction electrons at the Fermi energy largely because of the size of our computed $N(E_F)$. Further, with this picture of s-d conduction electrons occupying a band having a high density of states, one sees a strong qualitative resemblance to the transition metals and the role of d electrons in understanding the origin of magnetism in these materials. The difference is that in the rare-earth metals the bulk of the magnetization is carried by the $4f$ electrons which, however, lie well inside the atom and play no further direct role in interatomic exchange.

From our calculated $N(E_F)$ we obtain an electronic specific heat contribution of $\gamma = 4.2$ mJ/mole deg^2, which may be compared with an average measured value[3] of about 10 mJ/mole deg^2 for the $4f$ rare-earth metals with triply ionized cores, and with a free-electron value of 1.3 mJ/mole deg^2. Thus while our calculated $N(E_F)$ is some three times larger than the free-electron value, the calculated γ is smaller than experiment by about a factor of two. Crude estimates for Gd indicate that this difference could arise from electron-phonon contributions[10] to an apparent $N(E_F)$ deduced from measured γ values. As pointed out by Krebs,[10] this enhancement is expected to be appreciable when the electron energy differs considerably from the free-electron case which we found to be the case in Gd. Further theoretical work, including calculations for La, and other rare-earth metals, is in progress to answer this and other questions.

We are indebted to R. E. Watson who participated fully in almost all phases of this work. We are grateful to J. H. Wood for making the APW programs available to us and for many helpful discussions, and to A. Furdyna and R. Sheshinski for their help with many phases of the computations.

*Operated with support from the U. S. Air Force.

†Supported by the U. S. Air Force Office of Scientific Research.

[1]For example, see K. Yosida and A. Watabe, Progr. Theoret. Phys. (Kyoto) 28, 361 (1962). H. Miwa, Progr. Theoret. Phys. (Kyoto) 28, 208 (1962). R. J. Elliott and F. A. Wedgwood, Proc. Phys. Soc. (London) 81, 846 (1963); 84, 63 (1964). T. Kasuya, Trea-

tise on Magnetism, edited by H. Suhl and G. Rado (Academic Press, Inc., New York, 1964), Vol. IIA.

[2]H. Nigh, S. Legvold, and F. H. Spedding, Phys. Rev. 132, 1092 (1963).

[3]L. D. Jennings, R. E. Miller, and F. H. Spedding, J. Chem. Phys. 33, 1849 (1960). A. Berman, M. W. Zemansky, and H. A. Boorse, Phys. Rev. 109, 70 (1958). O. V. Lounasmaa, Phys. Rev. 126, 1352, 1357 (1962); 129, 2460 (1963); 133, A219 (1964).

[4]J. C. Slater, Phys. Rev. 51, 846 (1937); 92, 603 (1953). M. M. Saffren and J. C. Slater, Phys. Rev. 92, 1126 (1953).

[5]F. Herman and S. Skillman, Atomic Structure Calculations, (Prentice-Hall, Inc., Englewood Cliffs, New Jersey, 1963).

[6]A. J. Freeman and R. E. Watson, Phys. Rev. 127, 2058 (1962).

[7]A. J. Freeman and R. E. Watson, unpublished.

[8]T. A. Kaplan and D. H. Lyons, Phys. Rev. 129, 2092 (1963).

[9]R. E. Watson and A. J. Freeman, unpublished.

[10]K. Krebs, Phys. Letters 6, 31 (1963); R. E. Prange and L. P. Kadanoff, Phys. Rev. 134, A566 (1964).

LOCALIZED MOMENTS OF MANGANESE IMPURITIES IN FERROMAGNETIC IRON

V. Jaccarino, L. R. Walker, and G. K. Wertheim
Bell Telephone Laboratories, Murray Hill, New Jersey
(Received 18 November 1964)

Most studies of hyperfine fields in ferromagnetic transition-metal alloys have been concerned with the spatial distribution of the fields and little attention has been given to the thermal variation of the latter. Recently,[1] however, it has been observed that the temperature dependence of the Mn^{55} nmr frequency ν_T in a dilute (1.5% Mn) ferromagnetic FeMn alloy departs markedly from that of the magnetization σ_T of the Fe host. In particular, ν_T decreases much more rapidly than σ_T as may be seen in Fig. 1 where ν_T/ν_0 (open circles) and σ_T/σ_0 are plotted vs T/T_c.

We show here that an adequate explanation of the course of the Mn nmr may be obtained from the following assumptions: First, ν_T is proportional to the thermal average of the Mn moment $\langle S_T \rangle$; second, the Mn moment is localized, with a magnitude S that is independent of temperature; third, the thermal average of the Mn moment is taken over its levels in the exchange field of the iron $H_T{}^{Mn}$; fourth, $H_T{}^{Mn}$ is substantially weaker than that exchange field $H_T{}^{Fe}$ which acts between the iron ions. From this we conclude that little, if any, of the Mn magnetization is induced by the iron

host. As such the experiment and its interpretation provide information about the magnitudes of S and $H_0{}^{Mn}$ and constitute the first example of a magnetized localized state in a ferromagnetic transition metal.

The simplest quantitative expression of these ideas is to equate ν_T/ν_0 with the Brillouin function $B_S(y)$, with

$$y = \frac{g\beta S}{kT} H_T{}^{Mn}, \tag{1}$$

and $H_T{}^{Mn} = H_0{}^{Mn}\sigma_T/\sigma_0$. Then for various values of S and particular choices of $\zeta \equiv g\beta S \times H_0{}^{Mn}/kT_c$, families of curves may be generated, examples of which are shown in Fig. 2 for $S = \frac{1}{2}$ and $S = \frac{5}{2}$ for the values of ζ indicated. It is immediately apparent that the general shape of these curves, particularly for $0.5 < \zeta < 1$, resemble the behavior of the experimental data of Fig. 1. In particular, for $S = \frac{3}{2}$ and $H_0{}^{Mn} = 3.7 \times 10^6$ Oe ($g = 2.00$), a best fit to the experimental data could be obtained for which the average deviation $\Delta < 0.5\%$. Less satisfactory agreement was found for $S = 1$ ($\Delta > 1\%$) and for other half-integral values of S the fits were noticeably poorer.

Sec. 3. What we used was the crudest imaginable, and the error involved needs to be ascertained.[15a] Another approximation is that the response of the system to the perturbation that was used to determine the shielding was calculated only to first order in the perturbation. This lead to the result that the x, y, and z parts of

$S_l \cdot S_{k'k}$ get shielded in precisely the same way. It can be shown however that this "degeneracy" in the "triplet potential" is removed in higher order. This is usually a relatively minor effect, but it is interesting to note the changes in the character of the results when the approximations are relaxed.

PHYSICAL REVIEW   VOLUME 137, NUMBER 6A   15 MARCH 1965

Electronic Band Structure of TiC, TiN, and TiO†

V. Ern*

Laboratory for Insulation Research, Massachusetts Institute of Technology, Cambridge, Massachusetts

AND

A. C. Switendick‡

Solid State and Molecular Theory Group, Massachusetts Institute of Technology, Cambridge, Massachusetts

(Received 26 October 1964)

The band structure of metallic face-centered cubic TiC, TiN, and TiO has been obtained by the augmented-plane-wave (APW) method at the equivalent of 256 points in the Brillouin zone and for an energy range appropriate to cover the nonmetal 2s and 2p and the titanium 3d and 4s states. A density of states, the Fermi energy, and contours of constant energy were obtained for the three compounds. A charge distribution in the APW scheme was derived from the equivalent of 32 points in the zone, and the admixture of the bands was analyzed. The results are consistent with the available experimental data.

INTRODUCTION

THE carbides, nitrides, and oxides of transition metals have been studied intensively in the past years. Face-centered cubic titanium carbide and nitride belong to the group of so-called hard refractory metals. Their high melting point, hardness, brittleness, and metallic conductivity are common to all carbides and nitrides of the Group IV and V transition metals.[1] Metallic TiO crystallizes in the rock salt structure when quenched from the melt or annealed and quenched from 950 to 1225°C. The structure stabilizes with about 15% vacancies on both atomic sites.[2–4] The melting point of TiO is close to that of titanium metal, but its hardness is comparable to that of TiC or TiN.

The binding in the hard metals is expected to arise from simultaneous contributions of metallic, covalent, and ionic bonding to the cohesive energy. The relative position and degree of admixture of the 2s and 2p

metalloid levels with the d and s transition-metal states play a decisive role in the binding. Several models favoring metal-metal or metal-nonmetal interaction have been proposed[5–9] to account for the trends in the properties of these compounds. The orbital overlap and the character of the d band in the transition metal oxides have been analyzed by Morin[10,11] and Goodenough.[12] Other authors[9,13–15] have investigated the stability of the rock salt structure in the hard metals, in particular the vacancy problem in TiO.

Band-structure calculations using linear-combinations-of-atomic-orbitals (LCAO) methods have been made for some of these compounds: Bilz[9] has presented a model of band structure for the hard metals assuming (in the Slater and Koster[16] scheme) the values of the two-center integrals for the 3d, 4s, and 2p interactions.

† Sponsored by the U. S. Office of Naval Research and Air Force Materials Laboratory.
* Present address: Central Research Department, Experimental Station, E. I. DuPont de Nemours, Wilmington, Delaware.
‡ Present address: The Sandia Corporation, Albuquerque, New Mexico.
[1] For a review see, for example, R. Kieffer and F. Benesovsky, *Hartstoffe* (Springer-Verlag, Vienna, 1963).
[2] P. Ehrlich, Z. Elektrochem. **45**, 362 (1939); S. Anderson, B. Collén, U. Kuylenstierna, and A. Magnéli, Acta Chem. Scand. **11**, 1641 (1957).
[3] A. D. Pearson, J. Phys. Chem. Solids **5**, 316 (1958).
[4] S. P. Denker, Ph.D. thesis, Massachusetts Institute of Technology, 1963 (unpublished).

[5] Ya. S. Umanskii, Ann. Secteur Anal. Physicochim. Inst. Chim. Gen. (U.S.S.R.) **16**, No. 1, 127 (1943).
[6] E. Dempsey, Phil. Mag. **8**, 285 (1963).
[7] R. E. Rundle, Acta Cryst. **1**, 180 (1948).
[8] H. Krebs, Acta Cryst. **9**, 95 (1956).
[9] H. Bilz, Z. Physik **153**, 338 (1958).
[10] F. J. Morin, Bell System Tech. J. **37**, 1047 (1958).
[11] F. J. Morin, Phys. Rev. Letters **3**, 34 (1959); J. Appl. Phys. **32**, 2195 (1961).
[12] J. B. Goodenough, Phys. Rev. **117**, 1442 (1960).
[13] P. V. Geld and V. A. Ckaj, Zh. Strukt. Khim. **4**, 235 (1963).
[14] S. P. Denker, *Nuclear Metallurgy*, edited by J. T. Waber, P. Chiotti and W. N. Miner (Metallurgical Society of AIME, 1964), Vol. 10, p. 51.
[15] L. Kaufman and A. Sarney, Ref. 14, p. 267.
[16] J. C. Slater and G. F. Koster, Phys. Rev. **94**, 1498 (1954).

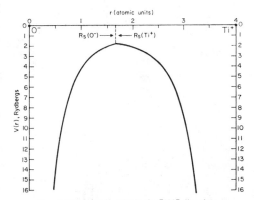

FIG. 1. Potential for TiO in the [100] direction.

Costa and Conte[17] computed a density of states in the $3d$ band of titanium for TiC and TiN, neglecting all but the d functions interaction. Yamashita[18] has obtained the eigenvalues at a few high-symmetry points in the zone for TiO and NiO by a modified tight-binding procedure with $3d$—$2p$ coupling.

The present band-structure calculation for TiC, TiN, and nondefective TiO was performed by the augmented-plane-wave (APW) method of Slater.[19] This method requires no a priori assumption on the degree of interaction between the different states. The results depend on the choice of the "muffin-tin" crystalline potential necessary to solve the one-electron Schrödinger equation within the scheme.

POTENTIALS

The APW method in its present form requires the knowledge of a starting one-electron potential spherically symmetric within spheres centered on the atomic sites and constant in between. This potential should resemble the one-electron potential due to the actual charge distribution in the crystal as closely as possible. An a posteriori comparison of the assumed starting electronic configuration with the charge distribution, as derived from the occupied states of the computed band structure, should give some indication of the degree of self-consistency achieved within the method. For compounds the choice of the starting potential is further complicated by the need for assuming some ionicity, that is, a possible transfer of charge between spheres of different types.

For the three compounds studied here the ionic character should increase from the carbide to the monoxide, i.e., with increasing electronegativity of the

nonmetal atom. For the present band-structure calculation the potentials of the constituent atoms were obtained with the programs of Herman and Skillman[20] for the self-consistent solution of the Hartree-Fock-Slater equations. The self-consistency criterion was 0.001 Ry. For TiC and TiN the potential in the respective spheres was taken as that obtained from the neutral atomic configurations: $Ti(3d)^2(4s)^2$, $C(2s)^2(2p)^2$, and $N(2s)^2(2p)^3$. For TiO an ionicity of ± 1 was assumed with the configurations for $Ti^+(3d)^2(4s)$ and for $O^-(2s)^2(2p)^5$. The free ion potentials should be corrected by the Madelung electrostatic field in the structure; this will raise all the one-electron states in the cation, and lower those in the anion sphere.

The Madelung interaction constant assumes nonoverlapping, spherically symmetric charge distributions. To account for the charge overlap between the first nearest neighbors, the following procedure was adopted to obtain the potential in the sphere of a particular ion: The Coulomb part of the potential and the radial charge density of each of the neighboring ions were expanded around the center of the chosen ion by the standard procedure of Löwdin,[21] and the expansions spherically averaged. The s-like terms of the expansions were added[22] to the Coulomb potential and to the radial charge density of the central ion, respectively. The total potential $V^s(r)$ in each sphere was then obtained as the sum of the superposed Coulomb part and the exchange term derived from the total charge density by Slater's[23] free-electron approximation

$$V_{exch}(r) = -6\{(3/8\pi)\rho(r)\}^{1/3},$$

which was used for all the potentials throughout this work.

In practice only a limited number of neighbors must be considered in the superposition procedure, and $V^s(r)$ can be adequately corrected for the presence of the remaining ions. Considering 26 neighbors around an ion A ($6B$ at $a/2$, $12A$ at $\sqrt{2}a/2$ and $8B$ at $\sqrt{3}a/2$ in the rock salt structure AB of lattice constant a), the total superposed radial charge density in sphere A was found to increase at most by 0.2% near the sphere radius when the next shell of neighbors (6 ions A at distance a) was added. This being a negligible charge overlap, the rest of the ions were treated as point charges. The superposed potential $V^s(r)$ was then corrected by using the remainder R_m of the Madelung sum

$$V_{Ti^+}(r) = V^s_{Ti^+}(r) + [2R_m/(a/2)],$$
$$V_{O^-}(r) = V^s_{O^-}(r) - [2R_m/(a/2)], \quad (1)$$

with

$$R_m \equiv \sum_{j=m+1}^{\infty} \frac{n_j(a/2)}{d_j} = 1.74756 - \sum_{j+1}^{m} \frac{n_j(a/2)}{d_j},$$

[17] P. Costa and R. R. Conte, Ref. 14, p. 3.
[18] J. Yamashita, J. Phys. Soc. Japan 18, 1010 (1963).
[19] J. C. Slater, Phys. Rev. 51, 846 (1937); 92, 603 (1953); M. M. Saffren and J. C. Slater, ibid. 92, 1126 (1953).

[20] F. Herman and S. Skillman, Atomic Structure Calculations (Prentice-Hall, Inc., Englewood Cliffs, New Jersey, 1963).
[21] Per-Olow Löwdin, Advan. Phys. 5, 96 (1956).
[22] L. F. Mattheiss, Bull. Am. Phys. Soc. 8, 222 (1963).
[23] J. C. Slater, Phys. Rev. 81, 385 (1951).

TABLE I. Potentials in the Ti sphere used for the band-structure calculation of TiO.

r	$-V(r)$	r	$-V(r)$
0.00158	27721.9468	0.42339	39.9693
0.00316	13795.2100	0.43603	38.0122
0.00474	9152.4032	0.44867	36.1909
0.00632	6830.6796	0.46131	34.4939
0.00790	5437.4595	0.47394	32.9111
0.00948	4508.5430	0.49922	30.0520
0.01106	3844.9812	0.52450	27.5482
0.01264	3347.2952	0.54978	25.3447
0.01422	2960.2161	0.57505	23.3945
0.01580	2650.5793	0.60033	21.6581
0.01738	2397.2781	0.62561	20.1028
0.01896	2186.2391	0.56088	18.7018
0.02054	2007.7184	0.67616	17.4337
0.02212	1854.7538	0.70144	16.2809
0.02370	1722.2397	0.72672	15.2292
0.02528	1606.3452	0.75199	14.2667
0.02686	1504.1407	0.77727	13.3836
0.02844	1413.3465	0.80255	12.5718
0.03002	1332.1627	0.82782	11.8239
0.03160	1259.1492	0.85310	11.1339
0.03476	1133.1787	0.87838	10.4964
0.03792	1028.3811	0.90365	9.9065
0.04108	939.8705	0.92893	9.3600
0.04423	864.1549	0.95421	8.8533
0.04739	798.6729	0.97949	8.3826
0.05055	741.5028	1.00476	7.9452
0.05371	691.1750	1.03004	7.5382
0.05687	646.5463	1.05532	7.1591
0.06003	606.7146	1.08059	6.8055
0.06319	570.9583	1.10587	6.4755
0.06635	538.6934	1.13115	6.1671
0.06951	509.4426	1.15642	5.8786
0.07267	482.8116	1.18170	5.6075
0.07583	458.4722	1.20698	5.3552
0.07899	436.1488	1.23226	5.1171
0.08215	415.6084	1.25753	4.8986
0.08531	396.6523	1.28281	4.6999
0.08847	379.1105	1.30809	4.5186
0.09163	362.8361	1.33336	4.3480
0.09479	347.7019	1.35864	4.1872
0.10111	320.4247	1.38392	4.0358
0.10743	296.5432	1.40920	3.8931
0.11375	275.4842	1.43447	3.7585
0.12007	256.7933	1.45975	3.6315
0.12639	240.1063	1.48503	3.5116
0.13270	225.1280	1.51030	3.3984
0.13902	211.6172	1.53558	3.2915
0.14534	199.3752	1.56086	3.1904
0.15166	188.2372	1.58613	3.0949
0.15798	178.0655	1.61141	3.0046
0.16430	168.7443	1.63669	2.9193
0.17062	160.1755	1.66197	2.8387
0.17694	152.2756	1.68724	2.7625
0.18326	144.9729	1.71252	2.6906
0.18958	138.2057	1.73780	2.6227
0.19590	131.9206	1.76307	2.5586
0.20222	126.0706	1.78835	2.4982
0.20854	120.6149	1.81363	2.4412
0.21485	115.5175	1.83891	2.3876
0.22117	110.7464	1.86418	2.3372
0.23381	102.0736	1.88946	2.2898
0.24645	94.4043	1.91474	2.2453
0.25909	87.5844	1.94001	2.2035
0.27173	81.4887	1.96529	2.1645
0.28437	76.0142	1.99057	2.1280
0.29701	71.0760	2.04112	2.0622

r	$-V(r)$	r	$-V(r)$
0.30964	66.6031	2.09168	2.0053
0.32228	62.5369	2.14223	1.9566
0.33492	58.8261	2.19278	1.9155
0.34756	55.4298	2.24334	1.8812
0.36020	52.3118	2.29389	1.8533
0.37284	49.4417	2.34445	1.8313
0.38548	46.7932	2.39500	1.8148
0.39811	44.3441	2.44555	1.8034
0.41075	42.0751	2.49611	1.7968

Potential for the titanium sphere in TiO.

r	$-V(r)$	r	$-V(r)$
0.00221	7203.4026	0.27466	35.8812
0.00443	3588.7623	0.28331	34.2709
0.00664	2383.7533	0.29216	32.7686
0.00885	1781.1624	0.30102	31.3647
0.01107	1419.5462	0.30987	30.0508
0.01328	1178.4237	0.32758	27.6640
0.01549	1006.1591	0.34528	25.5570
0.01771	876.9352	0.36299	23.6880
0.01992	776.4082	0.38070	22.0228
0.02213	695.9716	0.39840	20.5326
0.02435	630.1489	0.41611	19.1932
0.02656	575.2884	0.43382	17.9842
0.02877	528.8623	0.45152	16.8884
0.03099	489.0646	0.46923	15.8911
0.03320	454.5710	0.48694	14.9800
0.03541	424.3881	0.50464	14.1448
0.03763	397.7563	0.52235	13.3765
0.03984	374.0845	0.54006	12.6677
0.04205	352.9061	0.55777	12.0121
0.04427	333.8479	0.57547	11.4040
0.04869	300.9374	0.59318	10.8389
0.05312	273.5257	0.61089	10.3127
0.05755	250.3458	0.62859	9.8217
0.06197	230.4939	0.64630	9.3629
0.06640	213.3059	0.66401	8.9336
0.07083	198.2837	0.69942	8.1538
0.07525	185.0459	0.73483	7.4659
0.07968	173.2959	0.77025	6.8567
0.08411	162.7993	0.80566	6.3153
0.08853	153.3685	0.84107	5.8328
0.09296	144.8513	0.87649	5.4016
0.09739	137.1234	0.91190	5.0155
0.10181	130.0816	0.94732	4.6689
0.10624	123.6404	0.98273	4.3573
0.11067	117.7274	1.01814	4.0766
0.11509	112.2812	1.05356	3.8234
0.11952	107.2508	1.08897	3.5946
0.12395	102.5905	1.12438	3.3877
0.12837	98.2622	1.15980	3.2002
0.13280	94.2323	1.19521	3.0304
0.14165	86.9555	1.23062	2.8762
0.15051	80.5674	1.26604	2.7362
0.15936	74.9184	1.30145	2.6091
0.16821	69.8904	1.33687	2.4935
0.17707	65.3889	1.37228	2.3884
0.18592	61.3374	1.40769	2.2930
0.19478	57.6737	1.44311	2.2062
0.20363	54.3463	1.47852	2.1275
0.21248	51.3125	1.51393	2.0560
0.22134	48.5364	1.54935	1.9913
0.23019	45.9880	1.58476	1.9327
0.23904	43.6415	1.62017	1.8799
0.24790	41.4752	1.65559	1.8324
0.25675	39.4701	1.69100	1.7899
0.26560	37.6101	1.72642	1.7519

where a is the lattice constant, n_j the number of neighbors at distance d_j from the central ion, and m the number of *different* distances taken in the superposition. The final potentials given by Eq. (1) agreed within 0.0015 Ry when m was changed from 3 to 4. Table I gives the potentials used for the Ti$^+$ and O$^-$ spheres in the TiO band-structure calculation obtained by this procedure, with $m=3$.

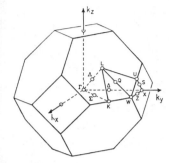

F. FIG. 2. Brillouin zone for the face-centered cubic lattice.

TABLE II. Lattice constants, APW sphere radii, and constant part of the potentials used in band calculations; in atomic units (1 a.u. = 0.529 Å, 1 Ry = 13.605 eV).

	a (a.u.)	R_s (a.u.)	V_c (Ry)
TiC	8.1777	Ti: 2.2736; C: 1.8153	−1.355
TiN	8.0038	Ti: 2.2736; N: 1.7283	−1.355
TiO	7.9036	Ti⁺: 2.3087; O⁻: 1.6431	−1.845

For the three compounds the APW sphere radii (R_s) were determined by requiring that the potentials be equal at the contact point of the two spheres around two nearest-neighbor atoms. The constant value V_c of the potential between the spheres was set equal to the common value at the spheres' surfaces. The experimental lattice constants were taken to be 4.326, 4.234, and 4.181 Å for TiC, TiN, and TiO, respectively.[3] Figure 1 shows the potential for TiO in the [100] direction. Table II summarizes the parameters used in the band-structure calculation.

METHOD OF COMPUTATION

The computational procedure used here for setting the matrix elements of the secular determinant is similar to that described by Wood.[24] For the more complicated NaCl structure[25] with two different atoms in the primitive cell, the plane-wave expansion is carried out around the different centers, and continuity with the atomic-like solution in each sphere is required. The potentials in the different spheres determine the respective solutions u_{lp} of the radial Schrödinger equation. The index p refers to the pth sphere in the primitive cell. The matrix elements (10) of Ref. 24 are now modified to

$$\langle \psi_i | H - E | R\psi_j \rangle = (\mathbf{k}_i \cdot R\mathbf{k}_j - E)$$

$$\times \Big[\Omega \delta_{ij} - 4\pi \sum_{p=1}^{\text{spheres}} R_{sp}^2 \exp\{i(R\mathbf{k}_j - \mathbf{k}_i) \cdot \mathbf{d}_p\}$$

$$\times j_1(|R\mathbf{k}_j - \mathbf{k}_i| R_{sp})/R\mathbf{k}_j - \mathbf{k}_i| \Big] + 4\pi \sum_{p=1}^{\text{spheres}} R_{sp}^2$$

$$\times \exp\{i(R\mathbf{k}_j - \mathbf{k}_i) \cdot \mathbf{d}_p\} \sum_{l=0}^{\infty} (2l+1) P_l \left(\frac{\mathbf{k}_i \cdot R\mathbf{k}_i}{|\mathbf{k}_i| |\mathbf{k}_j|} \right)$$

$$\times j_l(k_i R_{sp}) j_l(k_j R_{sp}) \frac{u_{lp}'(R_{sp}; E)}{u_{lp}(R_{sp}; E)}, \qquad (2)$$

---

[24] J. H. Wood, Phys. Rev. **126**, 517 (1962).
[25] A. C. Switendick, Ph.D. thesis, Massachusetts Institute of Technology, 1963 (unpublished).

where the summation over p is carried over all the spheres in the primitive cell (2 for the present structure). R_{sp} is the APW sphere radius, and the vectors $\mathbf{d}_p$ appearing in the phase factors are from a coordinate origin to the center of the pth sphere. As before, $\mathbf{k}_i \equiv \mathbf{k} + \mathbf{K}_i$ ($\mathbf{K}_i$ being the reciprocal lattice vectors) is the set of selected vectors appropriate for each irreducible representation of the group of the wave vector $\mathbf{k}$ in the first zone. The elements of the secular determinant for a particular irreducible representation are then computed from

$$(H - E)_{ij}^\alpha = \sum_R \frac{G}{n_\alpha} [\Gamma_{jl}(R)] \langle \psi_i | H - E | R\psi_j \rangle. \qquad (3)$$

The rest of the notation follows that of Ref. 24.

RESULTS OF THE COMPUTATION

The computer-time requirements pose practical restrictions on the extent of the band-structure calculation. At any desired point in k space the bulk of the machine time is spent in setting the matrix elements (2) for the different irreducible representations of the group of the wave vector and in evaluating the determinants (3) in a prescribed mesh of energy. Keeping

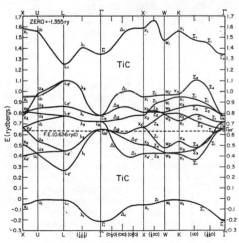

FIG. 3. Energy bands for TiC. Energies referred to a zero at −1.355 Ry, F. E. is the Fermi energy.

TABLE III. Calculated energies for TiC, TiN, and TiO at the equivalent of 32 points in the full zone. The values are referred to a zero at -1.355 Ry.

State	TiC	TiN	TiO
Γ_1	−0.210	−0.503	−1.073
	1.348	1.096	0.708
Γ_{15}	0.778	0.557	0.171
$\Gamma_{25'}$	0.651	0.653	0.556
Γ_{12}	0.722	0.728	0.705
X_1	−0.056	−0.416	−1.010
	0.953	0.881	0.818
	1.581		
$X_{4'}$	0.425	0.321	−0.039
		1.524	1.104
$X_{5'}$	0.671	0.492	0.130
X_2	0.777	0.786	0.807
X_3	0.510	0.507	0.305
X_5	0.804	0.815	0.842
L_1	−0.013	−0.362	−0.946
	1.253	1.209	0.785
$L_{2'}$	0.265	0.197	−0.160
	0.867	0.828	0.709
$L_{3'}$	0.453	0.354	0.035
	0.774	0.785	0.766
	1.11	1.029	0.978
W_1	−0.020	−0.391	−0.984
	0.913	0.862	0.820
	1.460		
W_2	0.804	0.828	0.852
$W_{2'}$	0.479	0.366	0.025
	0.964	0.936	0.920
W_3	0.436	0.354	0.007
	0.793	0.748	0.604
$\Delta_1(010)$	−0.113	−0.454	−1.015
	0.425	0.313	−0.037
	0.997	0.903	0.715
	1.523	1.322	0.983
$\Delta_{2'}(010)$	0.574	0.576	0.409
$\Delta_2(010)$	0.749	0.760	0.753
$\Delta_5(010)$	0.616	0.493	0.132
	0.858	0.795	0.741
$\Sigma_1(110)$	−0.022	−0.386	−0.972
	0.362	0.266	−0.087
	0.791	0.788	0.714
	0.924	0.873	0.805
	1.474	1.377	1.027
$\Sigma_2(110)$	0.732	0.743	0.706
$\Sigma_3(110)$	0.462	0.378	0.036
	0.872	0.792	0.628
$\Sigma_4(110)$	0.477	0.366	0.042
	1.11	1.020	0.969

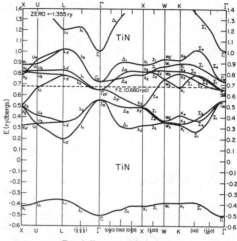

FIG. 4. Energy bands for TiN.

compounds were calculated[26] at the following points in the zone (Fig. 2): $\Gamma(000)$, $X(020)$, $\Delta(0\tfrac{1}{2}0)$, $\Delta(010)$, $\Delta(0\tfrac{3}{2}0)$, $Z(\tfrac{1}{2}20)$, $W(120)$, $K(\tfrac{3}{2}\tfrac{3}{2}0)$, $\Sigma(110)$, $\Sigma(\tfrac{1}{2}\tfrac{1}{2}0)$, $\lambda(\tfrac{1}{2}\tfrac{1}{2}\tfrac{1}{2})$, and $L(111)$. At $U(\tfrac{1}{2}2\tfrac{1}{2})$ the eigenvalues are identical to K. Figures 3 through 5 show the energy dependence with k along the paths Γ-K-W-X [in the (001) plane] and Γ-L-U-X. The bands are drawn through the eigenvalues determined at the labeled points along the abscissa and using the appropriate compatibility relations. The $\mathbf{k}$ components are given in

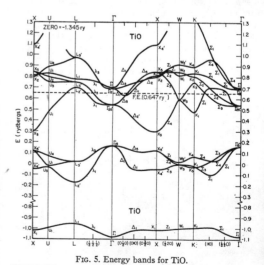

FIG. 5. Energy bands for TiO.

the size of the secular equation within the limits necessary to achieve some prescribed accuracy in the eigenvalues saves considerable time. Several convergence tests indicated that restricting the list of $\mathbf{k}_i = \mathbf{k} + \mathbf{K}_i$ to all vectors with modulus $(48)^{1/2}(\pi/a) \leqslant |\mathbf{k}_i| \leqslant (80)^{1/2}(\pi/a)$ results in an accuracy ranging from 0.003 Ry at Γ to 0.01 Ry at the zone boundaries. At Γ this corresponds to an expansion up to the eighth-nearest neighbor in reciprocal space (an effective inclusion of 113 unsymmetrized plane waves). The expansion in spherical harmonics was taken up to $l=12$. No change in the eigenvalues was observed at Γ with an expansion up to $l=18$. The energy range was restructed to include the states derived from the Ti $3d$ and $4s$, and nonmetal $2s$ and $2p$ states. With the restrictions specified above, the $E(k)$ values for the three

[26] This work was done in part using the facilities at the Computation Center at the Massachusetts Institute of Technology.

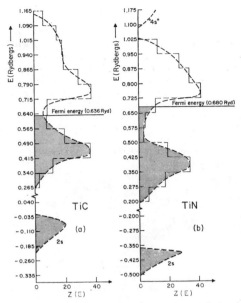

FIG. 6. Density-of-states histograms (spin included) for (a) TiC, (b) TiN, in electrons per primitive cell×Ry. Broken line schematic.

units of π/a. The standard notation of B.S.W.[27,28] for the different symmetry types has been used throughout this work. Table III gives the energy of states in the different bands for the subset of the equivalent of 32 high-symmetry points in the zone. These points uniformly cover the k space on a cubic grid of dimension π/a.

For a fairly stable density-of-states histogram a coverage of at least 256 uniformly distributed points in the zone (on a cubic mesh of side $\pi/2a$) is necessary. This requires, in addition to the states obtained, the eigenvalues at the points: $(\frac{1}{2}10)$, $(\frac{1}{2}\frac{3}{2}0)$, $(1\frac{3}{2}0)$, $(\frac{1}{2}1\frac{1}{2})$, $(\frac{1}{2}\frac{3}{2}\frac{1}{2})$, $(11\frac{1}{2})$, and $Q(1\frac{3}{2}\frac{1}{2})$, for which the group of the wave vector contains only two operations, and correspondingly large, computer-time-consuming, secular equations should be solved. For TiC and TiN these states were obtained by a graphical interpolation from the previously known energies. Whenever possible an average from different directions was taken. Several of the points were checked on the computer. The agreement ranged from 0.01 to 0.05 Ry, the best being for bands near the Fermi level. For TiO all of these states were obtained on the computer with a convergence to 0.02 to 0.03 Ry. For some points this required solving

[27] L. P. Bouckaert, R. Smoluchowski, and E. Wigner, Phys. Rev. 50, 58 (1963).
[28] H. Jones, The Theory of Brillouin Zones and Electronic State in Crystals (North-Holland Publishing Company, Amsterdam, 1960).

secular equations of the order of 32×32. The density-of-states curves were obtained by partitioning[29] the energy scale in equal intervals of width ΔE and counting the number of states in each interval for the 256 points in the full zone. Each state was weighted according to degeneracy and for both spin-up and -down occupancy. Different intervals ΔE were tried, and for each interval the partitions displaced along the energy scale in steps of $\frac{1}{3}\Delta E$. The most stable histograms were obtained for ΔE between 0.06 to 0.09 Ry. Figures 6 and 7 show the density of states for the three compounds for $\Delta E = 0.075$ Ry. The Fermi energy was obtained as follows: Starting from the nonmetal $2s$ band, the available states were filled for TiC, TiN, and TiO, with 8, 9, and 10 electrons per primitive cell, respectively. In the present mesh this corresponds to filling 1024, 1152, and 1280 doubly occupied states. The next lower states (about 2.5 Ry below the Fermi level for TiC) is the narrow filled Ti $3p$ band.

The following qualitative features (cf. Figs. 6 and 7) were reproducible in all histograms. For the first two compounds the conduction band presents two broad humps corresponding to bonding and antibonding mixtures of the $2p$–$3d$ bands (cf. Figs. 3 and 4). The Fermi level lies near a minimum for TiC, and on the rising portion of the density of states for TiN. For the monoxide the density of states of the $3d$ bands still rises at the Fermi level, reaching a maximum at about 2 eV above the Fermi energy. At the Fermi level the

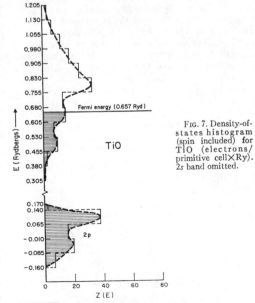

FIG. 7. Density-of-states histogram (spin included) for TiO (electrons/primitive cell×Ry). $2s$ band omitted.

[29] G. A. Burdick, Phys. Rev. 129, 138 (1963).

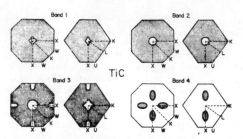

FIG. 8. Contours in k space at the Fermi level for TiC. Distance Γ-$X = 0.77$ (a.u.)$^{-1}$. Shaded regions filled with electrons.

density of states is 0.4 to 0.5 electrons per primitive cell-eV for TiC and about 1 for TiN and TiO. Costa and Conte[17] found values of 0.23 and 0.49 from low-temperature specific-heat and magnetic-susceptibility measurements, respectively, for TiC. The superconducting transition temperature is reported higher for TiN than for TiC,[1] in agreement, according to the BCS formula,[30] with the trends derived for the density-of-states curves assuming a similar pair-interaction constant for the two compounds. The Debye temperature is reported slightly lower for TiN than for TiC.[31]

Some qualitative information about the intersections of the Fermi surface with symmetry planes in the zone, as given by the present APW calculation, seemed worthwhile in the hope that these orbits may help in interpreting the de Haas–van Alphen or magneto-resistance experiments when these data become available for the three materials studied here. Figures 8 through 10 give the contours of constant energy at the Fermi level in the (001) and (110) planes through Γ. The orbits are drawn in the reduced zone scheme through the marked $\mathbf{k}$ points as determined graphically from the computed APW states. Band 1 refers to the first not-completely-filled zone.

For TiC, pockets of holes occur in the first three bands. Piper[32] has proposed a simple mixed-conductivity two-band model to explain the temperature dependence of the Hall coefficient for TiC.

CHARGE DISTRIBUTION

If $E_n(\mathbf{k}) \equiv E$ is a particular eigenvalue in the nth band, the APW crystal function can be written in a compact form, as

$$\psi \mathbf{k} = \alpha \sum_i A_i{}^n e^{(i \mathbf{k}_i \cdot \mathbf{r})} + \sum_{p=1}^{\text{spheres}} \beta_p e^{(i \mathbf{k} \cdot \mathbf{d}_p)}$$

$$\times \sum_{l=0}^{\infty} \sum_{m=-l}^{+l} B_{lm}{}^p \frac{u_{lp}(r_p; E)}{u_{lp}(R_{sp}; E)} Y_l{}^m(\theta_p \varphi_p),$$

[30] J. Bardeen, L. N. Cooper, and J. R. Schrieffer, Phys. Rev. 108, 1175 (1957).
[31] C. R. Houska, J. Phys. Chem. Solids 25, 359 (1964).
[32] J. Piper, Ref. 14, p. 29.

with

$$B_{lm}{}^p \equiv \sum_i A_i{}^n C_{lm}{}^P(\mathbf{k}_i),$$

where $\mathbf{k}_i \equiv \mathbf{k} + \mathbf{K}_i$, $A_i{}^n$ are the components of the APW eigenvector determined from the secular equation, $Y_l{}^m(\theta_p, \varphi_p)$ the normalized spherical harmonics for the pth sphere, $C_{lm}{}^P(\mathbf{k}_i)$ the APW matching coefficients at each sphere surface,[24,25] and $u_{lp}(r_p; E)$ the solutions of the radial Schrödinger equation for the energy E in the pth sphere. α is defined as zero within the sphere and 1 between them; β_p is 1 in the pth sphere and zero elsewhere.

If $\Psi_\mathbf{k}$ is normalized over the volume of the Wigner-Seit cell, one obtains

$$1 = \frac{1}{N} \int_{\text{cell}} \psi_\mathbf{k}{}^* \psi_\mathbf{k} d$$

$$= \frac{1}{N} \sum_{i,j} A_i{}^n A_j{}^n \int_{\text{outside spheres}} e^{i(\mathbf{k}_i - \mathbf{k}_j) \cdot \mathbf{r}} d\tau$$

$$+ \sum_{p=1}^{\text{spheres}} \sum_{l=0}^{\infty} \int_0^{R_{sp}} P_{lp}{}^2(r_p) dr_p, \quad (4)$$

where $\sqrt{N}$ is the normalization constant, and the functions

$$P_{lp}{}^2(r_p) \equiv \frac{1}{N} \sum_{m=-l}^{+l} |B_{lm}{}^P|^2 \frac{u_{lp}{}^2(r_p; E)}{u_{lp}{}^2(R_{sp}; E)} r_p{}^2$$

can be interpreted as the spherically averaged radial charge densities for a given l in the pth sphere. The number of electronic charges in a given sphere is

$$Q^p = \sum_{l=0}^{\infty} q_l{}^p \equiv 2 \sum_{l=0}^{\infty} \int_0^{R_{sp}} P_{lp}{}^2(r_p) dr_p,$$

and in the plane-wave region

$$Q^{\text{P.W.}} = \frac{2}{N} \sum_{i,j} A_i{}^n A_j{}^n \int_{\text{outside spheres}} e^{i(\mathbf{k}_i - \mathbf{k}_j) \cdot \mathbf{r}} d\tau,$$

the factor 2 deriving from the double occupancy of each Bloch state. As before, previous symmetrization[24] simplifies the problem.

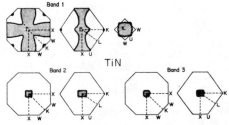

FIG. 9. Contours in k space at the Fermi level for TiN. Distance Γ-$X = 0.78$ (a.u.)$^{-1}$. Shaded region filled with electrons.

TABLE IV. Number of valence electrons in the APW spheres and in the intermediate region in the Wigner-Seitz cell. "Valence" includes 2s states for the nonmetal spheres. The states are labeled following the atomic notation according to l and the number of nodes of the radial part of the wave function in a given sphere. "Bands" refer to the charge distribution given by the average on the occupied states at the 32 points in the full zone (Table III). Atomic or ionic refers to the valence electrons of the free atom or ion in the same spherical volume for the configurations Ti: $(3d)^2(4s)_2^2$, C: $(2s)^2(2p)^2$, N: $(2s)^2(2p)^3$, Ti$^+$: $(3d)^2(4s)$, and O$^-(2s)^2(2p)^5$.

	TiC						TiN						TiO					
	In Ti sphere			In C sphere			In Ti sphere			In N sphere			In Ti$^+$ sphere			In O$^-$ sphere		
state	bands	atomic	state	bands	atomic	state	bands	atomic	state	bands	atomic	state	bands	ionic	state	bands	ionic
3d	2.36	1.78	2s	1.19	1.44	3d	1.90	1.78	2s	1.51	1.61	3d	1.78	1.80	2s	1.54	1.69
4s	0.17	0.32	2p	1.81	1.26	4s	0.14	0.32	2p	3.20	2.21	4s	0.16	0.21	2p	3.70	3.59
4p	0.26	...	3d	0.02	...	4p	0.27	...	3d	0.02	...	4p	0.36	...	3d	0.03	...
4f	0.03	...				4f	0.05	...				4f	0.09	...			
	2.82	2.10		3.02	2.70		2.36	2.10		4.73	3.82		2.39	2.01		5.27	5.22
														2.86ᵃ			5.45ᵃ
	In plane waves: 2.16						In plane waves: 1.90						In plane waves: 2.31				

ᵃ After the charge superposition procedure previously described. Obtained by subtracting from the total superposed charge, the 1s atomic core charge in the O$^-$ sphere, and the atomic core up to 3p (17.93 electrons) in the Ti$^+$ sphere. The core states are considered to be localized in the spheres.

Table IV gives the number of valence electrons in the APW spheres and in the plane-wave region, obtained from the average of the filled state at the equivalent of 32 points in the zone (Table III). A comparison with the free atomic or ionic charge in the same spherical volume is made. The pictorial description obtained for TiC is that of positive spheres of approximately $+1$ charge with 2 electronic charges in the intermediate region of each cell. Figure 11 shows the components and the total radial charge density $P_{p^2}(r) \cong \sum_{l=0}^{3} P_{lp^2}(r)$ for the two spheres in TiO, obtained from the average of the filled states of Table III. A comparison is made with the initial-valence (see footnote of Table IV) radial charge density.

Reasonable agreement exists between the starting and the derived charges for the C and O$^-$ spheres. The nitrogen sphere contains approximately one extra electronic charge in 2p states, indicating that some intermediate ionicity should have been assumed for a more consistent charge distribution. In the Ti spheres 4p- and 4f-like functions became important. Their contribution is specially noticeable at the sphere radius where higher l components can drastically affect the behavior of the wave function. The 4p function is responsible for the "hump" in the radial charge density at $r=0.88$ a.u.

The 3d radial function has a more diffuse (bonding) character than does a free atom d function. The same was found true for the 2p functions in TiC and to a lesser degree in TiN. An analysis of all the computer states at $\Delta(010)$ in the 2p–3d bands of TiC showed a progressively localized (antibonding) character of the functions for the high-energy empty states. Similar behavior was found by Wood[33] for the 3d functions in iron. Tables V through VII give the percentage of charge contained in the APW spheres from the different spherical harmonics (up to $l=3$) for the filled states of Table III, including the empty states at $\Delta(010)$. For each point in k space the states are ordered in increasing energies starting from the nonmetal 2s band (Figs. 3 to 5). The amount in the plane-wave region can be obtained approximately as the complement to the sum of the given percentages for each state [cf. Eq. (4)].

Because of the strong mixing in the bands, only a fit of the pure t_{2g} symmetry (xy type) 3d bands was attempted with the LCAO scheme.[16] Fitting in the nearest-neighbor approximation for the states Γ_{25}', Δ_2',

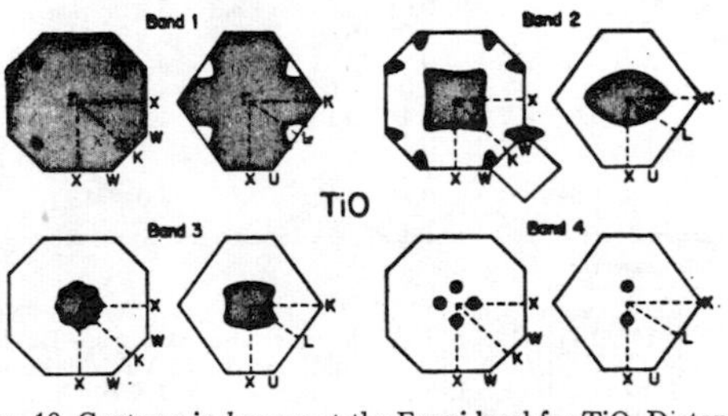

FIG. 10. Contours in k space at the Fermi level for TiO. Distance Γ-$X=0.79$ (a.u.)$^{-1}$. Shaded regions filled with electrons.

TABLE V. Analysis of the charge in the APW spheres for TiC (percent).

	In C sphere				In Ti sphere			
State	2s	2p	3d	4f	4s	4p	3d	4f
Γ_1	50.5		0.00		13.8		0.00	
X_1	60.7		0.00		1.7		16.6	
$X_{4'}$		42.2		0.05		15.5		0.03
X_3			2.2				68.1	
L_1	65.0		0.1		9.5			0.8
$L_{2'}$		29.6		0.1	10.2		20.1	
$L_{3'}$		33.8		0.1			48.3	
W_1	63.0		0.01	0.01	2.6		13.9	0.3
$W_{2'}$		40.5	0.00	0.04	4.1		34.0	0.7
W_3		30.4	0.5	0.05		9.0	23.0	0.04
Σ_1	55.9	0.4	0.1	0.00	4.5	5.8	3.5	0.6
Σ_1	2.4	32.5	0.03	0.04	6.2	0.2	27.5	0.4
$\Sigma_{3'}$		27.0	0.6	0.07		5.9	33.7	0.2
Σ_4		36.5	0.02	0.08		0.4	46.3	0.3
Δ_1	54.6	0.7	0.03	0.00	8.1	3.2	2.5	0.1
Δ_1	2.1	36.1	0.1	0.02	2.6	1.2	33.0	0.6
$\Delta_{2'}$		1.9		0.04			73.7	0.2
Δ_5		33.1	0.3	0.1		3.3	41.6	1.1
Δ_2		2.31		0.01			91.9	0.05
Δ_5		39.2	0.1	0.05		2.0	48.3	1.4
Δ_1	12.3	16.3	0.5	0.2	2.8	0.1	54.3	1.1
Δ_1	4.2	31.5	0.1	0.01	11.9	2.4	4.6	0.7

33 J. H. Wood, Phys. Rev. 117, 714 (1960).

TABLE VI. Analysis of the charge in the APW spheres for TiN (percent).

State	In N sphere				In Ti sphere			
	2s	2p	3d	4f	4s	4p	3d	4f
Γ_1	67.4		0.00		9.2		0.00	
Γ_{15}		81.6		0.00		1.9		3.1
$\Gamma_{25'}$			1.3				84.2	
X_1	75.3		0.00		1.0		8.5	
$X_{4'}$		54.7		0.03		13.2		0.00
$X_{5'}$		73.4		0.00		6.0		1.7
X_3			1.9				69.1	
L_1	77.5		0.01			6.5		0.8
$L_{2'}$		39.8		0.02	9.9		14.9	
$L_{3'}$		49.4		0.1			33.0	
W_1	76.7		0.00	0.00		2.0	6.6	0.3
W_3		47.5	0.2	0.02		9.1	12.4	0.1
$W_{2'}$		55.6	0.00	0.02	3.7		20.6	0.7
Σ_1	75.4	0.1	0.01	0.00	1.3	4.3	2.1	0.5
Σ_1	0.8	45.4	0.02	0.02	6.8	0.4	17.4	0.4
Σ_4		52.7	0.01	0.06		0.3	30.5	0.3
Σ_3		46.7	0.3	0.03		6.1	19.3	0.3
Δ_1	72.1	0.1	0.00	0.00	4.0	2.4	1.9	0.2
Δ_1	1.2	49.9	0.04	0.01	3.6	1.4	19.5	0.6
Δ_5		64.1	0.1	0.03		3.7	12.1	1.7
$\Delta_{2'}$			1.7	0.02			74.9	0.2
Δ_2			2.1	0.00			92.2	0.1
Δ_5		15.7	0.2	0.1		0.2	76.9	0.5
Δ_1	8.9	8.8	0.5	0.2	3.7	0.2	65.9	0.5
Δ_1	10.9	29.4	0.03	0.00	11.6	3.4	7.0	0.3

X_3, X_5, and Σ_2 gave the following parameters for the energy integrals:

	$-E_{xy,xy}(110)$	$E_{xy,xy}(011)$	$E_{xy,x\varepsilon}(011)$
TiC	0.381 eV	0.120 eV	0.134 eV
TiN	0.401 eV	0.124 eV	0.155 eV
TiO	0.715 eV	0.213 eV	0.220 eV

The values for TiC and TiN are close to the corresponding integrals calculated by Costa and Conte.[17] In the two-center approximation[16] the eigenvalues were best fitted by the following $(dd\sigma)$, $(dd\pi)$, and $(dd\delta)$ two-center integrals: -0.51, 0.25, and -0.02 eV for TiC; -0.52, 0.28, and -0.03 eV for TiN; -0.90, 0.44, and -0.05 eV for TiO.

COMPARISON WITH X-RAY DATA

The $K\beta_5$ emission band observed in transition metals is usually attributed to the transitions to the $1s$ levels from the $3d$ band hybridized with $4s$ and $4p$ functions.[34] Blokhin and Shuvaev[35] made a comparative study of K-emission spectra of TiO, TiN, and TiC. For TiO they find a weak $K\beta_5'$ line in coincidence with the usual Ti $K\beta_5$ line and two other bands lying, respectively, -5.8 eV $(K\beta_5)$ and -21 eV [36] $(K\beta'')$ below that line. The band calculation for TiO gives the position of the maxima of the density of states for the $2p$- and $2s$-like bands approximately as -5.1 and 20.8 eV, respectively, below the middle of the filled portion of the $3d$ conduction band (Figs. 7 and 12). The width of the $K\beta_5$

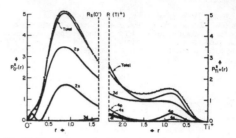

FIG. 11. Radial charge densities in the two spheres of TiO from the filled states at 32 points in the zone (——— from average of bands at 32 points; —·—·—·— charge density).

line (4.36 eV) agrees with the computed width (4.5 eV) of the $2p$ bands. Further agreement exists between the $K\beta_5$-$K\beta''$ distances as measured by several investigators[35,37] for TiC and TiN and the respective separation of the $(2s)$ and $(3d+2p)$ filled maxima in the density of states of Fig. 6. The comparison is as follows:

	$K\beta_5$-$K\beta''$ [35]	$K\beta_5$-$K\beta''$ [37]	Density of states
TiC:	7.0 eV	7.0 eV	7.1 eV
TiN:	10.0 eV	11.0 eV	10.7 eV

The long-wave K-absorption band[38] found in TiC re-

TABLE VII. Analysis of the charge in the APW spheres for TiO (percent).

State	In O sphere				In Ti sphere			
	2s	2p	3d	4f	4s	4p	3d	4f
Γ_1	71.5		0.00		8.4		0.00	
Γ_{15}		79.4		0.00		2.1		3.8
$\Gamma_{25'}$			1.8				76.4	
X_1	78.7		0.00		0.9		5.9	
$X_{4'}$		52.4		0.03		16.0		0.00
$X_{5'}$		70.2		0.03		7.1		2.1
X_3			2.1				56.6	
L_1	77.1		0.00			9.5		1.0
$L_{2'}$		40.9		0.02	11.7		10.1	
$L_{3'}$		59.6		0.05			20.3	
W_1	78.6		0.01	0.00		3.4	4.4	0.3
W_3		50.6	0.1	0.02		11.7	6.1	0.2
$W_{2'}$		61.5	0.00	0.00	4.5		11.2	1.0
W_3		16.2	1.0	0.1		0.07	57.3	1.6
Σ_1	76.6	0.02	0.00	0.00	1.0	6.8	1.4	0.7
Σ_1	0.5	47.8	0.02	0.02	8.7	0.8	10.1	0.5
Σ_3		53.6	0.2	0.02		8.1	9.5	0.5
Σ_4		62.5	0.00	0.02		0.5	18.0	0.4
Σ_3		20.5	0.8	0.1		0.2	52.6	2.0
Δ_1	74.5	0.02	0.01	0.00	3.8	3.9	1.4	0.3
Δ_1	0.9	52.8	0.01	0.00	5.3	2.3	10.0	0.9
Δ_5		70.3	0.04	0.02		4.5	3.8	2.4
$\Delta_{2'}$			2.0	0.03			61.8	0.7
Δ_1	20.6ᵃ	2.0	0.4	0.1	11.4	1.6	32.2	0.4
Δ_5		5.9	0.5	0.1		0.1	81.3	0.6
Δ_2			2.4	0.01			89.9	0.2
Δ_1	1.6ᵃ	25.5	0.24	0.02	3.5	4.0	45.1	0.06

ᵃ $3s$ character.

[34] W. W. Beeman and H. Freedman, Phys. Rev. 50, 150 (1939); D. E. Bedo and D. H. Tomboulian, ibid. 113, 464 (1959).
[35] M. A. Blokhin and A. T. Shuvaev, Bull. Acad. Sci. U.S.S.R., Phys. Ser. 26, 429 (1962).
[36] Obtained graphically from Fig. 1 of Ref. 35.
[37] E. E. Vainshtein and V. I. Chirkov, Dokl. Akad. Nauk SSSR 145, 1031 (1962) [English transl.: Soviet Phys.—Doklady 7, 724 (1963)]; E. A. Shurakovskii and E. E. Vainshtein, ibid. 129, 1269 (1959) [English transl.: ibid. 4, 1308 (1960)].
[38] E. E. Vainshtein et al., Dokl. Akad. Nauk SSSR 122, 365 (1958) [English transl.: Soviet Phys.—Doklady 3, 960 (1958)].

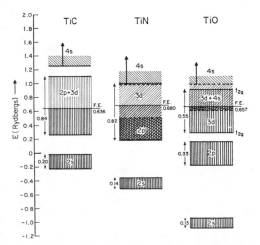

Fig. 12. Schematic trends in the band structures of TiC, TiN, and TiO. Labels indicate the predominant character of the band. The t_{2g} lines mark the width of the $3d$ band of that symmetry in the Δ direction.

sembles the empty portion of the density of states of Fig. 6(a). The higher intensity of the $K\beta''$ line for TiC[37] may correspond to an enhanced transition probability because of a stronger hybridization in the $2s$ band in the carbide (Tables V–VII). L and M spectra will be of great aid in assessing the present interpretation of the K-emission data.

The experimental shifts toward longer wavelengths of the $K\beta''$ and $K\beta_5$ lines for TiC and TiN relative to the respective lines for TiO[35] compare with the corresponding shifts in the maxima in the computer density of states:

	$K\beta_5$	$2p+3d$	$K\beta''$	$2s$
TiC:	+4.4 eV	+4.8 eV	+12.6 eV	+13.3 eV
TiN:	+2.0 eV	+3.9 eV	+6.3 eV	+8.9 eV

The discrepancy for the nitride would indicate that the $2s$ and $2p$ bands should be about 2–3 eV lower than predicted, giving a picture more closely resembling that for TiO. This is consistent with the discrepancy between the initial and derived charges in the nitrogen sphere (Table IV).

Denker[4] has measured the optical reflectivity on a single crystal of TiO and on an arc-melted polycrystal-line sample of TiO. Companion and Wyatt[39] measured diffuse reflectance spectra from $TiO_{1.09}$ powder. Kramers-Kronig analysis[40] on Denker's data on TiO seem to indicate that interband transitions are responsible for the kink in reflectivity at about 2 eV and a plasma effect for the big drop in reflectivity at 3.8 eV. Figure 5 shows several filled and empty bands of almost parallel slope and about 2 eV separation, which could be responsible for the observed transition (like $\Sigma_1 \to \Sigma_4$, $\Sigma_3 \to \Sigma_1$, $\Delta_5 \to \Delta_1$, $\lambda_3 \to \lambda_1$, λ_3).

SUMMARY

The results of Table IV and the comparison with the x-ray emission data tend to indicate that a fairly correct position of the nonmetal $2p$ and $2s$ levels with respect to the titanium $3d$ band has been obtained by the present band calculation, at least for TiC and TiO. For TiN some intermediate ionicity should have been assumed for the starting potential. Figure 12 summarizes the relative position and the widths of the bands for the three compounds. The Γ_1–$\Gamma_1(2s$–$4s)$ interaction pushes the titanium $4s$-like band toward the higher energies above the $3d$ bands. With increasing nuclear charge of the nonmetal atom, the $2s$ band becomes more localized, and a corresponding lowering of the upper Γ_1 state occurs. For TiO the upper portion of the d band is strongly hybridized with $4s$ states. A calculation for a hypothetical face-centered cubic Ti metal without the nonmetal atoms gave the eigenvalues in the usual order Γ_1, Γ_{25}', Γ_{12} found in $3d$ transition metals. The hybridization of the $2s$ band with titanium states and the $3d$–$2p$ (metal–nonmetal) interaction decrease in the sequence from the carbide to the monoxide. The metal–metal $3d$ interaction is strong for the three compounds. The existence of a wide $3d$ band for these compounds of Ti, as given by the present one-electron picture agrees with the predictions of several authors[9–12] and with previous LCAO computations.[17,18]

ACKNOWLEDGMENTS

The authors are greatly indebted to Professor Arthur von Hippel for the continuous support given to this work and to the Solid-State and Molecular Theory Group of MIT for many helpful discussions.

[39] A. L. Companion and R. E. Wyatt, J. Phys. Chem. Solids 24, 1025 (1963).
[40] S. P. Denker, Columbia University (private communication). We are greatly indebted to Professor D. J. Epstein, at M.I.T., for many helpful discussions on these data.

RELATIVISTIC ENERGY BANDS FOR TUNGSTEN*

T. L. Loucks

Institute for Atomic Research and Department of Physics, Iowa State University, Ames, Iowa

(Received 15 March 1965)

In this Letter the results of an <u>ab initio</u> relativistic calculation of the electronic structure of tungsten are presented. The predicted splitting of the energy bands is in complete agreement with the experimental results obtained from size effect measurements.[1]

The method used in these calculations was developed by the author and has recently been submitted for publication.[2] It can be thought of as a relativistic generalization of the augmented plane wave (APW) method of Slater.[3]

The basic function consists of a Dirac plane wave in the outer region of the unit cell and an expansion of Dirac central-field orbitals inside the APW sphere. The expansion coefficients are chosen such that the upper (large) components of the wave function are continuous on the sphere. The lower (small) components are, in general, discontinuous on this surface. A variational expression, which is appropriate for this type of trial function, is developed. The resulting matrix elements have the following form:

$$M\binom{NM}{nm} = (k_N{}^2 - E)\Omega_{nN}\delta_{mM} + 4\pi R^2 \sum_\kappa D_\kappa\binom{NM}{nm} j_l(k_n R)\left\{ j_l(k_N R)\left(\frac{cf_\kappa(R,E)}{g_\kappa(R,E)}\right) - j_l{}'(k_N R)k_N S_\kappa \right\}, \tag{1}$$

where

$$\Omega_{nN} = \Omega\delta_{nN} - 4\pi R^2 \frac{j_1(|\vec{k}_N - \vec{k}_n|R)}{|\vec{k}_N - \vec{k}_n|}, \tag{2}$$

and

$$D_\kappa\binom{N+}{n+} = |\kappa| P_l(\hat{N}\cdot\hat{n}) - iS_\kappa(\hat{N}\times\hat{n})_z P_l{}'(\hat{N}\cdot\hat{n}), \quad (3)$$

$$D_\kappa\binom{N-}{n+} = -S_\kappa P_l{}'[(\hat{N}\times\hat{n})_y + i(\hat{N}\times\hat{n})_x], \quad (4)$$

$$D_\kappa\binom{N-}{n-} = D_\kappa{}^*\binom{N+}{n+}, \quad (5)$$

$$D_\kappa\binom{N+}{n-} = -D_\kappa{}^*\binom{N-}{n+}. \quad (6)$$

The notation introduced by the relativistic considerations is the same used by Rose,[4] with the exception that units are given by $e^2 = 2$, $m = \frac{1}{2}$, $h = 2\pi$. A more thorough discussion of these results is given in the original article.

The method has been applied to tungsten, and the energy bands along the symmetry direction ΓH are shown in Fig. 1. In these calculations the muffin-tin potential was constructed from a superposition of atomic potentials and charge densities[5] (this procedure is discussed in detail by the author in a paper[6] on the nonrelativistic Fermi surfaces of Cr, Mo, and W). The same 39 reciprocal lattice vectors were used to calculate the eigenvalues for all points along ΓH. These consisted of the 38 vectors which minimize $|\vec{k} + \vec{k}_n|$ for $\vec{k}$ at the point H (plus one additional vector which was required to complete the set of 19 vectors nearest to Γ). The

Table I. Comparison with size-effect experiments.

Dimension	Experiment[a] (a.u.)$^{-1}$	Theory
ab	0.59	0.57
cd	0.41	0.41

[a]See reference 1.

Fermi energy was calculated by the requirement of equal hole and electron volumes.

These results are in excellent agreement with the size-effect measurements by Walsh.[1] The distances indicated on Fig. 1 as determined by these experiments are compared in Table I with the present results. This is the first verification of these experimental results by an ab initio energy-band calculation. For comparison the reader is referred to a spin-orbit perturbation calculation by Matheiss and Watson[7] in which the strength of the interaction was treated as an arbitrary parameter. There is, of course, no such arbitrary parameter in the present relativistic theory.

From these calculations it is also possible to predict the disappearance of the electron lenses along the ΓH axis. One can see from the energy bands that if these lenses occur at all, they will most assuredly be small. Preliminary results along the ΓN axis indicate that this is accompanied by the disappearance of the hole pockets at N.

It is a pleasure to acknowledge the cooperation of the group at Los Alamos Scientific Laboratory[5] in making available in convenient form its results on the relativistic self-consistent-field atomic calculations.

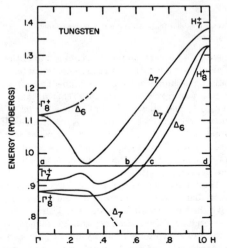

FIG. 1. Relativistic energy bands for tungsten along the ΓH axis.

*Contribution No. 1689. Work was performed in the Ames Laboratory of the U. S. Atomic Energy Commission.

[1]W. M. Walsh and C. C. Grimes, Phys. Rev. Letters 13, 523 (1964).
[2]T. L. Loucks, Phys. Rev. (to be published).
[3]J. C. Slater, Phys. Rev. 51, 846 (1937).
[4]M. E. Rose, Relativistic Electron Theory (John Wiley & Sons, Inc., New York, 1961).
[5]D. Liberman, J. T. Waber, and Don T. Cromer, Phys. Rev. 137, A27 (1965).
[6]T. L. Loucks, to be published.
[7]L. F. Mattheiss and R. E. Watson, Phys. Rev. Letters 13, 526 (1964).

RELATIVISTIC ENERGY BANDS FOR LEAD
BY THE RELATIVISTIC AUGMENTED PLANE-WAVE METHOD*

T. L. Loucks

Institute for Atomic Research and Department of Physics, Iowa State University, Ames, Iowa
(Received 26 April 1965)

A method for calculating relativistic energy bands was recently developed by the author.[1] This method, which can be thought of as a generalization of the augmented plane-wave method,[2] was shown to give accurate results for a transition element in its first application to tungsten.[3] For that metal it was found that the spin-orbit splitting of degenerate levels as predicted by those calculations was in quantitative agreement with experimental results.

In this Letter we present the results of an ab initio energy-band calculation for lead using the relativistic augmented plane-wave (RAPW) method. These results are shown as solid curves in Fig. 1 and will be compared with the Fermi surface and band structure proposed by Anderson and Gold.[4-6] On the basis of de Haas–van Alphen measurements, these authors

have given a very complete description of the Fermi surface using a pseudopotential interpolation scheme in which the spin-orbit interaction was taken into account. This parametrized Fermi surface was also found to be in very good agreement with experimental results obtained by other workers. The energy bands predicted by Anderson and Gold[6] are shown as dashed curves in Fig. 1 for comparison with the present results.

The theoretical Fermi energy was chosen such that intersections with the bands would give the best possible agreement with the parametrized Fermi surface; this surface was shown to very closely satisfy the requirement of equal hole and electron volumes. To facilitate comparison, the zero of energy for the RAPW bands has been shifted to bring the Fer-

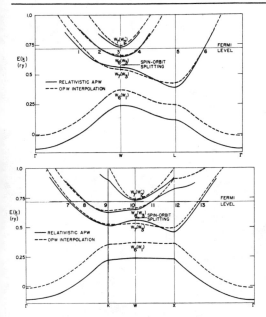

FIG. 1. Relativistic energy bands for lead using the RAPW method (solid curves) and energy bands from the four-parameter model used by Anderson and Gold[6] to fit experimental de Haas-van Alphen measurements (dashed curves).

mi levels for the two sets of bands into coincidence. The various dimensions of the Fermi surface as indicated on Fig. 1 are compared with those of the parametrized model in Table I. The agreement between these results can be seen to be very close. In addition there are two general features of the parametrized model which are retained in the theoretical bands: There is an energy gap between the first and second bands, and the fourth zone is empty. There are, however, noticeable

Table I. Dimensions of lead Fermi surface (a.u.$^{-1}$).

Dimension	Relativistic APW	Anderson and Gold
1-3	0.356	0.318
2-3	0.178	0.181
3-4	0.158	0.157
5-6	0.259	0.250
7-9	0.338	0.318
8-9	0.184	0.199
10-11	0.146	0.141
12-13	0.239	0.206

differences in the two sets of energy bands. These are to be expected for several reasons. Firstly, only four orthogonalized plane waves were used in the parametrized fit of the Fermi surface to the experimental data, as compared to a basis set of 39 RAPW's in the theoretical calculation. Secondly, the fitting parameters in the pseudopotential scheme were determined from experimental information which reflects the electronic structure only in the immediate vicinity of the Fermi energy. For these reasons one would not necessarily expect the parametrized model to represent accurately the states away from the Fermi energy. In this respect it is perhaps unfortunate that the largest spin-orbit splitting occurs beneath the Fermi energy. The only degenerate level (nonaccidental) which is split by this interaction is the level W_3. Since this level is below the Fermi energy, the splitting is not directly reflected in the Fermi surface. There are, however, several bands around the symmetry points W, K, and X which (although nondegenerate) are spread further apart by the spin-orbit interaction, and this spreading certainly has an over-all effect on the Fermi surface. Finally, since no attempt was made toward self-consistency in the theoretical calculation, there is sufficient uncertainty in the potential to account for the differences between the two sets of results.

This is the first application of the RAPW method to a nearly free-electron metal. The agreement with experiment is very good, as it was in the first application of the method to the transition element tungsten. The method can therefore be recommended for theoretical studies of the electronic structures of any of the heavier elements.

It has been my pleasure to have many interesting discussions on this subject with Dr. J. R. Anderson and Dr. A. V. Gold. Also the cooperation of Dr. J. T. Waber at Los Alamos Scientific Laboratory in providing the results of relativistic atomic calculations for constructing the crystal potential is greatly appreciated.

*Work was performed in the Ames Laboratory of the U. S. Atomic Energy Commission. Contribution No. 1708.
[1]T. L. Loucks, Phys. Rev. (to be published).
[2]J. C. Slater, Phys. Rev. 51, 846 (1937).
[3]T. L. Loucks, Phys. Rev. Letters 14, 693 (1965).

Reprinted from THE PHYSICAL REVIEW, Vol. 139, No. 3A, A934–A940, 2 August 1965
Printed in U. S. A.

ERRATION

On page A937, in the fourth paragraph of section III, the phrase, "Along the (100) (110) or Σ direction" should be corrected to read,

"Along the (110) or Σ direction . . ."

Band Structure of Silver Chloride and Silver Bromide*

PETER M. SCOP†

Massachusetts Institute of Technology, Cambridge, Massachusetts

(Received 12 January 1965; revised manuscript received 26 March 1965)

The valence and conduction bands of silver chloride and silver bromide were calculated using the augmented-plane-wave (APW) method. For both crystals the calculated bands were adjusted so that the experimental value of the direct band gap at Γ was duplicated ($E_g=5.13$ eV in AgCl, $E_g=4.29$ eV in AgBr). Several possible correction terms to the APW potential were considered. The effects of the nonspherical cubic field inside APW spheres and the varying cubic field outside the spheres were negligible. The mass-velocity correction was large for states which arise from the Ag$^+$($4d$) electron. The calculated indirect band gaps were 3.28 and 2.89 eV for AgCl and AgBr, respectively. These values are within 10% of the experimental values. The indirect gap may occur along the [110] direction or at the point L.

I. INTRODUCTION—APW CALCULATIONS

THE augmented-plane-wave (henceforth abbreviated APW) method has been employed in calculating the electronic band structure of silver chloride and silver bromide crystals. This method was originally proposed by Slater[1] and later used by Wood[2] in his calculation of the band structure of iron. More recently,

Switendick[3] has extended the method to deal with problems involving two atoms per unit cell in his band calculation of nickel oxide. The APW calculation of the band structure of silver chloride and silver bromide has been performed using the programs written by Wood and Switendick for the IBM 709 computer.

In the APW method the one-electron potential energy is constructed as follows. Spheres are inscribed about each ionic site in the crystal; within each sphere the potential energy of an electron is assumed to be the

* Research supported by the U. S. Office of Naval Research and the National Science Foundation.
† Presently employed by the National Research Corporation, a Subsidiary of Norton Company, Cambridge, Massachusetts.
[1] J. C. Slater, Phys. Rev. **51**, 846 (1937).
[2] J. H. Wood, Phys. Rev. **126**, 517 (1962).

[3] A. C. Switendick, MIT Solid-State and Molecular Theory Group, Quarterly Progress Report No. 49, July 1962 (unpublished).

spherical average of the one-electron potential energy for an electron in the appropriate ion. In the region between spheres, the potential is assumed to be constant and put equal to zero.

Corresponding to this choice of potential energy, the one-electron wave function is expanded in augmented plane waves. An APW is a plane wave outside the spheres, joined continuously to a solution of the spherical-potential problem corresponding to a definite energy inside the spheres. The assumed solution to the one-electron problem in the crystal is a linear combination of APW's, the coefficients being determined by a secular equation. The last step in the process is to equate the assumed energy inside the spheres to the eigenvalues of the secular equation.

Since the APW functions are constructed to correspond to the assumed potential, the convergence (the number of APW's needed to adequately represent a particular state) will be fairly rapid. However, one must face some serious questions about the validity of the assumed potential.

The general form of this potential is sensible from physical reasoning, but the problem of choosing the various parameters entering into the calculations is a difficult one. One must determine the sizes of the APW sphere radii; in addition, the ionic potentials themselves usually depend on several parameters, especially the "ionicity" (the limit of $r/2$ times the ionic potential, for large r).

If one attempts to choose these parameters by physical reasoning, the results may be quite confusing. For example, in a real ionic crystal the previous simple definition of ionicity cannot even be applied since an electron never experiences a single ionic potential far from ionic sites. In addition, the concept of sphere radii may be misleading if there is any covalent bonding in the crystal.

In order to avoid these (and other) physical arguments, the present author has chosen the parameters in a rather arbitrary manner, and then varied one of them in order to obtain some agreement with experimental results.

II. DETAILS OF THE CALCULATIONS FOR AgBr AND AgCl

AgBr and AgCl both have the NaCl structure, that is, two displaced face-centered cubic lattices. One lattice is composed of silver ions, the other contains the halogen ions. A silver ion is located at the origin of coordinates. The six neighboring halogen ions are located at the points $\pm\frac{1}{2}a(1,0,0)$, $\pm\frac{1}{2}a(0,1,0)$, $\pm\frac{1}{2}a(0,0,1)$. There are 12 nearest-neighbor silver ions located at $\pm\frac{1}{2}a(1,1,0)$, $\pm\frac{1}{2}(1,-1,0)$, $\pm\frac{1}{2}a(0,1,1)$, $\pm\frac{1}{2}a(0,1,-1)$, $\pm\frac{1}{2}a(1,0,1)$, $\pm\frac{1}{2}a(1,0,-1)$. All translations which leave the lattice invariant are given by $\mathbf{T}(n_1,n_2,n_3)=n_1\mathbf{a}_1+n_2\mathbf{a}_2+n_3\mathbf{a}_3$ where n_1, n_2, n_3 are integers and $\mathbf{a}_1$, $\mathbf{a}_2$, $\mathbf{a}_3$ are three primitive translations:

$\mathbf{a}_1=\frac{1}{2}a(0,1,1)$; $\mathbf{a}_2=\frac{1}{2}a(1,0,1)$; $\mathbf{a}_3=\frac{1}{2}a(1,1,0)$. For AgCl $\frac{1}{2}a=5.23$ a. u., for AgBr, $\frac{1}{2}a=5.46$ a. u.[4] (a. u.=atomic units).

The ionicity parameters were chosen in accordance with the ordinary ideas of chemical valence (i. e., ionicity of $Ag^+=+1$, ionicity of Cl^-=ionicity of $Br^-=-1$).

The free-ion one-electron potential energies used are those determined by the Hartree-Fock-Slater equations and calculated using programs described by Herman and Skillman.[5]

These potential energy functions for an electron within each sphere are modified in two ways. First the Madelung energy

$$V_M=-2\alpha/(a/2)=-4\alpha/a$$

($\alpha=1.747558$ is the Madelung constant for an NaCl structure[6]) is added to or subtracted from the original potential energy. That is,

about silver sites $\quad V(r)=(V_{\text{Herman-Skillman}})_{Ag^+}-V_M$;

about halogen sites $V(r)=(V_{\text{Herman-Skillman}})_{\text{halogen}}+V_M$.

Finally a positive constant V_0 is added to the potential energy in each sphere. This constant will be treated as an adjustable parameter that is eventually determined by fitting the calculated value of the band gap at $\mathbf{k}=0$ to the experimental value.

The choice of the sphere radii and the initial determination of V_0 were made in the following way. First the Herman-Skillman free-ion potential energies for Ag^+ and Cl^- were superimposed and plotted in the [100] direction [Fig. 1(a)]. Then these potential energies were corrected by adding or subtracting the Madelung energy. The point where the Madelung-corrected potential energies cross defines the sphere radii and the first determination of V_0 [Fig. 1(b)]. The net result of the Madelung correction and addition of V_0 is that the Herman-Skillman potential energies have been altered by different amounts called V_{shift}:

for Ag^+ $\qquad V_{\text{shift}}=V_0-V_M$,
for halogen $\quad V_{\text{shift}}=V_0+V_M$.

Thus, the corrected potential energies become:

for Ag^+ $\quad V(r)=(V_{\text{Herman-Skillman}})_{Ag^+}+(V_{Ag^+})_{\text{shift}}$;

for halogen

$$V(r)=(V_{\text{Herman-Skillman}})_{\text{halogen}}+(V_{\text{shift}})_{\text{halogen}}.$$

This corrected potential energy is shown in Figs. 1(c) and 1(d) for the [100] and [110] directions.

When the above scheme is used in determining the sphere radii and V_0, the bands subsequently found do

[4] R. Wyckoff, *Crystal Structures* (Interscience Publishers, Inc., New York, 1963), 2nd ed., Vol. I, p. 86.
[5] F. Herman and S. Skillman, *Atomic Structure Calculations* (Prentice-Hall, Inc., Englewood Cliffs, New Jersey, 1963).
[6] C. Kittel, *Introduction to Solid-State Physics* (John Wiley & Sons, Inc., New York, 1956), 2nd ed., p. 77.

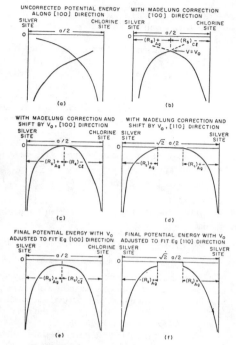

FIG. 1. Determination of V_0 and sphere radii.

Although the size of the band gap at $k=0$ depends in a critical way on the value of V_0, the relative spacing of core and valence states is almost independent of this quantity. This corresponds to the physical fact that the charge density associated with the p and d states lies almost entirely within the APW spheres. Hence, varying V_0 shifts the valence bands rigidly relative to the conduction band. In fact, changing V_0 by as much as a few tenths of a rydberg only altered the relative spacings of valence bands by less than 0.01 Ry and left their qualitative features virtually unchanged.

The APW bands for AgCl and AgBr are shown in Figs. 2 and 3, respectively. Values for the sphere radii, V_{shift}, V_M, the free-ion potential energies as functions of r, and the points in the Brillouin zone actually calculated for the bands in Figs. 2 and 3 are given in Ref. 7.

At this point it should be mentioned that because our basis functions are located on different sites in the unit cell, the symmetry properties of certain eigenstates of the Hamiltonian depend on which ion is located at the origin of coordinates. Switendick[8] has shown that within the Brillouin zone it makes no difference which ion is at the origin; but on the surface of the Brillouin zone, the representation matrices for the ion located at $R_n = \frac{1}{2}a(1,0,0)$ must be multiplied by the factor

not agree with experimental facts. Specifically, the band gap at $k=0$ is too small for both AgCl and AgBr. This discrepancy may be resolved by varying the magnitude of V_0 until agreement is obtained. For both AgCl and AgBr the experimental band gap at $k=0$, E_g, was duplicated when the magnitude of V_0 was reduced. The final form of the potential energy is shown in Figs. 1(e) and 1(f) for the [100] and [110] directions, respectively.

This corrected potential energy should be more representative of the actual crystalline potential energy than that shown in Figs. 1(c) and 1(d). Along the line joining the APW sphere centers (x, y, or z directions) the ionic potential energies employed will have some value V at the sphere radii. However, in some other direction the actual crystalline potential energy just beyond either of the APW spheres will not be equal to V as in Fig. 1(d), but will have some larger value as in our corrected potential energy [Fig. 1(f)]. Hence, a jump discontinuity in the potential energy at the sphere radii is needed to allow the APW method to represent the behavior of the potential energy in different directions. The magnitude of this discontinuity is the difference of the initial value of V_0 [which makes $V(r)$ continuous] and the final value of V_0 needed to fit E_g. For AgCl this jump is $0.869357 - 0.579357 = 0.29$ Ry; for AgBr it is $0.87501 - 0.69465 = 0.18036$ Ry.

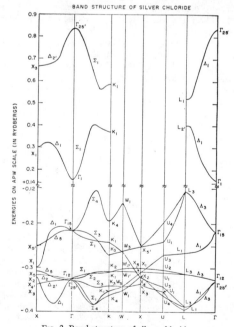

FIG. 2. Band structure of silver chloride.

[7] P. M. Scop, MIT Solid-State and Molecular Theory Group, Quarterly Progress Report No. 54, October 1964 (unpublished).
[8] A. C. Switendick, doctoral thesis, MIT (1963) (unpublished).

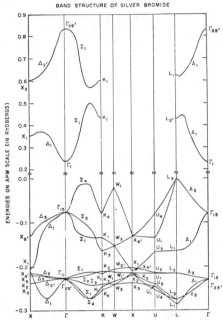

BAND STRUCTURE OF SILVER BROMIDE

FIG. 3. Band structure of silver bromide.

$\exp[i(RK_l - K_l) \cdot R_n]$ (here R is an operation of the group of the wave vector and K_l is a vector of the reciprocal lattice). One finds that the symmetries at L, W, and Q are affected. The results are shown in Table I.

After solving the secular equations and obtaining eigenvalues, the eigenfunctions may also be determined. For points of major interest in the Brillouin zone, we have obtained the spherically-averaged radial charge densities within each APW sphere. The total amount of charge in each sphere associated with a given l value, q_l, and the amount of plane-wave charge (between spheres) have also been calculated and are tabulated in Ref. 7.

TABLE I. Representations for face-centered cubic structure displaying different symmetries about different centers.

Center A at origin	Center B at $(a/2)$ $(1,0,0)$
L_1	$L_{2'}$
L_2	$L_{1'}$
L_3	$L_{3'}$
$L_{1'}$	L_2
$L_{2'}$	L_1
$L_{3'}$	L_3
W_1	$W_{2'}$
W_2	$W_{1'}$
$W_{1'}$	W_2
$W_{2'}$	W_1
W_3	W_3
Q_+	Q_-
Q_-	Q_+

In order to determine the slopes of the bands at symmetry points within and on the surface of the Brillouin zone, the expectation value of the momentum vector was determined using $\mathbf{k} \cdot \mathbf{p}$ perturbation theory and well known selection rules.[9] Thus, because of parity, the slopes in any direction of all bands are zero at Γ, X and L. At U the bands have zero slope along U to W, but nonzero slope along U to X and U to L. At W the bands associated with the one-dimensional representations all have zero slope, the slopes of bands associated with representation W_3 are zero along W to L but nonzero along W to X, W to U, and W to K. At K the slopes of all bands are zero along K to W and nonzero along K to L and K to Γ.

III. DISCUSSION OF APW BANDS

The gross features of the APW bands shown in Figs. 2 and 3 are simply interpreted using the appropriate charge densities and symmetry of the various states. The lowest conduction band in either crystal arises mostly from s-like ionic functions and is nearly spherical in the neighborhood of its minimum at Γ_1.

Most of the features of the wide valence band can be explained by the variation in strength of the interaction between states arising from the Cl^- $(3p)$ or Br^- $(4p)$ and $Ag^+(4d)$ functions. Since the group of the wave vector at $\mathbf{k}=0$, (point group O_h) contains the inversion, the bands are parity eigenstates at Γ. By examining the charge within each APW sphere, the valence bands at this point are seen to arise predominantly from either p or d functions with no mixing of p and d states. At Γ_{15} the eigenfunction is mostly $Cl^-(3p)$ or $Br^-(4p)$ with some $Ag^+(5p)$. The Γ_{12} and $\Gamma_{25'}$ states are almost entirely $Ag^+(4d)$.

As one departs from along any of the three symmetry directions, the valence bands exhibit a strong p-d mixing.

In the [100] or Δ direction, the p-d mixing is zero at Γ, increases until $\mathbf{k} = (\pi/a)(1,0,0)$, and then decreases to zero at the point X where $\mathbf{k} = (2\pi/a)(1,0,0)$ (the point group at X is D_{4h} and includes the inversion operation). Along the [100][110] or Σ direction, the mixing is greatest at the point $\mathbf{k} = \pi/a(1,1,0)$. Because of the transformation properties listed in Table I, the $Ag^+(4d)$ function located at the origin and the $Cl^-(3p)$ [or $Br^-(4p)$] function located at $\frac{1}{2}a(1,0,0)$ both have even parity at the point L. Consequently, this point is one of greatest p-d mixing along the [111] direction.

For both AgCl and AgBr, the point at which the valence band maximum lies is difficult to determine. In either crystal both the uppermost Σ_4 and L_3 points have very nearly the same energy. For AgCl the Σ_4 eigenvalue is 0.001 Ry higher than that of L_3; in AgBr the L_3 state is 0.0177 Ry higher than that of Σ_4. Thus the APW calculations do not clearly resolve the location of the valence-band maximum in either crystal.

[9] J. Zak, J. Math. Phys. 3, 1278 (1962).

The APW valence bands for AgCl and AgBr are quite similar to those recently calculated by Bassani, Knox, and Fowler[10] (henceforth abbreviated BKF) who used the tight-binding method. Although the techniques of calculation are quite different in the two methods, the only important differences in the results are that their Δ_1 and Δ_5 states for the highest valence bands in the [100] direction rise higher than those found by the APW method.

The most glaring discrepancy in the APW calculation is in the comparison of the calculated value of the indirect band gap with experiment. For both crystals the calculated indirect band gap is approximately 0.5 eV larger than the observed value.[11,12] In the remainder of this paper we will consider possible corrections to the APW bands and show that the final calculations are consistent with experiment.

IV. ESTIMATES OF CORRECTION TERMS TO THE APW CALCULATION—INTRODUCTION

There are a number of possible causes for the discrepancy of 0.5 eV in the APW value of the indirect band gap. Some of these are: the lack of self-consistency in the calculation, errors in the ionic potentials employed, the effects of a varying potential outside the APW spheres, the effect of the nonspherical portion of the cubic field inside APW spheres, spin-orbit coupling, and other relativistic effects such as the Darwin and mass-velocity corrections.

In the absence of a self-consistent calculation it is very difficult to estimate how closely the present calculation approaches self-consistency. It is the opinion of the author that since the Herman-Skillman ionic potentials employed were self-consistent, and since the crystalline potential has been adjusted to fit the bands at Γ, that the APW calculation is not far from self-consistency.

Even though the Herman-Skillman potentials are self-consistent, the one-electron energies are higher than those determined by Hartree-Fock calculations because of the $\rho^{1/3}$ approximation. The $Cl^-(3p)$ eigenvalue is about 0.106 Ry higher, the $Br^-(4p)$ eigenvalue is 0.092 Ry higher, and the $Ag^+(4d)$ eigenvalue is 0.122 Ry higher. Since the bands were fit at Γ_{15}, only the variation of the difference between the Herman-Skillman and Hartree-Fock eigenvalues for the halogen and silver ions could affect the shapes of the energy bands (to first order). Because of the p-d mixing away from Γ, the uppermost Σ_4 and L_3 valence band states would be shifted downward relative to Γ_{15} by at most 0.01 Ry. This correction not only is small compared to the discrepancy in the indirect gap, but has the wrong sign (i.e., it would tend to increase the error).

For KCl, DeCicco[13] has studied the effect of a varying cubic field outside APW spheres and the nonspherical cubic field inside APW spheres. He concluded that even though these fields vary substantially in the regions of interest, their net effect on the energy bands is quite small—usually of the order of a few thousandths of a rydberg for valence bands and rarely more than a hundredth of a rydberg for conduction bands. An estimate by first-order perturbation theory indicates that these effects are of the same order of magnitude in AgCl and AgBr. Since these corrections are roughly a factor of five or ten times smaller than the discrepancy we are trying to resolve, we may conclude that the effects of the cubic field not taken into account by the APW method are negligible.

The Herman-Skillman parameters which characterize the spin-orbit and mass-velocity effects for $Cl^-(3p)$, $Br^-(4p)$, and $Ag^+(4d)$ electrons are of the order of a few tenths of an electron volt. As we shall show in Secs. V and VI the spin-orbit splitting will not resolve the discrepancy of 0.5 eV, but the mass-velocity correction by itself can account for this error.

V. SPIN-ORBIT INTERACTION

As we shall show in this section, the spin-orbit interaction cannot account for the discrepancy in the size of the indirect band gap. However, since spin-orbit effects are of intrinsic interest, the details of the calculation will be discussed for three valence band states: Γ_{15}, and the Σ_4 and L_3 states at the valence band maximum along the [110] and [111] directions, respectively.

The APW wave functions at each of these three points in the Brillouin Zone were multiplied by the usual two-component spinors and the matrix elements for the spin-orbit operator were calculated. Because of the form of the APW potential energy, there are no contributions to the matrix elements from the region between spheres [$V(\mathbf{r})$ = constant in this region]. Thus the spin-orbit matrix elements are a sum of terms arising from the regions inside the halogen and silver spheres. There are no overlap terms to be considered because of the form of the APW wave functions.

The spin-orbit interaction splits the Γ_{15} state into two levels: a fourfold-degenerate Γ_8^- state with energy $+\lambda$, and a doubly-degenerate Γ_6^- state with energy -2λ. For the Γ_{15} state, the amount of charge within the silver sphere is very small and to a good approximation one finds that

$$\lambda = \frac{\alpha^2}{4} \int_0^{R_h} \frac{1}{r} \frac{dV_h(r)}{dr} \rho_h(r) dr \quad \text{Ry}.$$

Here α is the fine-structure constant (equal to 1/137), $\rho_h(r)$ is the spherically-averaged radial charge density within the halogen sphere, $V_h(r)$ is the halogen free-ion

[10] F. Bassani, R. S. Knox, and W. B. Fowler, Phys. Rev. **137**, A1217, (1965).
[11] F. C. Brown, J. Phys. Chem. **66**, 2368 (1962).
[12] Y. Okamoto, Nachr. Akad. Wiss. Göttingen II Math. Physik. Kl. **1956**, 275 (1956).

[13] P. DeCicco, MIT Solid-State and Molecular Theory Group, Quarterly Progress Report No. 54, October 1964 (unpublished).

potential energy, and R_h is the radius of the halogen sphere. If $\rho_h(r)$ were exactly equal to the free-ion charge density and R_h were replaced by infinity, λ would equal one half the free-ion spin-orbit parameter. However, since the halogen wave function is slightly compressed in the crystal, λ turns out to be about 10% higher than its free-ion value. For AgCl, $\lambda = 0.0033$ Ry and the $\Gamma_8^- - \Gamma_6^-$ splitting (equal to 3λ) is 0.0099 Ry or 0.13 eV; for AgBr $\lambda = 0.0143$ Ry and the splitting is 0.0429 Ry or 0.58 eV.

When spin is included, all bands in the [110] or Σ direction are doubly degenerate and have symmetry Σ_5. At the valence band maximum in this direction the spin-orbit perturbation is zero to first order; the energy is shifted in second order by an amount $\lambda^2(\Delta E)^{-1}$ where λ is of the order of the appropriate spin-orbit parameters and ΔE is the difference in energy of a neighboring band. For AgCl and AgBr this shift is roughly a few thousandths of a rydberg and may be safely neglected.

The L_3 state at the valence band maximum in the [111] direction is split by the spin-orbit interaction into two levels: a doubly-degenerate L_6^+ state and L_4^+ and L_5^+ states which are degenerate with each other because of time reversal symmetry. The energy levels are given by $\pm\epsilon$ (L_4^+ and L_5^+ have energy $+\epsilon$, L_6^+ has energy $-\epsilon$) where

$$\epsilon = \begin{matrix} \lambda_{3p}{}^c - K\lambda_{4d}{}^s & \text{for AgCl,} \\ \lambda_{4p}{}^b - K\lambda_{4d}{}^s & \text{for AgBr.} \end{matrix}$$

Here K is a parameter which is a measure of the distortion of the Ag^+ free-ion wave function by the cubic field. For zero cubic field, K would equal unity; for AgCl, $K = 0.67$; for AgBr, $K = 0.83$ (AgBr has a larger lattice constant than AgCl and hence a smaller cubic field strength). After approximating λ_{nl} by $(q_l)(\tfrac{1}{2})\zeta_{nl}$ and inserting the numerical values of the q's, ζ_{nl}'s and K's, one obtains $\epsilon = -0.0032$ Ry for AgCl and $\epsilon = +0.0029$ Ry for AgBr. Thus, first-order perturbation theory gives a small splitting at L_3, and indicates that in AgBr L_4^+ and L_5^+ lie above L_6^+; in AgCl the L_6^+ state is highest. Since the magnitude and sign of ϵ depend on the difference of two almost identical numbers, either of which may be error by ten percent, these results are far from being precise. However, we may conclude that the spin-orbit splitting at L_3 should be less than 0.007 Ry or 0.1 eV.

VI. MASS-VELOCITY PERTURBATION

The mass-velocity perturbation may be approximated by a spherically-symmetric operator about each site in the crystal. Since the electron's speed is largest in the neighborhood of the nucleus, we ignore the mass-velocity effect for the plane waves between APW spheres, and restrict ourselves to calculating the correction to a given energy level by considering only the portion of the wave function within spheres.

Using first-order perturbation theory, an APW level is shifted by

$$\Delta E(\mathbf{k}) = \sum_i [q_{ih}(\mathbf{k})\nu_{ih} + q_{is}(\mathbf{k})\nu_{is}],$$

where the q_i's are the amounts of charge within the halogen and silver spheres associated with the APW state, and the ν_i's are the ionic mass-velocity parameters.

We must now determine the mass-velocity parameters. For a first estimate we can use the free-ion parameters since the radial wave functions within APW spheres for the free ions and the crystal are substantially the same, especially near the nucleus where the mass-velocity effect is largest.

For the free ions, Herman and Skillman calculated the mass-velocity shift by first-order perturbation theory, averaging the mass-velocity operator $V' = -\alpha^2 (E-V)^2$ over the free-ion wave function. However, a more accurate calculation has been performed by Waber[14] who solved the Dirac equation for the energies of the two possible j values of a given electron. By taking the appropriate weighted average of Waber's two eigenvalues one obtains the energy for an electron with all relativistic effects included with the exception of spin-orbit coupling.

In Table II, we compare the Herman-Skillman and Waber calculations for $Cl^-(3p)$, $Br^-(4p)$, and $Ag^+(4d)$ ionic eigenvalues. Waber's eigenvalues are higher than those of Herman-Skillman for every case shown. This may be explained by the fact that the mass-velocity operator in reality produces two effects for a valence electron:

1. It lowers the eigenvalue because the mass-velocity operator is always negative.

2. It raises the eigenvalue because the core electrons are drawn closer to the nucleus, producing a stronger inner shielding of the nucleus.

The Herman-Skillman calculation ignores the second effect which, as Waber's calculation indicates, is actually greater in magnitude than the first.

It is interesting to note that Waber's eigenvalues are very close to the Herman-Skillman nonrelativistic energies. Therefore, in our perturbation calculation, we may approximate the mass-velocity parameters by the difference of the Waber and Herman-Skillman (nonrelativistic) levels given in column four of Table II. After using these mass-velocity parameters and the appropriate q_i's, one obtains the following shifts in energy for the uppermost valence bands at Γ_{15}, Σ_4, and L_3 (in rydbergs):

Γ_{15}	Σ_4	L_3	
+0.0002	+0.0389	+0.0399	AgCl
+0.0009	+0.0343	+0.0269	AgBr

Thus the mass-velocity perturbation raises the Σ_4 and L_3 states relative to the Γ_{15} state by 0.37 to 0.55 eV, a large correction that virtually eliminates any discrepancy in the final value for the indirect band gap.

[14] J. Waber (private communication).

TABLE II. Comparison of Herman-Skillman[a] and Waber free-ion eigenvalues.

	H-S (nonrelativistic)	H-S (including mass-velocity)	Waber (relativistic)	Waber minus H-S (nonrelativistic)
$Cl^-(3p)$	−0.19094587	−0.19794587	−0.1906440	+0.00030187
$Br^-(4p)$	−0.18183391	−0.21283391	−0.1807204	+0.00104187
$Ag^+(4d)$	−1.5682048	−1.6152048	−1.5082592	+0.0599456

[a] The Herman-Skillman mass-velocity energy was found by interpolation from their tables which list only the energies for atoms with even Z.

VII. FINAL RESULTS AND COMPARISON WITH EXPERIMENT

We shall present only a few remarks on the over-all band structures of AgCl and AgBr since BKF have given a detailed analysis of the experimental data and its relationship to the energy bands.

The value of the indirect band gap found by the APW method is about 0.5 eV too small for both AgCl and AgBr. After a preliminary survey of several possible correction terms omitted in the APW calculation, it was shown that the mass-velocity correction by itself could account for the discrepancy. In Table III we compare the calculated values for the direct and indirect band gaps. By examining Table III one can see that the mass-velocity correction is needed in order that the calculated value for the indirect band gap be in reasonable agreement with experiment.

The energies for the Σ_4 and L_3 points at the valence-band maximum in the [110] and [111] directions, respectively are practically identical in both crystals after the mass-velocity correction has been included. For AgCl the energies are equal to within 0.01 eV, for AgBr the L_3 state is about 0.1 eV higher. Thus the location of the valence-band maximum cannot be clearly determined in either crystal; BKF indicate that both possibilities are consistent with experiment.

At Γ_{15} the spherically-averaged radial charge density inside the halogen sphere was compared with that of the free ion (found from Herman-Skillman's program). For both AgCl and AgBr, the crystalline charge density was slightly larger near the nucleus than in the free ion, accounting for the larger spin-orbit splittings. For

AgBr the calculated splitting is about 0.58 eV and is in agreement with experiment; for AgCl the calculated splitting is 0.13 eV and more than twice the observed value. A plausible explanation for the smaller splitting in AgCl may be given in terms of many-body effects.[15]

At L_3 the spin-orbit contributions from the halogen and silver ions have opposite sign. The theoretical upper limit to the splitting is 0.1 eV and is in agreement with the observed exciton splitting in both crystals.

The details of the conduction bands hypothesized by BKF do not agree with those calculated by the APW method, the chief difference occurring for the symmetry labels at L. In the absence of a calculation BKF tentatively assigned the lowest conduction band to have $L_{2'}$ symmetry (L_1 in our convention) and the second lowest conduction band to have L_1 symmetry ($L_{2'}$ in our convention). Strictly speaking, because of parity, electric dipole transitions can occur only between primed and unprimed states at L. However, since one may consider $L_1 \rightarrow L_3$ transitions (which actually take place near L) in the sense described by Phillips,[15] the parity of the states at L is not of the utmost importance.

VIII. CONCLUSIONS

The band structure for both AgCl and AgBr appear to be in quite reasonable agreement with experimental facts. The success of this calculation not only illustrates the validity of the energy band method but shows that many of the details of the crystalline potential not explicitly taken into account by the APW method are negligible. Furthermore, the importance of relativistic corrections and their effect on some of the important features of the over-all band structure has been demonstrated.

ACKNOWLEDGMENT

The author wishes to thank Professor John Wood under whose supervision this work was performed. He also would like to thank the members of the Solid State and Molecular Theory Group of the Massachusetts Institute of Technology for their discussions and assistance, especially Dr. A. C. Switendick who supplied virtually all of the necessary computer programs. Finally, the author thanks Professor J. C. Slater for his many comments and suggestions regarding the manuscript.

TABLE III. Comparison of calculated and experimental[a] values for band gaps.

	Direct gap (at $k=0$) E_g	Indirect gap, E_{ig} (experimental)	E_{ig} (Calculated-APW)	E_{ig} (Calculated APW and mass-velocity)
AgCl	5.13 eV	3.25 eV	3.84 eV	3.28 eV
AgBr	4.29 eV	2.68 eV	3.24 eV	2.89 eV

[a] The experimental values quoted for the band gaps are the values of the absorption edges and have not been corrected for the exciton binding energy which is of the order of a few tenths of an electron volt (based on a hydrogenic model). If the exciton binding energy were constant for all k values, one could (because of the fitting procedure employed) correct all the experimental and calculated values listed by simply adding this constant. However, since the valence and conduction bands have considerable width, the exciton bands will exhibit k dependence. In the absence of a detailed knowledge of the exciton bands, these corrections were not included in the present calculation.

[15] J. C. Phillips, Phys. Rev. 136, A1705, A1714, A1721 (1964).

PHYSICAL REVIEW   VOLUME 139, NUMBER 4A   16 AUGUST 1965

Fermi Surfaces of Cr, Mo, and W by the Augmented-Plane-Wave Method*

T. L. LOUCKS

Institute for Atomic Research and Department of Physics, Iowa State University, Ames, Iowa

(Received 16 March 1965)

The Fermi surfaces of chromium, molybdenum, and tungsten were calculated using linear-variation functions consisting of 19 augmented plane waves (APW). The muffin-tin potential was constructed from a superposition of atomic potentials centered on the lattice sites. The atomic orbitals were solutions of the Hartree-Fock-Slater self-consistent field. Constant-energy surfaces throughout the Brillouin zone and the volume contained by each of the regions were determined. The Fermi surface was selected from these energy surfaces by the requirement of equal hole and electron volumes. The density of states at the Fermi energy was determined from the slope of the volume-vs-energy curve. The Fermi surfaces of Mo and W were found to be almost identical and similar to the model postulated by Lomer for the Cr-group metals. The Fermi surface of Cr, however, differs from the other two by the disappearance of the hole pockets around N and a shrinking of the knobs on the electron jack. A quantitative comparison between experimental results and the Fermi surface of Mo is presented.

I. INTRODUCTION

A MODEL for the Fermi surface of the chromium-group metals was proposed in 1962 by Lomer.[1] This model was not the result of *ab initio* electronic-structure calculations for these elements. It was deduced from the energy bands for iron which had been determined theoretically by Wood[2] using the augmented-plane-wave (APW) method. Also available for consideration at that time was a tight-binding calculation for Cr by Asdente and Friedel[3] in which only the *d* bands were considered. Prior to this, there was work done on W by Manning and Chodorow[4] using the cellular method.

The Lomer model has met with varying degrees of success in comparisons with experimental results. In the original paper the larger pieces of the surface (holes at *H*, electrons at Γ) were discussed qualitatively, and the antiferromagnetic state of Cr was considered. In a brief note two years later, Lomer[5] corrected the model such that it was consistent with the requirements im-posed by crystal symmetry. Here again the qualitative features of the larger pieces of the surface were discussed.

In 1963 Brandt and Rayne[6] reported de Haas–van Alphen data for the three metals. However, these frequencies corresponded to very small pieces of the surface not well defined in the model (holes at *N* and either electrons or hole pockets along Γ*H*). Nevertheless, it was observed that the results for Mo and W were quite similar to each other and different from those for Cr. Further low-field measurements on W by Sparlin and Marcus[7,8] have been interpreted by these authors as suggesting that the electron surface at Γ has the shape of a child's jack with knobs at the end of each arm. Additional de Haas–van Alphen data for W has been reported by Girvan,[9] which lends further support to the general features of the larger pieces of the Lomer model. The size-effect experiments by Walsh[10] have pointed out the separation of the electron and hole regions along Γ*H*, attributed to spin-orbit coupling.

* Contribution No. 1674. Work was performed in the Ames Laboratory of the U. S. Atomic Energy Commission.
[1] W. M. Lomer, Proc. Phys. Soc. (London) 80, 489 (1962).
[2] J. H. Wood, Phys. Rev. 126, 517 (1962).
[3] M. Asdente and J. Friedel, Phys. Rev. 124, 384 (1961).
[4] M. F. Manning and M. I. Chodorow, Phys. Rev. 56, 787 (1939).
[5] W. M. Lomer, Proc. Phys. Soc. (London) 84, 327 (1964).

[6] G. B. Brandt and J. A. Rayne, Phys. Rev. 132, 1945 (1963).
[7] D. M. Sparlin and J. A. Marcus, Bull. Am. Phys. Soc. 8, 258 (1963).
[8] D. M. Sparlin and J. A. Marcus, Bull. Am. Phys. Soc. 9, 250 (1964).
[9] R. F. Girvan, M.S. thesis, Iowa State University, 1964 (unpublished).
[10] W. M. Walsh, Jr., and C. C. Grimes, Phys. Rev. Letters 13, 523 (1964).

In light of the general qualitative success of this model, it was decided to perform *ab initio* calculations of the Fermi surfaces for the chromium group, in the hope of obtaining quantitative information which could be compared with experiment. In these calculations no *a priori* consideration was given to the antiferromagnetic state of Cr, nor to the relativsitic effects which should yield small corrections in W. In all three metals the Fermi surfaces were computed in the same manner, using the APW method. These calculations were programmed such that constant-energy surfaces could be traced out in the Brillouin zone. The volumes contained by the various pieces of surface were determined, and the Fermi energy chosen by the requirement of equal hole and electron volumes. A discussion of the methods employed is given in the following sections.

THEORY

Hartree-Fock-Slater Self-Consistent-Field Calculation

The potential was constructed from a superposition of atomic potentials centered on the lattice sites. The atomic potentials were found from Hartree-Fock-Slater (HFS) self-consistent-field calculations similar to those described in detail by Herman and Skillman[11] (HS). Although the program established for these calculations was different in some details from the one published by HS it provided no additional information. This aspect of the project served only as an independent check of their results. Agreement was established for the Cr-group metals out to the fourth figure in all of the eigenvalues.

In performing these calculations, however, it was found to be more convenient to use a logarithmic scale. Because the distance between radial nodes increases rapidly for a given orbital, it is necessary to use an expanding scale of some sort. HS chose to periodically increase the increment size. This can be avoided by using $x = \ln r$ as the independent variable. By simultaneously changing the dependent variable from R to $r^{1/2}R$, we obtain a radial equation containing no first derivative. This has been pointed out by Hartree.[12]

A different method for the numerical integration of the radial equation was used. The method commonly employed is due to Hartree and consists of comparing inward and outward integrations of the radial equation (for a trial eigenvalue) in the region of the outermost inflection point. This technique assures that the solutions have the proper behavior at the two boundaries. The trial eigenvalue is adjusted on the basis of the mismatch in logarithmic derivatives at the joining point. The method for this is developed from perturba-

tion theory and involves an integration over the radial coordinates. A method is presented in the Appendix which eliminates the need for this joining point and hence avoids the problems associated with making the function continuous at this point. In addition, the corrections to the eigenvalue are given by an algebraic expression which can be easily evaluated after each sweep over the range of the radial coordinate.

The result of the HFS calculations is a tabular record of the self-consistent potential and the atomic orbitals with corresponding eigenvalues. In the construction of the muffin-tin potential, the only information needed is the total electronic charge density which one obtains from the orbitals.

The crystal potential was constructed by superposing atomic potentials centered on neighboring lattice sites. In the Slater free-electron approximation the average exchange potential is proportional to $\rho^{1/3}$, where ρ is the total electronic charge density. This requires that the superposing be done in two steps. The ordinary electrostatic potential given by the solution of Poisson's equation, using the charge density ρ, is superposed to give the electrostatic contribution to the crystal potential. The charge density itself is then independently superposed to approximate the crystal charge density. The $\rho^{1/3}$ exchange potential is then computed using this superposed charge density. The resulting contribution is added point by point to the crystal electrostatic potential to yield the total crystal potential.

The method of superposing the radial functions should be discussed. Starting with the function (it might be the electrostatic potential or the charge density) on a particular site, we consider the contributions from the same function centered on neighboring sites. It we limit ourselves to constructing a spherically symmetric potential, then the contributions from neighboring centers will depend only on the distance from the origin to the site. There will, in general, be several equidistant neighbors, and hence these can all be taken into account simultaneously by an appropriate factor.

A procedure for determining the contribution from the function $\chi(r)$ centered on a lattice site a distance R_n from the origin was given by Löwdin[13] and is known as the alpha summation method. This method is very general and allows the construction of a nonspherically symmetric potential. By retaining only the lowest order term in the spherical-harmonic expansion, the resulting expression is simply

$$\chi(r, R_n) = \frac{1}{2rR_n} \int_{|r-R_n|}^{r+R_n} t\chi(t)dt. \tag{1}$$

This gives the spherically symmetric contribution at r due to the function $\chi(t)$ centered at R_n. Thus the super-

[11] F. Herman and S. Skillman, *Atomic Structure Calculations* (Prentice-Hall, Inc., Englewood Cliffs, New Jersey, 1963).
[12] D. R. Hartree, *Calculation of Atomic Structures* (John Wiley & Sons, Inc., New York, 1957).

[13] P. O. Löwdin, Advan. Phys. 5, 1 (1956).

position consists of summing these contributions from all the lattice sites in the vicinity of the origin.

The resulting potential, it is hoped, will be slowly varying in the region between atomic sites because of the overlapping of the functions from adjoining neighbors. Of course, it will not be exactly constant; but in many cases it is meaningful to spherically average the potential in this outer region and replace it by a constant value. This was the procedure followed in these calculations. This constant was then subtracted from the spherically-symmetric potential inside the Slater sphere so that the potential in the outer region could be taken as zero. The resulting potential was used in constructing the APW matrix elements as discussed in the following section.

APW Method

The APW method has certainly been established as an important tool in the calculation of electronic properties of crystals. In order to avoid listing the impressive array of theoretical results already produced by this method, only the recent results by Mattheiss[14] will be cited. One can easily trace the abundant literature by starting with this reference. For the most recent results the reader is referred to the Progress Reports of the Solid State and Molecular Theory Group at MIT. All of this work has been motivated by J. C. Slater who was responsible for the original formulation of the method in 1937.[15]

The method takes full advantage of the muffin-tin form of the potential and constructs a basis function from plane waves and from atomic orbitals in the spherically-symmetric potential. The APW for an electronic state $\bar{k}$ consists of a plane wave in the outer region and a summation of atomic orbitals inside the Slater sphere. The coefficients in the atomic-orbital expansion are chosen such that the functions in each region are continuous on the Slater sphere. The resulting APW, however, has a kink due to a discontinuity in the slope. This is taken into account by including appropriate surface integrals in the matrix elements. These integrals give the contribution to the kinetic energy due to the kink in the wave function. The resulting matrix elements are given here for one atom in the unit cell of volume Ω:

$$(H-E)_{ij} = (\bar{k}_i \cdot \bar{k}_j - E)\left(\delta_{ij} - \frac{4\pi R^2}{\Omega}\frac{j_1(|\bar{k}_j - \bar{k}_i|R)}{|\bar{k}_j - \bar{k}_i|}\right)$$

$$+\frac{4\pi R^2}{\Omega}\sum_{l=0}^{\infty}(2l+1)P_l(\hat{k}_i \cdot \hat{k}_j)j_l(k_iR)$$

$$\times j_l(k_jR)[\mu_l'(R,E)/\mu_l(R,E)]; \quad (2)$$

R is the radius of the Slater sphere and can be any

[14] L. F. Mattheiss, Phys. Rev. 134, A970 (1964).
[15] J. C. Slater, Phys. Rev. 51, 846 (1937).

TABLE I. Some parameters and results of APW calculation.

	Cr	Mo	W
Lattice constant	5.4512	5.9468	5.9810
Slater-sphere radius	2.34	2.46	2.46
Fermi energy	0.647	0.542	0.548
Density of states $G(E)$	0.0895	0.0695	0.0673
Electronic-specific-heat coefficient (cal/mole°K²)	3.00(−4)	3.04(−4)	2.98(−4)

value (less than half of the interatomic spacing) such that the potential in the region outside the sphere is nearly constant. The radii used in this calculation are listed in Table I. The l summation was truncated at $l=10$. The Legendre polynominals $P_l(Z)$ were calculated from the recurrence relation

$$lP_l(Z) = (2l-1)ZP_{l-1}(Z) - (l-1)P_{l-2}(Z), \quad (l \geq 2) \quad (3)$$

starting with $P_0(Z)=1$ and $P_1(Z)=Z$. The spherical Bessel functions were computed from the recurrence relation

$$j_l(Z) = \frac{2(l-\frac{1}{2})}{Z}j_{l-1}(Z) - j_{l-2}(Z). \quad (4)$$

The standard method for calculating these functions is to start with two arbitrary values $j_L(Z)$ and $j_{L-1}(Z)$ where L is large enough that $j_L(Z)$ is in the asymptotic region. After determining the functions $j_l(Z)$ from $l=L$ down to $l=0$ with the recurrence relation, the normalization can be fixed by computing any of the lower order functions explicitly. This method avoids the loss in accuracy resulting from repeatedly subtracting numbers which are almost equal. Finally, the logarithmic derivatives of the radial functions can be determined from outward integrations of the radial equation, using finite-difference approximations similar to those described in Appendix A.

The secular determinant resulting from the linear variation function using APW's gives the dispersion relation $E(\bar{k})$ for the conduction electrons. It should be noticed that the energy appears both explicitly and implicitly in these matrix elements. Hence the eigenvalue problem necessarily involves finding the roots of the secular equation numerically. Having specified the quantum numbers of the crystalline state $(\bar{k})$, it is necessary to examine the determinant as a function of energy and find the roots. For a given value of energy it is necessary to perform an outward integration of the radial equation for each value of l. This requires extensive computing, and so in this work it was decided to fix the energy parameter and solve the resulting eigenvalue problem for the constant-energy surfaces. In this way the integrations could be performed once and for all, and only the algebra associated with the other terms in the matrix elements had to be repeated each time. This does not represent a great saving of computer time, but it does yield important information

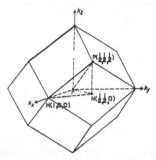

about the energy surfaces near the Fermi surface. Of
course one does not know the Fermi energy *a priori*.
However, the requirement that electron and hole
volumes be equal is sufficient to determine the Fermi
energy. This aspect of the calculations will be discussed
in more detail later in the paper. It might be mentioned
for the sake of completeness that the secular determinants were solved by the method of triangularzation.
This amounts to getting zeros under the main diagonal
by adding and subtracting multiples of the rows.
A few systematic attempts at this will lead one to the
expression

$$D_{\mu\nu} = d_{\mu\nu} - \sum_{i=1}^{I-1} \frac{D_{\mu i} D_{i\nu}}{D_{ii}} \qquad (5)$$

where I is the minimum value of ν or μ. This gives the
rule for transforming the original matrix elements $d_{\mu\nu}$
into the triangularized form. The value of the determinant is then πD_{ii}.

Lattices

The crystal structure for the chromium group metals
is bodycentered cubic. The lattice constants[16] are
listed in Table I.[17] This structure and the associated

 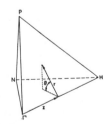

[16] *International Tables for X-ray Crystallography* (Kynoch
Press, Birmingham, England, 1962), Vol. III.
[17] Units are such that $e^2 = 2$, $m = \frac{1}{2}$ and $h = 2\pi$. Thus energies are
in rydbergs and distances in Borh radii.

reciprocal lattice are reviewed by Jones.[18] The Brillouin
zone is shown in Fig. 1. The 1/48 zone is outlined by
the points of high symmetry $\Gamma P N H$. The coordinates
of these points are indicated on the figure in units of
$2\pi/d$. In this calculation the set of 19 reciprocal lattice
vectors nearest the origin were used for all points
throughout the zone. This is a slight disadvantage to the
points near the P, N, and H. By increasing the basis set
to 26 lattice vectors, one can include all those vectors
for which $|\bar{k} + \bar{K}| \leq 4\pi/d$ with $\bar{k}$ anywhere in the 1/48
zone. This probably would have been better, but the
calculations were much too extensive to repeat for this
reason alone.

In the Lomer model the Fermi surface is located
along the ΓH axis and at the point N. Anticipating this,
two coordinate systems for tracing out the energy
contours were established: cylindrical coordinates with
ΓH as the azimuthal axis and angles measured from
the $\Gamma N H$, and spherical coordinates centered at N with
NP as the azimuthal axis and angles measured from
the plane $N\Gamma P$. These coordinate systems in the 1/48
zone are shown in Fig. 2.

Constant-Energy Contours

The procedure for tracing out the constant-energy
surfaces will be discussed. Along ΓH for instance, the
polar angle between the planes $\Gamma P H$ and $\Gamma N H$ was
divided into four equal intervals. Then for a particular
plane the z coordinate was specified, and the secular
determinant was examined as a function of the radial
coordinate to determine the roots. These roots were
located by searching for a change of sign and then using
repeated linear interpolations. The roots represent the
intersection of the energy surface with the plane. A
similar procedure was carried out at the symmetry
point N where the azimuthal angle between the planes
$NP\Gamma$ and $N\Gamma H$ was also divided into four intervals.

RESULTS AND DISCUSSION

Fermi Energy and Density of States

The volume contained by each of the pieces of surface
for a particular value of the energy were numerically
determined from the tabular data. The assignment of
electrons and holes to the various regions was determined on the basis of whether the volume increased or
decreased with an increase in the energy. In Fig. 3
these volumes are plotted as a function of the energy
for the three metals. The Fermi energy is determined by
the requirement of equal hole and electron volumes. The
results are given in Table I.

The density of states at the Fermi energy can be
determined from Fig. 3. The definition of the density of

[18] H. Jones, *The Theory of Brillouin Zones and Electronic States
in Crystals* (Interscience Publishers, Inc., New York, 1960).

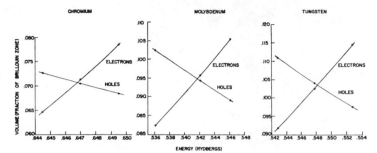

FIG. 3. Hole and electron volumes contained by energy surfaces.

states is

$$G(E) = (1/4\pi^3)dV_k/dE, \qquad (6)$$

where $G(E)dE$ is the number of electrons per unit volume of the crystal (the factor of 2 for spin degeneracy is already included) with energy in the range E to $E+dE$. dV_k is the volume in reciprocal space between the constant energy surfaces E and $E+dE$. dV_k/dE is therefore the slope of the volume-versus-energy curve. Thus

$$dV_k/dE = 48[(dv_e/dE) - (dv_h/dE)]. \qquad (7)$$

The v corresponds to volume in the 1/48 zone; subscripts refer to electrons and holes. The minus sign is needed because an increase in energy results in a decrease in the hole volume. The values of $G(E)$ determined from Fig. 3 are given in Table I. The low-temperature electronic-specific-heat coefficient is related to this by

$$\gamma = (\pi^2/3)(k^2/\rho)G(E), \qquad (8)$$

where k is the Boltzmann constant and ρ is molar density. The predicted specific-heat coefficients are listed in Table I.

Fermi Surfaces

The energy surfaces calculated for the middle set of points in each of the curves in Fig. 3 are shown in Figs. 4, 5, and 6. One notices immediately that the surfaces for Mo and W are quite similar and exhibit the qualitative features of the Lomer model (see Fig. 7). Cr differs from these by the absence of the hole pockets at N and by a reduction in the size of the knobs on the electron jack. The pockets along ΓH are found to contain electrons. A quantitative comparison between these surfaces and experimental results will now be considered. Because Cr is complicated by the magnetic state and W is heavy enough for relativistic effects to be important, the characteristics of the Fermi surface of Mo will be emphasized.

The de Haas–van Alphen frequencies can be predicted from extremal areas of the Fermi surface using the Onsager relation $f = KA_0$ where $K = ch/2\pi e = 374.1(6)$. This gives f in G with A_0 measured in atomic units. The various extremal orbits are shown in Figs. 8 and 9. The corresponding de Haas–van Alphen frequencies

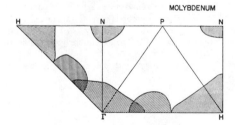

MOLYBDENUM

FIG. 5. Intersection of molybdenum Fermi surface with 1/48 zone faces.

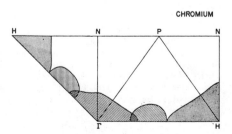

CHROMIUM

FIG. 4. Intersection of chromium Fermi surface with 1/48 zone faces.

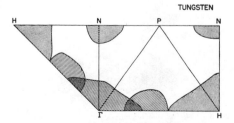

TUNGSTEN

FIG. 6. Intersection of tungsten Fermi surface with 1/48 zone faces.

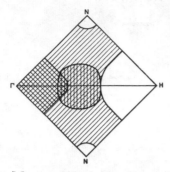

FIG. 7. Lomer model for chromium-group metals.

are listed in Table II. Without detailed angular dependence of these frequencies it is difficult to compare all of them with experiment. For instance, the holes at N and the electron pockets along ΓH should have complicated angular dependence because of the different possible orientations of each in the Brillouin zone. There are the equivalent of 6 hole pockets and 6 electron pockets in the first zone (Fig. 1). However, Brandt and Rayne[6] have reported a large number of frequencies for Mo ranging from 5.03 to 8.00(6) G. Most of these can apparently be associated with the small electron pockets along ΓH. The larger frequencies reported approach the magnitude predicted for the $J_1(100)$ orbit around the necks of the jack. They also report two frequencies at 24.2 and 25.8(6) G for the (110) direction. These fall in the range of frequencies predicted for the holes at N. In fact, the extremal area of the hole pockets in the plane NPH [which corresponds to one of the (110) frequencies] yields the frequency 24.1(6) G. For completeness, the $NP\Gamma$ cross section yields 30.6(6) and ΓNH yields 16.5(6) G.

A further comparison can be made with the de

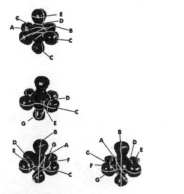

FIG. 8. Orbits on molybdenum electron jack. (A)-J_1 (111); (B)-J_1(110) (C)-J_1(100); (D)-J_2(100); (E)-J_3(100); (F)-J_4(110); (G)-J_5(111).

Haas–van Alphen measurements on Mo communicated by Girvan.[19] In the (111) direction he has preliminary results which indicate frequencies at 5.7, 25.5, 31.6, 37.2, 91 and 110(6) G. The first of these could be assigned to the electron pockets along ΓH. The next three are in the range predicted for the holes at N. Of course, the frequencies from orbits on the knobs of the jack (orbit J_3) are expected to be about 35(6) G. Thus, the higher frequencies from the holes at N and the ones from the knobs are the of same magnitude. Considering the two larger frequencies, the value 91(6) G could be associated with either the orbit $J_1(111)$ or $J_5(111)$. The latter was not determined exactly, but is probably a little larger than $J_1(111)$ which yields a frequency of 72.3(6) G. The experimental value 110(6) G agrees closely with the theoretical value for the hole orbit $H(111)$.

Girvan also reports the following possible frequencies in the (100) direction: 5.43, 10.8, 24.0, 33.3, and 165(6) G. The smallest value is gain attributed to the elec-

FIG. 9. Orbits on molybdenum hole octahedron. H-H(100); I-H(110); J-H(111).

tron pockets along ΓH. The next frequency 10.8(6) G is either a harmonic or might be associated with the neck orbit $J_2(100)$. The intermediate values are of the same order of magnitude as the predicted frequencies for the holes at N or for the knob orbit $J_3(100)$. The largest frequency agrees closely with the predicted value 168(6) G for the holes at H.

From the above discussion it is concluded that the large orbits on the electron jack and the hole octahedron are easily identified and agree quantitatively with the experimental results of Girvan. Also it is likely that the smaller frequencies reported by Brandt and Rayne are due to orbits on the electron pockets along ΓH. The frequencies of the orbits on the hole pockets at N range from about 16 to 32(6) G, but the frequencies from the knobs on the jack should overlap the upper portion of this range. Only the availability of the

[19] R. F. Girvan (private communication). I am grateful to Mr. Girvan for informing me of these results prior to publication.

TABLE II. Predicted de Haas–van Alphen frequencies (G).

	Orbit	Frequency
Electron jack		
	$J_1(100)$	227. $\times 10^6$
	$J_2(100)$	11.3
	$J_3(100)$	33.6
	$J_1(110)$	154.
	$J_4(110)$	$64.7 \to 76.4$
	$J_1(111)$	72.3
	$J_5(111)$	Not measured
Hole octahedron		
	$H(111)$	108
	$H(110)$	130
	$H(100)$	168
Holes at N		
	All directions	$16.5 \to 32.3$
Electron pockets ΓH		
	Not calculated—Same order of magnitude as $J_2(100)$.	

TABLE IV. Electron specific heat coefficient $\gamma(10^{-4}$ cal/mole°K²).

	Cr	Mo	W
Present work	3.00	3.04	2.98
Manning and Chodorow (Ref. 4)	...	...	4.8
Horowitz and Daunt (Ref. 22)	...	5.1 ±0.4	1.8 ±0.7
Gupta, Cheng, and Beck (Ref. 23)	3.76	...	...
White and Woods (Ref. 24)	3.60	5.24	2.88
Kirillin, Sheindlin, and Chekhovskoi (Ref. 25)	...	...	10.1
Shimizu, Takahashi, and Katsuki (Ref. 26)	3.7 –3.8	5.05–5.25	1.8 –5.0
Clusius and Franzosini (Ref. 27)	3.6	...	...

The theoretical values are presented in Table IV with a variety of experimental results.[22-27]

As a final comparison with experiment, those properties which depend on the surface area of the Fermi surface were predicted for Mo. The surface area of the jack was determined in a rather crude fashion. Therefore all values are quoted to only two significant figures. The results are given in Table V. Fawcett and Griffiths[28] have experimentally examined the anomalous skin effect for the Cr-group metals. The quantity measured is $\langle 1/\Sigma \rangle$ where Σ is the surface conductance. By using $\langle 1/\Sigma \rangle^{-3}$ for $\langle \Sigma^3 \rangle$ they were able to calculate the surface area S using

$$S = (6\sqrt{3}\pi^2\omega^2h/e^2)\langle \Sigma \rangle^3. \qquad (9)$$

The above approximation in the averaging procedure is known to underestimate S for anisotropic surfaces. The experimentally determined value for Mo is 1.74 a.u. as compared to our value of 6.7 a.u. Using the

experimentally determined angular dependence of the frequencies would clarify this assignment of orbits.

The size-effect data of Walsh et al.,[20] on W provide a further comparison with the theoretical results. The extremal dimensions of the jack and the octahedron are listed in Table III.[21] Since Mo and W have essentially the same Fermi surfaces if relativistic effects are neglected, one can presumably see from this table the changes in the surface caused by these effects. As Walsh[10] has pointed out, the jack and octahedron must be split apart along ΓH by the spin-orbit coupling.

Another experimental result which can be predicted is the low temperature electronic-specific-heat coefficient γ. This was discussed in a previous section of the paper.

TABLE III. k vectors of Fermi surface.

	W (expt)[a]	W (theory)[b]	Mo (htheory)[c]
Electron jack			
(100)	0.587	0.613	0.608
(110)	...	0.270	0.257
(111)	0.219	0.248	0.232
Hole octahedron			
(100)	0.411	0.428	0.445
(110)	0.316	0.317	0.332
(111)	0.265	0.264	0.282
Holes at N			
along NP	...	...	0.195
along $N\Gamma$	...	...	0.141
along ΓH	...	...	0.100

[a] Walsh et al.
[b] Matheiss (Ref. 21) APW calculation.
[c] Present work.

TABLE V. Surface area of Mo and related parameters.

Electron jack	3.2
Hole octahedron	1.6
Electron pockets (6)	0.4
Holes at N (6)	1.5
	—
Total surface area	6.7 atomic units (a. u.)
$\langle 1/v \rangle^{-1}$	7.6×10⁷ cm/sec
$\sigma/\langle l \rangle$	7.4×10¹⁴ esu

[20] W. M. Walsh, Jr., and C. C. Grimes, Phys. Rev. Letters 13, 523 (1964).
[21] L. F. Mattheiss and R. E. Watson, Phys. Rev. Letters 13, 526 (1964).

[22] M. Horowitz and J. G. Daunt, Phys. Rev. 91, 1099 (1953).
[23] K. P. Gupta, C. H. Cheng, and P. A. Beck, J. Phys. Radium 23, 721 (1962).
[24] G. K. White and S. B. Woods, Phil. Trans. Roy. Soc. London 215A, 35 (1959).
[25] V. A. Kirillin, A. E. Sheindlin and V. Ya. Chekhovskoi, Chem. Abstr. 57, 1632 F (1962).
[26] M. Shimizu, T. Takahashi and A. Katsuki, J. Phys. Soc. Japan 17, 1740 (1962).
[27] K. Clusius and P. Franzosini, Gazz. Chim. Ital. 93, 221 (1963).
[28] E. Fawcett and D. Griffiths, J. Phys. Chem. Solids 23, 1631 (1962).

theoretical values for S and γ, two additional physical quantities can be calculated[29]:

$$\sigma/\langle l \rangle = (e^2 S)/(6\pi^2 h), \tag{10}$$

$$\langle 1/v \rangle = (6h\gamma)/(k^2 S). \tag{11}$$

σ is the dc conductivity, $\langle l \rangle$ is the electron mean free path, and v is the electron velocity at the Fermi surface. These results are also listed in Table V although they are not readily compared with experiment.

APPENDIX

An algorithm for the numerical of the radial Schrödinger equation is discussed in this Appendix. This equation takes the form

$$Y''(x) = g(x)Y(x) \tag{A1}$$

where $Y = r^{1/2}R$ and $x = \ln r$. Here

$$g(x) = e^{2x}[\lambda + V(e^x)] + (l + \tfrac{1}{2})^2 \tag{A2}$$

with $\lambda = -E$. By writing the Taylor series expansion at r, it is easy to show that

$$Y_{j+1} - 2Y_j + Y_{j-1} = \Delta^2 Y_j'' + (\Delta^4/12)Y_j{}^{iv}. \tag{A3}$$

Differentiating this twice and dropping the highest order term, the fourth derivative can be expressed in terms of second derivatives at neighboring points. Using the original differential equation to eliminate the second derivative we find

$$A_j Y_{j+1} + B_j Y_j + C_j Y_{j-1} = 0, \tag{A4}$$

where

$$\begin{aligned} A_j &= 1 - (\Delta^2/12)G_{j+1}, \\ B_j &= -2 - (5\Delta^2/12)G_j, \\ C_j &= 1 - (\Delta^2/12)G_{j-1}. \end{aligned} \tag{A5}$$

The differential equation is thus replaced by a tridiagonal system of linear equations with coefficients which depend on the eigenvalue and the potential. We approach the solution of this set of equations by taking

$$\begin{aligned} \lambda + \lambda\delta &= \lambda^*, \\ Y_j + \delta Y_j &= Y_j^*. \end{aligned} \tag{A6}$$

The philosophy is to assume that the true solution λ and Y_j differ from a trial solution (indicated by a star) only by the small quantities $\delta\lambda$ and δY_j. This necessitates a reasonable initial guess for the wave function and eigenvalue. Since in general λ^* and Y_j^* will not satisfy the difference equation, we write

$$A_j^* Y_{j+1}^* + B_j^* Y_j^* + C_j^* Y_{j-1}^* = Q_j. \tag{A7}$$

29 A. B. Pippard, Rept. Progr. Phys. 23, 176 (1960).

Q_j is called the residual; it will approach zero as λ^* and Y_j^* approach the correct solution. Using (A5) and (A6) it is not difficult to show that (A7) becomes

$$A_j \delta Y_{j+1} + B_j \delta Y_j + C_j \delta Y_{j-1} + D_j \delta\lambda = Q_j, \tag{A8}$$

where

$$D_j = -(\Delta^2/12)e^{2x}(e^{2\Delta}Y_{j+1}^* + 10Y_j^* + e^{-2\Delta}Y_{j-1}^*). \tag{A9}$$

We assume a solution in the form

$$\delta Y_j = E_j \delta Y_{j+1} + F_j \delta\lambda + G_j. \tag{A10}$$

Repeated substitution into (A8) yields

$$\begin{aligned} E_j &= -A_j/R_j, \\ F_j &= -(D_j + C_j F_{j-1})/R_j, \\ G_j &= (Q_j - C_j G_{j-1})/R_j, \end{aligned} \tag{A11}$$

with

$$R_j = B_j + C_j E_{j-1}. \tag{A12}$$

The solution at each stage of the iteration then follows after the boundary conditions are specified. The inner boundary condition at $x \to -\infty$ allows us to set

$$E_1 = \bar{e}^{\Delta/2}, \quad F_1 = 0 \quad \text{and} \quad G_1 = Y_1^* - E_1 Y_2^*. \tag{A13}$$

From repeated application of (A11) we can then determine E_J, F_J and G_J corresponding to a grid point in the outer tail region of the wave function. In this region the WKB approximation is valid, and it is not difficult to show from a comparison of (A10) and the asymptotic form of the wave function that

$$\delta\lambda = (Y_{J-1}^* - G_{J-1} - a_J)/(F_{J-1} - b_J a_J), \tag{A14}$$

where

$$\begin{aligned} a_J &= Y_J^* \exp(\Delta\sqrt{g_J}), \\ b_J &= \Delta \exp(-2x_J)/(2\sqrt{g_J}). \end{aligned}$$

Here J corresponds to the grid point at the outer boundary and x_J is the value of x at that point. Having determined $\delta\lambda$ from (A14), we set $\delta Y_J = 0$ in order to specify the normalization. Then repeated application of (A10) yields the corrections to the trial wave function.

This algorithm has been found to converge after only a few iterations in most instances. However, it is usually necessary to do some preliminary calculations before using this method. It should be obvious that the trial function must have the same number of nodes desired for a particular orbital. Hence, the same procedure suggested by Hartree and used by HS for counting nodes and getting an approximate eigenfunction and eigenvalue is recommended. This is particularly important for the higher orbitals where the eigenvalues get very close together.

PHYSICAL REVIEW VOLUME 139, NUMBER 4A 16 AUGUST 1965

Relativistic Electronic Structure in Crystals. I. Theory*

T. L. LOUCKS

Institute for Atomic Research and Department of Physics, Iowa State University, Ames, Iowa

(Received 10 March 1965)

A relativistic generalization of the augmented-plane-wave (APW) method is presented. The upper components of a Dirac plane wave are joined continuously on the Slater sphere to a linear expansion of central-field Dirac orbitals. The lower components of the functions in the two regions are discontinuous. A variational expression for the energy which is appropriate for this type of basis function is developed. The matrix elements between these relativistic APW's are derived and compared with the nonrelativistic case.

INTRODUCTION

A N increasing number of references in the current literature dealing with the electronic states in crystals have attempted to include relativistic effects. Most of these calculations begin with the two-component Hamiltonian which results from application of the Foldy-Wouthuysen transformation to the Dirac Hamiltonian.[1] This yields three relativistic correction terms to the nonrelativistic Hamiltonian: mass velocity, Darwin, and spin-orbit coupling. The spin-orbit term is the only one which mixes spinor components. The other two are radial functions which are simply corrections to the nonrelativistic crystal potential. By absorbing these radial terms in the Fourier coefficients of the pseudopotential, Anderson and Gold[2] were able to fit experimental de Haas–van Alphen data for lead by adjusting several parameters, one of which was the spin-orbit parameter. Herman, *et al.*[3,4] have considered the corrections to the band structure of tetrahedrally bonded semiconductors due to all three of the relativistic corrections. Mattheiss and Watson[5] have shown that the spin-orbit interaction term can (by an appropriate choice of the spin-orbit parameter) lead to band splitting in W which is of the same magnitude as determined experimentally by Walsh.[6] Scop[7] has included mass-velocity and spin-orbit perturbation corrections in an augmented-plane-wave (APW) calculation of the band structure of AgCl and AgBr.

Conklin, Johnson, and Pratt[8,9] have used the relativistic Hamiltonian discussed above for lead telluride

with a linear variation function consisting of eigenfunctions determined from a nonrelativistic APW calculation. The first complete formulation of the relativistic theory for energy bands in crystals was reported recently by Soven.[10] His approach was to generalize the orthogonalized-plane-wave method (OPW) by orthogonalizing four-component Dirac plane waves to the four-component central-field solutions of the core states. The results of this theory compare favorably with the experimental data available for thallium. More recently a theory of spin-orbit interaction in metals has been presented by Animalu.[11] It is essentially a generalization of the model potential of Heine and Abarenkov[12] which takes into account the observed spin-orbit splitting of atomic levels. This experimental information is used to evaluate quantities in the crystal theory which otherwise require a knowledge of the crystal potential near the core.

The theory presented here is the relativistic generalization of the Slater[13] APW method. The basis function consists of an expansion of four-component central-field orbitals of the Dirac Hamiltonian inside the Slater sphere and a Dirac plane wave outside. The expansion coefficients are chosen such that the upper (large) components of the two functions in each region are continuous on the Slater sphere. As a result the lower (small) components of this relativistic APW (RAPW) are discontinuous on this boundary. A variational expression for the energy which is suitable for this type of function is developed.

Matrix elements between the states arising in a reciprocal lattice expansion of the wave function are evaluated. The resulting expression is very similar to the nonrelativistic APW theory. Using this method, relativistic calculations can be performed as easily as nonrelativistic calculations. Hence all of the advantages of the APW method are available with the added benefit that the procedure is completely relativistic. The size of the basis set is necessarily doubled by the inclusion of both spin states, but as Soven[10] has pointed out in the relativistic OPW theory there are relations among the matrix elements which allow the triangularization procedure to be carried out for two rows simultaneously.

* Work was performed in the Ames Laboratory of the U. S. Atomic Energy Commission. Contribution No. 1676.
[1] M. E. Rose, *Relativistic Electron Theory* (John Wiley & Sons, Inc., New York, 1961).
[2] J. R. Anderson and A. V. Gold, U. S. Atomic Energy Commission, Research and Development Report No. 1S-762, 1963 (unpublished).
[3] F. Herman, C. Kuglin, K. Cuff, and R. Kortum, Phys. Rev. Letters 11, 541 (1963).
[4] F. Herman, *Physics of Semiconductors* (Dunod et Cie., Paris, 1964), p. 3.
[5] L. F. Mattheiss and R. E. Watson, Phys. Rev. Letters 13, 526 (1964).
[6] W. M. Walsh, Jr., and C. C. Grimes, Phys. Rev. Letters 13, 523 (1964).
[7] P. M. Scop, Massachusetts Institute of Technology, Quarterly Progress Report No. 54, SSMTG, 1964 (unpublished).
[8] J. B. Conklin, Jr., L. E. Johnson, and G. W. Pratt, Jr., Phys. Rev. 137, A1282 (1965).
[9] J. B. Conklin, Jr., Massachusetts Institute of Technology, Technical Report No. 1, 1964 (unpublished).

[10] P. Soven, Phys. Rev. 137, A1706 (1965).
[11] A. O. E. Animalu (to be published).
[12] V. Heine and I. Abarenkov, Phil. Mag. 9, 451 (1964).
[13] J. C. Slater, Phys. Rev. 51, 846 (1937).

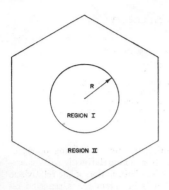

FIG. 1. Unit cell in crystal showing Slater sphere.

REGION I

REGION II

R

In this paper only the theory will be presented. Although the calculations for tungsten are nearly completed, it was felt that the method itself should be made available as soon as possible so that others could take advantage of its relative ease of application. The preliminary results for tungsten are very encouraging, however, since it has been possible to perform *ab initio* calculations which predict the observed spin-orbit splitting of the energy bands. The complete relativistic calculation of the Fermi surface of tungsten will be presented in a later companion article.

THEORY

Form of the RAPW

Let us consider a unit cell which contains only one Slater sphere (Fig. 1). Our results can easily be generalized to more than one sphere. In region II the potential is zero and the wave function in this region is

$$\Psi_{nm}{}^{II}=\left(\frac{k_n{}^*+1}{2k_n{}^*}\right)^{1/2}\left[\begin{matrix}\chi(m)\\ \dfrac{\sigma\cdot\mathbf{k}_n}{k_n{}^*+1}\chi(m)\end{matrix}\right]e^{i\mathbf{k}_n\cdot\mathbf{r}}(m=\pm\tfrac{1}{2}). \quad (1)$$

The normalization is one particle per unit volume.[14] $k_n{}^*=(k_n{}^2+1)^{1/2}$. $\mathbf{k}_n$ is the reciprocal space vector, $\mathbf{k}+\mathbf{K}_n$. σ is the usual notation for the Pauli matrices, and $\chi(\pm\tfrac{1}{2})$ are the Pauli spinors.[1] The Dirac Hamiltonian is

$$H=\alpha\cdot\mathbf{p}+\beta+V. \quad (2)$$

For zero potential the eigenvalue equation is

$$H\Psi_{nm}{}^{II}=k_n{}^*\Psi_{nm}{}^{II}. \quad (3)$$

In region I the wave function is a linear combination of the central field orbitals[15]:

$$\Psi_{nm}{}^{I}=\sum_{\kappa\mu}A_{\kappa\mu}{}^{nm}\begin{pmatrix}g_\kappa(r) & \chi_\kappa{}^\mu\\ if_\kappa(r) & \chi_{-\kappa}{}^\mu\end{pmatrix}. \quad (4)$$

---

[14] Units are $m=c=\hbar=1$. Later in the paper we will convert to atomic units with $e^2=2$, $m=\tfrac{1}{2}$, and $\hbar=1$.

[15] The subscripts nm are in anticipation of the joining requirement which will be discussed.

TABLE I. C coefficients $C(l\tfrac{1}{2}j;\,m-m_2,\,m_2)$.

	$m_2=+\tfrac{1}{2}$	$m_2=-\tfrac{1}{2}$
$j=l+\tfrac{1}{2}$	$\left(\dfrac{l+m+\tfrac{1}{2}}{2l+1}\right)^{1/2}$	$\left(\dfrac{l-m+\tfrac{1}{2}}{2l+1}\right)^{1/2}$
$j=l-\tfrac{1}{2}$	$-\left(\dfrac{l-m+\tfrac{1}{2}}{2l+1}\right)^{1/2}$	$\left(\dfrac{l+m+\tfrac{1}{2}}{2l+1}\right)^{1/2}$

The spin-angular functions $\chi_\kappa{}^\mu$ are

$$\chi_\kappa{}^\mu=\sum_{m=\pm\frac{1}{2}}C(l\tfrac{1}{2}j;\mu-m,m)Y_l{}^{\mu-m}(\hat{r})\chi(m) \quad (5)$$

and they have the properties

$$(\sigma\cdot\mathbf{l}+1)\chi_\kappa{}^\mu=-\kappa\chi_\kappa{}^\mu, \quad (6)$$

$$\sigma\cdot\hat{r}\chi_\kappa{}^\mu=-\chi_{-\kappa}{}^\mu. \quad (7)$$

These functions are orthonormal in the sense that

$$\int\chi_\kappa{}^{\mu\dagger}\chi_{\kappa'}{}^{\mu'}\sin\theta d\theta d\phi=\delta_{\mu\mu'}\delta_{\kappa\kappa'}. \quad (8)$$

The C coefficients as given by Rose[1] are reproduced in Table I for completeness. Notice that they satisfy

$$\sum_{m_2=\pm\frac{1}{2}}C^2(j)=1. \quad (9)$$

The radial functions are solutions of the following coupled linear differential equations:

$$\frac{df}{dr}=\frac{(\kappa-1)f}{r}-(W-1-V)g, \quad (10)$$

$$\frac{dg}{dr}=(W-V+1)f-\frac{(\kappa+1)}{r}g. \quad (11)$$

The expansion coefficients $A_{\kappa\mu}{}^{nm}$ are chosen such that the upper components of $\Psi_{nm}{}^{I}$ and $\Psi_{nm}{}^{II}$ are equal on the Slater sphere. This is easily done if the plane wave is expanded in terms of the spin-angular functions. The result is[1]

$$\Psi_{nm}{}^{II}=\sum_{\kappa\mu}a_{\kappa\mu}{}^{nm}\left[\begin{matrix}j_l(k_nr)\chi_\kappa{}^\mu\\ \dfrac{ik_nS_\kappa}{k_n{}^*+1}j_{l'}(k_nr)\chi_{-\kappa}{}^\mu\end{matrix}\right], \quad (12)$$

where

$$a_{\kappa\mu}{}^{nm}=4\pi i^l\left(\frac{k_n{}^*+1}{2k_n{}^*}\right)^{1/2}C(l\tfrac{1}{2}j;\mu-m,m)Y_l{}^{(\mu-m)\dagger}(\hat{k}_n). \quad (13)$$

$j_l(x)$ is a spherical Bessel function. S_κ means "sign of κ." The κ summation is over all positive and negative integers (not zero). j, l, and l' are specified by κ according to the rules

$$l=\kappa, \qquad j=l-\tfrac{1}{2}, \quad l'=\kappa-1 \quad (\kappa>0),$$
$$l=-\kappa-1, \quad j=l+\tfrac{1}{2}, \quad l'=-\kappa \quad (\kappa<0). \qquad (14)$$

For fixed κ, the μ summation is between j and $-j$.

The expansion coefficient is taken to be

$$A_{\kappa\mu}{}^{nm}=a_{\kappa\mu}{}^{nm}[j_l(k_nR)/g_\kappa(R)], \qquad (15)$$

which establishes the desired continuity of the upper components. The lower components, however, are discontinuous on the Slater sphere. Before forming matrix elements between the RAPW's, it is necessary to consider the appropriate variational expression for the energy.

Variational Expression for the Energy

The Dirac Hamiltonian has been shown by Swirles[16] to yield a variational expression for the energy if an infinite region is considered. Schlosser and Marcus[17] have developed variational expressions which apply to nonrelativistic trial wave functions which are discontinuous on a surface inside the unit cell. We will consider the combined situation of a relativistic trial function discontinuous on the Slater sphere.

From the divergence theorem we have

$$\int_\Omega \nabla\cdot(\phi^\dagger\alpha\Psi)d\tau=\int_S \phi^\dagger\alpha\cdot\hat{n}\Psi d\sigma. \qquad (16)$$

The volume integration is over regions I and II of the unit cell. In region I the outward unit normal $\hat{n}$ is equal to $\hat{r}$. In region II it is in the opposite direction. The surface integration in both cases is over the Slater sphere. Expanding the integrand of the left-hand side, it is easy to show that

$$\int_\Omega \phi^\dagger\alpha\cdot\nabla\Psi d\tau=-\int_\Omega (\Psi^\dagger\alpha\cdot\nabla\phi)^* d\tau+\int_S \phi^\dagger\alpha\cdot\hat{n}\Psi d\sigma. \qquad (17)$$

Setting $p=-i\nabla$ and using the Hermiticity of $\beta+V$, we find

$$\int_\Omega \phi^\dagger H\Psi d\tau=\int_\Omega (\Psi^\dagger H\phi)^* d\tau-i\int_S \phi^\dagger\alpha\cdot\hat{n}\Psi d\sigma. \qquad (18)$$

A comparison of the above surface term and the analogous term in the nonrelativistic theory[17] leads us to assume the following form for the energy:

$$W\int_\Omega \Psi^\dagger\Psi d\tau=\int_\Omega \Psi^\dagger H\Psi d\tau-(i/2)$$
$$\times\int_S (\Psi^{II}+\Psi^I)^\dagger\alpha\cdot\hat{r}(\Psi^{II}-\Psi^I)d\sigma, \qquad (19)$$

[16] B. Swirles, Proc. Roy. Soc. (London) **152**, 625 (1935).
[17] H. Schlosser and P. M. Marcus, Phys. Rev. **131**, 2529 (1963).

where Ψ^I and Ψ^{II} are the forms of the trial function in regions I and II, respectively. It is implied that in the volume integrations the appropriate form of Ψ is to be used in each region. It is not difficult to show that this expression has the desired properties: W is both variational and real for arbitrary trial functions Ψ^I and Ψ^{II}. In the following section the matrix elements between RAPW's corresponding to different wave vectors and different spin states will be determined using the above variational expression.

RAPW Matrix Elements

If we expand the crystal wave function in a linear combination of RAPW's (a reciprocal lattice expansion), then the secular equation is

$$\left| M\binom{NM}{nm} \right|$$
$$= \left| H\binom{NM}{nm}-WQ\binom{NM}{nm}-S\binom{NM}{nm} \right|=0, \qquad (20)$$

where

$$H\binom{NM}{nm}=\int_\Omega \Psi_{nm}{}^\dagger H\Psi_{NM}d\tau, \qquad (21)$$

$$Q\binom{NM}{nm}=\int_\Omega \Psi_{nm}{}^\dagger\Psi_{NM}d\tau, \qquad (22)$$

$$S\binom{NM}{nm}=(i/2)\int_S (\Psi_{nm}{}^{II}+\Psi_{nm}{}^I)^\dagger\alpha\cdot\hat{r}$$
$$\times(\Psi_{NM}{}^{II}-\Psi_{NM}{}^I)d\sigma. \qquad (23)$$

We consider first the Hamiltonian and overlap matrix elements. For convenience the energy parameter W in the central-field orbital equations [Eqs. (10) & (11)] is identified with the crystal eigenvalue in the secular equation. This simplifies the expression for the matrix elements because the volume integration of $(H-W)$ over region I is identically zero. However, the price we pay is that the final form of the matrix elements will have an implicit dependence on the energy parameter.

In the outer region the eigenvalue of the Hamiltonian is $k_N{}^*$. The first two terms in the secular equation can therefore be written

$$H\binom{NM}{nm}-WQ\binom{NM}{nm}=(k_N{}^*-W)Q^{II}\binom{NM}{nm}, \qquad (24)$$

where the superscript indicates that the volume integration is only over region II. It can be shown using Ψ^{II}

from Eq. (1) that

$$Q^{II}\binom{NM}{nm}=\Omega\delta_{nN}\delta_{mM}-4\pi R^2\frac{j_1(|\mathbf{k}_N-\mathbf{k}_n|R)}{|\mathbf{k}_N-\mathbf{k}_n|}\left(\frac{k_n^*+1}{2k_n^*}\right)^{1/2}$$

$$\times\left(\frac{k_N^*+1}{2k_N^*}\right)^{1/2}\left\{\left[1+\frac{\mathbf{k}_N\cdot\mathbf{k}_n}{(k_n^*+1)(k_N^*+1)}\right]\delta_{mM}\right.$$

$$\left.+\frac{i\mathbf{k}_n\times\mathbf{k}_N\cdot\langle m|\boldsymbol{\sigma}|M\rangle}{(k_n^*+1)(k_N^*+1)}\right\},\quad(25)$$

where Ω is the volume of the unit cell. The spin-matrix elements are given by

$$\langle\pm|\boldsymbol{\sigma}|\pm\rangle=\pm\hat{e}_z,\quad\langle\pm|\boldsymbol{\sigma}|\mp\rangle=\hat{e}_x\pm i\hat{e}_y.\quad(26)$$

The integration in the surface term of Eq. (23) is over the Slater sphere: $d\sigma=R^2\sin\theta d\theta d\phi$. Hence all the radial functions are evaluated at $r=R$. We use Ψ^I given in Eq. (4) [with $A_{\kappa\mu}{}^{nm}$ from Eq. (15)] and Ψ^{II} from Eq. (12). Operating $\boldsymbol{\alpha}\cdot\hat{r}$ on $\Psi^{II}-\Psi^I$ and performing the angular integrations yields

$$S\binom{NM}{nm}=4\pi R^2\left(\frac{k_n^*+1}{2k_n^*}\right)^{1/2}\left(\frac{k_N^*+1}{2k_N^*}\right)^{1/2}$$

$$\times\sum_\kappa D_\kappa\binom{NM}{nm}j_l(k_nR)\left\{\left(\frac{k_NS_\kappa}{k_N^*+1}\right)j_{l'}(k_NR)\right.$$

$$\left.-j_l(k_NR)\frac{f_\kappa(R)}{g_\kappa(R)}\right\},\quad(27)$$

where

$$D_\kappa\binom{NM}{nm}=4\pi\sum_\mu C(l\tfrac{1}{2}j;\mu-m,m)C(l\tfrac{1}{2}j;\mu-M,M)$$

$$\times Y_l{}^{(\mu-M)\dagger}(\hat{k}_N)Y_l{}^{\mu-m}(\hat{k}_n).\quad(28)$$

The coefficients D_κ are evaluated using the addition theorem for spherical harmonics:

$$(2l+1)P_l(\hat{N}\cdot\hat{n})=4\pi\sum_{m=-l}^{m=+l}Y_l{}^{m\dagger}(\hat{N})Y_l{}^m(\hat{n}).\quad(29)$$

In some instances the necessary expressions are found by applying the orbital-angular-momentum operators to the addition theorem. The results are

$$D_\kappa\binom{N+}{n+}=|\kappa|P_l(\hat{N}\cdot\hat{n})-iS_\kappa(\hat{N}\times\hat{n})_zP_l'(\hat{N}\cdot\hat{n}),\quad(30)$$

$$D_\kappa\binom{N-}{n+}=-S_\kappa P_l'[(\hat{N}\times\hat{n})_y+i(\hat{N}\times\hat{n})_x],\quad(31)$$

$$D_\kappa\binom{N-}{n-}=D_\kappa{}^*\binom{N+}{n+},\quad(32)$$

$$D_\kappa\binom{N+}{n-}=-D_\kappa{}^*\binom{N-}{n+}.\quad(33)$$

This completes the derivation of the matrix elements. In the next section various simplifications will be considered, and the procedure for the relativistic calculation will be compared to the nonrelativistic APW method.

DISCUSSION

Our results to this point are expressed in relativistic units: $m=c=\hbar=1$. Let us now convert to atomic units with $e^2=2$, $m=\frac{1}{2}$ and $\hbar=1$. The energy will be expressed in the form $W=E+mc^2$, where E is the energy measured with respect to the rest mass in the region of zero potential energy. If we agree to neglect terms of the order $(137)^{-2}$ as compared to unity, the expression for the matrix elements becomes

$$M\binom{NM}{nm}=(k_N^2-E)\Omega_{nN}\delta_{mM}+4\pi R^2$$

$$\times\sum_\kappa D_\kappa\binom{NM}{nm}j_l(k_nR)\left\{j_l(k_NR)\right.$$

$$\left.\times\left(\frac{cf_\kappa(R,E)}{g_\kappa(R,E)}\right)-j_{l'}(k_NR)k_NS_\kappa\right\},\quad(34)$$

where

$$\Omega_{nN}=\Omega\delta_{nN}-4\pi R^2\frac{j_1(|\mathbf{k}_N-\mathbf{k}_n|R)}{|\mathbf{k}_N-\mathbf{k}_n|}\quad(35)$$

In our present units $c=2/\alpha$, where $\alpha\approx1/137$ is the fine-structure constant. Of course, lengths are in Bohr radii and energies in rydbergs.

By considering the divergence theorem for the case of plane waves in region II, it can be shown that

$$\Omega_{nN}\delta_{mM}(k_N^2-k_n^2)$$

$$=4\pi R^2\sum_\kappa S_\kappa D_\kappa\binom{NM}{nm}$$

$$\times\{k_nj_l(k_nR)j_{l'}(k_NR)-k_Nj_l(k_NR)j_{l'}(k_nR)\}.\quad(36)$$

This can be substituted into Eq. (34) to yield an index-symmetric form for the matrix elements:

$$M\binom{NM}{nm}=\left(\frac{k_N^2+k_n^2}{2}-E\right)\delta_{mN}\Omega_{nN}+4\pi R^2\sum_\kappa D_\kappa\binom{NM}{nm}$$

$$\times\left\{j_l(k_nR)j_l(k_NR)\left(\frac{cf_\kappa(R,E)}{g_\kappa(R,E)}\right)\right.$$

$$-\tfrac{1}{2}S_\kappa[k_Nj_l(k_nR)j_{l'}(k_NR)$$

$$\left.+k_nj_l(k_NR)j_{l'}(k_nR)]\right\}\quad(37)$$

It is interesting to compare the above expression with the nonrelativistic APW matrix elements[13]:

$$\text{APW}\binom{N}{n} = (\mathbf{k}_N \cdot \mathbf{k}_n - E)\Omega_{nN} + 4\pi R^2 \sum_{l=0}^{\infty} (2l+1) P_l(\hat{N} \cdot \hat{n})$$

$$\times j_l(k_n R) j_l(k_N R) \frac{u_l'(R,E)}{u_l(R,E)} . \quad (38)$$

Instead of a single sum over atomic orbitals labeled by l, we have the double sum over κ which includes both possible orientations of the spin. In place of the logarithmic derivative of the radial wave function u, it is necessary to evaluate the ratio of the two central-field functions f and g. These satisfy Eqs. (10) and (11), which are repeated here in a convenient form:

$$\frac{d(cf)}{dr} = \left(\frac{\kappa-1}{r}\right)cf - (E-V)g , \quad (39)$$

$$\frac{dg}{dr} = \left(\frac{(E-V)}{c^2}+1\right)cf - \frac{(\kappa+1)}{r}g . \quad (40)$$

The following comparison can be made in the nonrelativistic limit:

$$\lim_{c\to\infty} cf/g = (\kappa+1)/r + u'/u . \quad (41)$$

Methods for solving the coupled equations have been discussed by Hartree[18] and by Rose.[1] For numerical work the Runge-Kutta method and the Milne method are applicable.

The last term on the right-hand side of Eq. (37) does not appear in the nonrelativistic theory, but it increases the necessary computing only trivially because the spherical Bessel functions must also be determined for the preceding term in the expression. Hence the only significant complication which the relativistic theory imposes on the matrix elements is in the coefficients D_κ. Because these are complex one must use complex algebra in triangularizing the secular determinant. Here again, however, the additional computing requirements are negligible.

There is a significant increase in computing time which results from the spin-doubling of the basis set. However, this can be substantially reduced because of the relations between matrix elements indicated in Eqs. (32) and (33). It is found that if the matrix elements are ordered according to the following scheme[10]

$$n_1+, \ n_1-, \ n_2+, \ n_2-, \ \text{etc.,} \quad (42)$$

it is necessary to apply the triangularization procedure only to the odd rows. If $M(i,j)$ is the matrix element as determined by either Eq. (34) or (37), the operation necessary to triangularize the determinant can be written

$$M(i,j) \to M(i,j) - \sum_{\nu \text{ odd}}^{i-2} \frac{[M^*(\nu,i)M(\nu,j) + (-1)^{j+1}M^*(\nu,\ j+(-1)^{j+1})M(\nu,i+1)]}{M(\nu,\nu)} . \quad (43)$$

Because the even rows are not needed, there are gaps in the machine storage of the matrix. It has been found convenient to store the real parts and the imaginary parts each in vectors. There is a one-to-one relation between matrix elements (I,J) in the odd rows (above and including the main diagonal) and the vector component KV, where

$$KV = \frac{(I-1)}{2}\left(N+2-\left(\frac{I+1}{2}\right)\right) + J - I + 1; \quad (44)$$

N is the dimension of the matrix (two times the number of reciprocal lattice vectors included in the expansion).

The maximum storage locations required for the complex matrix elements using this identification is $2[N(N+2)/4-1]$.

ACKNOWLEDGMENTS

The encouragement and advice offered by Professor R. H. Good, Jr., Professor J. M. Keller, and Professor D. L. Pursey on this project is greatly appreciated. The author also benefited from several discussions with N. Folland and is very grateful for his assistance.

[18] D. R. Hartree, *The Calculation of Atomic Structures* (John Wiley & Sons, Inc., New York, 1957).

PHYSICAL REVIEW   VOLUME 139, NUMBER 6A   13 SEPTEMBER 1965

Fermi Surface in Tungsten

L. F. MATTHEISS

Bell Telephone Laboratories, Murray Hill, New Jersey

(Received 29 April 1965)

The results of nonrelativistic, augmented-plane-wave energy-band calculations have been used to calculate the Fermi surface in body-centered cubic tungsten, neglecting spin-orbit coupling. The resulting Fermi surface is very similar to one proposed earlier by Lomer for group-VI transition metals and agrees qualitatively with the available experimental results. Spin-orbit coupling is found to have little effect on the basic Fermi-surface topology in tungsten and its consequences can be understood qualitatively in terms of a simplified tight-binding calculation. Within the energy range of the tungsten $5d$ bands, the electronic density of states contains four distinct peaks, three of which lie below the tungsten Fermi energy. Assuming a rigid-band model, the present energy-band results have been used to predict the Fermi surface in the group-V transition metals.

I. INTRODUCTION

TUNGSTEN is one of the first transition metals to become available in high-purity, single-crystal form. As a result, most of the experimental techniques for studying the electronic properties of metals have been applied to tungsten. These have included measurements of the anomalous skin effect,[1] magnetoresistance,[2-5] the magnetoacoustic effect,[6] the de Haas-van Alphen effect,[7-9] Azbel'-Kaner cyclotron resonance,[10,11] and the Gantmakher size effect.[12] The majority of the experimental results, as well as their interpretation, remain unpublished. The objectives of the present investigation are: (i) to calculate a model Fermi surface for body-centered cubic tungsten from the results of nonrelativistic augmented-plane-wave (APW) energy-band calculations; (ii) to determine semiempirically the effects of spin-orbit coupling on this model Fermi surface; (iii) to compare this calculated Fermi surface and other electronic properties with the available experimental results.

Interest in the energy-band structure of tungsten dates back to calculations by Manning and Chodorow[13] in the late thirties using the cellular method. More recently, a Fermi surface for the chromium-group metals has been proposed by Lomer.[14] This model Fermi surface has been based primarily on Wood's APW calculations for iron.[15] Recently, Lomer has revised this model Fermi surface (Lomer II) and limited its application to molybdenum.[16] This revised Fermi surface is sketched in Fig. 1. It consists of two main, closed surfaces that have been described as an electron "jack" centered at the origin of the Brillouin-zone Γ and hole "octahedra" at the symmetry points H. The electron "jack" consists of an octahedral body connected to six ball-like protrusions along the $\langle 100 \rangle$ or ΓH directions. Within the "necks" which join the octahedral body to the balls are the electron "lenses." Neglecting spin-orbit coupling, these "lenses" contact the "necks" in the (100) and (110) planes. In this approximation, the electron "jack" at Γ contacts hole "octahedra" at H along the $\langle 100 \rangle$ directions in the Brillouin zone. Finally, this model predicts small hole pockets at N. In his original model (Lomer I), Lomer overlooked the presence of the ball-like protrusions on the electron surface at Γ and assumed that this surface tapered smoothly along the $\langle 100 \rangle$ directions.

In the present investigation, two fairly complete APW calculations have been carried out for tungsten, using slightly different crystal potentials. The results of these two calculations differ mainly in the calculated s-d energy separation and the $5d$ bandwidths. These $5d$ band widths vary from approximately 0.8 to 1.0 Ry, the latter value agreeing quite well with that found by Manning and Chodorow.[13] The present energy-band results are quite similar to those obtained by Manning and Chodorow, except that they found that the bottom of the $6s$ conduction band was above the bottom of the $5d$ bands while the present results indicate that it lies about 0.1 Ry below the $5d$ bands.

The Fermi surface for tungsten which results from the present nonrelativistic APW calculations agrees qualitatively with the Lomer II model shown in Fig. 1.

[1] E. Fawcett and D. Griffiths, J. Phys. Chem. Solids **23**, 1631 (1962).

[2] E. Justi and H. Scheffers, Physik. Z. **37**, 700 (1936).

[3] E. Fawcett, Phys. Rev. Letters **7**, 370 (1961); E. Fawcett, Phys. Rev. **128**, 154 (1962).

[4] N. V. Volkenshtein, V. N. Kachinskii, and L. S. Starostina, Zh. Eksperim i Teor. Fiz. **45**, 43 (1963) [English transl.: Soviet Phys.—JETP **18**, 32 (1964)].

[5] E. Fawcett and W. A. Reed, Phys. Rev. **134**, A723 (1964).

[6] J. A. Rayne and H. Sell, Phys. Rev. Letters **8**, 199 (1962); J. A. Rayne, Phys. Rev. **133**, A1104 (1964); C. K. Jones and J. A. Rayne, Proceedings of the Ninth International Conference on Low Temperature Physics, Columbus, 1964 (to be published).

[7] G. B. Brandt and J. A. Rayne, Phys. Letters **3**, 148 (1962); Phys. Rev. **132**, 1945 (1963).

[8] D. Sparlin and J. A. Marcus, Bull. Am. Phys. Soc. **8**, 258 (1963); **9**, 250 (1964).

[9] R. F. Girvan and A. V. Gold (private communication).

[10] E. Fawcett and W. M. Walsh, Jr., Phys. Rev. Letters **8**, 476 (1962).

[11] W. M. Walsh, Jr., Phys. Rev. Letters **12**, 161 (1964).

[12] W. M. Walsh, Jr. and C. C. Grimes, Phys. Rev. Letters **13**, 523 (1964).

[13] M. F. Manning and M. I. Chodorow, Phys. Rev. **56**, 789 (1939).

[14] W. M. Lomer, Proc. Phys. Soc. (London) **80**, 489 (1962).

[15] J. H. Wood, Phys. Rev. **126**, 517 (1962).

[16] W. M. Lomer, Proc. Phys. Soc. (London) **84**, 327 (1964).

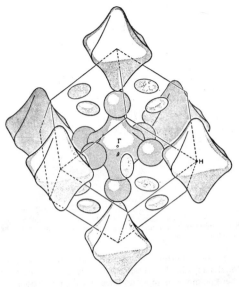

FIG. 1. A three-dimensional stretch of Lomer's revised Fermi surface for chromium-group metals.

However, there has been some reluctance to apply the Lomer II model Fermi surface for chromium-group metals to tungsten, mainly because the low-field de Haas–van Alphen results for molybdenum and tungsten differ significantly.[7] This has been attributed to an enhanced spin-orbit coupling in the latter element.[7,16] However, the data from de Haas–van Alphen measurements on tungsten by Sparlin and Marcus[8] and their interpretation by Sparlin[17] are consistent with the Lomer II model Fermi surface. According to Sparlin, the Fermi surfaces for molybdenum and tungsten differ in two respects: First, the dimensions of the hole pockets at N are smaller in tungsten than in molybdenum. Second, the extremal areas for orbits associated with the "lenses" in tungsten have not been observed, whereas they have been measured in molybdenum. Sparlin and Marcus have inferred the re-entrant nature of the electron surface at Γ from their analysis of the de Haas–van Alphen results and introduced the term electron "jack."

The most striking experimental verification of the Lomer II model Fermi surface in tungsten is a consequence of the size-effect experiments by Walsh and Grimes,[12] who mapped out the extremal linear dimensions of portions of the electron "jack" and the entire hole "octahedron" in a (110) plane. Walsh and Grimes have shown that the electron "jack" at Γ fails to contact the hole "octahedra" at H, as the nonrelativistic energy-

band results predict. Rather, these electron and hole surfaces are separated by a gap equal approximately to 5% the $\bar{\Gamma}\bar{H}$ distance. This splitting has been attributed to the effects of spin-orbit coupling.[18] Using a simplified model, it has been possible to use the measured separation between the electron "jack" and hole "octahedra" to estimate the $5d$ spin-orbit coupling parameter ξ_{5d} in metallic tungsten to be approximately 0.03 Ry (0.4 eV). Another consequence of spin-orbit coupling is that it could cause the "lenses" to disappear in tungsten.

A brief description of the present calculation is contained in the following section, including a discussion of the approximate crystal potentials which have been used. The results of these APW calculations are presented in Sec. III, including for each calculation, $E(\mathbf{k})$ curves along symmetry directions in the Brillouin zone, a density-of-states, and the resulting Fermi surface. In Sec. IV, a brief description of the simplified model used to estimate the effects of spin-orbit coupling is presented. In Sec. V, a Fermi-surface model for the group-V transition metals vanadium (V), niobium (Nb), and tantalum (Ta) is proposed. The final section contains a discussion of the present energy-band results and comparisons with experiment.

II. DESCRIPTION OF THE CALCULATION

The present nonrelativistic energy-band calculations for body-centered cubic tungsten have been carried out using the APW method,[19] as programmed for the IBM computers by Wood.[15] The crystal potential has been approximated by a "muffin-tin" potential, which is calculated by superimposing atomic potentials in a manner that has been described earlier in connection with an energy-band study of the $3d$ transition series.[20] Exchange has been treated approximately using Slater's free-electron exchange approximation.[21]

Instead of using the self-consistent atomic Hartree-Fock charge densities that have been used previously in calculations for the $3d$ transition series, the present calculations utilize potentials which have been obtained from Hartree-Fock-Slater charge densities, as provided by Herman and Skillman.[22] Unpublished calculations by the author indicate that equivalent results are obtained in the $3d$ transition series using potentials which are derived from either atomic Hartree-Fock or Hartree-Fock-Slater charge densities.

The potentials used in the present calculations have been obtained using an assumed atomic configuration of $(5d)^5(6s)^1$ for tungsten, which is probably close to that in the solid. Two fairly complete calculations have

---

[17] D. M. Sparlin, thesis, Northwestern University, 1964 (unpublished).

[18] L. F. Mattheiss and R. E. Watson, Phys. Rev. Letters 13, 526 (1964).
[19] J. C. Slater, Phys. Rev. 51, 846 (1937).
[20] L. F. Mattheiss, Phys. Rev. 134, A970 (1964).
[21] J. C. Slater, Phys. Rev. 81, 385 (1951).
[22] F. Herman and S. Skillman, *Atomic Structure Calculations* (Prentice-Hall, Inc., Englewood Cliffs, New Jersey, 1963).

TABLE I. An abbreviated tabulation of the potentials used in the present calculations for tungsten. The radial distance r is tabulated in terms of r/r_0 (where $r_0=0.005272$ a.u.) and $V(r)$ is in Ry. For both potentials, the APW sphere radius $R_s=2.59$ a.u.; the constant value of the potential between the APW spheres equals 1.466 and 1.181 Ry for V_1 and V_2, respectively.

r/r_0	$-V_1(r)$	$-V_2(r)$
1	27256.823	27211.528
2	13229.229	13194.117
3	8568.264	8540.645
4	6248.878	6226.470
6	3950.230	3933.161
8	2818.407	2803.394
10	2149.628	2136.018
12	1710.687	1698.456
16	1174.998	1165.263
20	865.262	857.146
24	666.864	659.589
28	530.645	523.922
36	358.680	353.076
44	257.127	252.636
52	191.808	188.103
60	147.461	144.138
76	92.926	89.944
92	62.301	59.723
108	43.921	41.796
124	32.750	30.523
156	19.067	17.849
188	12.350	11.368
220	8.505	7.670
252	6.121	5.408
316	3.527	3.009
380	2.310	1.920
444	1.727	1.408
508	1.483	1.197

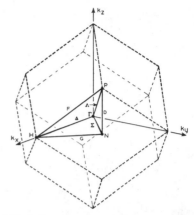

FIG. 2. The Brillouin zone for the body-centered cubic structure with symmetry points and lines labeled in accordance with the standard notation.

been carried through using two slightly different potentials, $V_1(r)$ and $V_2(r)$. These potentials differ only in the exchange contribution to the potential. In $V_2(r)$, the exchange potential in $V_1(r)$ has been reduced by 30%. This has been done in order to vary the $6s$-$5d$ energy separation in the simplest possible manner without modifying the potential drastically.

An abbreviated tabulation of the two potentials $V_1(r)$ and $V_2(r)$ which have been used in the present calculations for tungsten is presented in Table I. In this table, the radial distance r is tabulated in terms of r/r_0, where $r_0=0.005272$ atomic units (a.u.) for tungsten. This radial mesh corresponds to the one used by Herman and Skillman,[22] being proportional to the inverse cube-root of the atomic number Z.

The lattice constant for tungsten which has been used in these calculations is the room-temperature value tabulated by Pearson[23] of 5.9811 a.u. (3.1651 Å). The lattice constant at 4.2°K has been estimated to be approximately 5.973 a.u. (3.161 Å),[12] using the thermal-expansion data of Nix and MacNair.[24]

III. RESULTS

The Brillouin zone for the body-centered cubic Bravais lattice is shown in Fig. 2. In this figure as well

[22] W. B. Pearson, *A Handbook of Lattice Spacings and Structures of Metals and Alloys* (Pergamon Press, Inc., New York, 1958).
[24] F. C. Nix and D. MacNair, Phys. Rev. **61**, 74 (1942).

as in the following discussions, the notation due to Bouckaert, Smoluchowski, and Wigner[25] is used to label symmetry points and lines and the corresponding irreducible representations.

Two extensive APW calculations have been carried out for tungsten using the potentials $V_1(r)$ and $V_2(r)$ of Table I. The results of these calculations, which will be referred to either as W_1 and W_2 or $E_1(\mathbf{k})$ and $E_2(\mathbf{k})$, are shown in Figs. 3 and 4, respectively. Here, the energy bands $E_1(\mathbf{k})$ and $E_2(\mathbf{k})$ are plotted along symmetry directions in the Brillouin zone for tungsten. These APW results have been obtained at a total of 55 points in 1/48 of the Brillouin zone. The W_1 results are listed in Table II. The calculations have been carried out for $\mathbf{k}$ values which are distributed on a uniform mesh in the Brillouin zone such that the entire zone is subdivided into 1024 cubic subzones, each having edge dimensions $(\pi/4a)$.

The $5d$-band states are readily distinguished in Figs. 3 and 4. At the symmetry points, they correspond to the following states: Γ_{12}, $\Gamma_{25'}$; $H_{25'}$, H_{12}; N_3, N_4, N_1, N_2, N_1; P_3, P_4. It is clear from Fig. 4 that the $5d$ bandwidth is approximately 0.8 Ry. The state with Γ_1 symmetry represents the bottom of the $6s$ conduction band in both cases, while $N_{1'}$ represents a $6p$-type state. The ordering of states at symmetry points in the Brillouin zone in Figs. 3 and 4 is identical with that obtained by Wood for iron,[15] who found a $3d$ bandwidth slightly less than 0.5 Ry. The main differences between the results shown in Figs. 3 and 4 are the $5d$ bandwidth and the relative position of $E(N_{1'})$ with respect to the Fermi energy.

The energy-band results can be used to calculate a density-of-states for tungsten. However, due to the

[25] L. P. Bouckaert, R. Smoluchowski, and E. Wigner, Phys. Rev. **50**, 58 (1936).

TABLE II. Energy-band results for tungsten obtained using the potential $V_1(r)$ of Table I. Energies are in Ry, the zero of energy coinciding with the constant potential between the APW spheres, 1.466 Ry. The eigenvalues are identified using the notation of Bouckaert, Smoluchowski, and Wigner.

$4(a/\pi)\mathbf{k}$	Band 1	Band 2	Band 3	Band 4	Band 5	Band 6
$\Gamma(0,0,0)$	1 0.341	25′ 0.746	25′ 0.746	25′ 0.746	12 0.957	12 0.957
$\Delta(1,0,0)$	1 0.366	5 0.745	5 0.745	2′ 0.759	2 0.920	1 0.973
$\Delta(2,0,0)$	1 0.434	5 0.746	5 0.746	2′ 0.795	2 0.828	1 1.013
$\Delta(3,0,0)$	1 0.517	2 0.717	5 0.762	5 0.762	2′ 0.850	1 1.067
$\Delta(4,0,0)$	1 0.571	2 0.610	5 0.804	5 0.804	2′ 0.923	1 1.131
$\Delta(5,0,0)$	2 0.520	1 0.552	5 0.877	5 0.877	2′ 1.006	1 1.225
$\Delta(6,0,0)$	2 0.452	1 0.484	5 0.981	5 0.981	2′ 1.086	1 1.356
$\Delta(7,0,0)$	2 0.410	1 0.421	5 1.099	5 1.099	2′ 1.147	1 1.49
$H(8,0,0)$	12 0.396	12 0.396	25′ 1.169	25′ 1.169	25′ 1.169	15 1.554
$\Sigma(1,1,0)$	1 0.389	2 0.716	1 0.737	3 0.797	1 0.923	4 0.960
$(2,1,0)$	+ 0.448	− 0.699	+ 0.726	− 0.854	+ 0.871	+ 0.997
$(3,1,0)$	+ 0.514	+ 0.695	− 0.704	+ 0.831	− 0.923	+ 1.057
$(4,1,0)$	+ 0.551	+ 0.629	− 0.737	+ 0.844	− 1.002	+ 1.142
$(5,1,0)$	+ 0.521	+ 0.573	− 0.803	+ 0.867	− 1.085	+ 1.260
$(6,1,0)$	+ 0.467	+ 0.503	− 0.898	+ 0.938	− 1.154	+ 1.41
$G(7,1,0)$	1 0.428	4 0.441	3 1.011	1 1.038	2 1.179	4 1.538
$\Sigma(2,2,0)$	1 0.473	2 0.655	1 0.729	1 0.927	3 0.939	4 0.976
$(3,2,0)$	+ 0.487	− 0.638	+ 0.751	+ 0.921	− 1.027	+ 1.028
$(4,2,0)$	+ 0.495	− 0.655	+ 0.718	+ 0.911	− 1.115	+ 1.144
$(5,2,0)$	+ 0.498	+ 0.651	− 0.707	+ 0.867	− 1.181	+ 1.304
$G(6,2,0)$	1 0.487	4 0.568	3 0.790	1 0.877	2 1.202	4 1.45
$\Sigma(3,3,0)$	1 0.458	2 0.602	1 0.856	1 0.975	4 1.006	3 1.128
$(4,3,0)$	+ 0.455	− 0.601	+ 0.854	+ 0.969	+ 1.104	− 1.203
$G(5,3,0)$	1 0.467	3 0.637	4 0.761	1 0.901	2 1.226	4 1.249
$N(4,4,0)$	1 0.435	2 0.582	1′ 0.976	1 0.978	4 1.023	3 1.235
$\Lambda(1,1,1)$	1 0.411	3 0.709	3 0.709	1 0.840	3 0.942	3 0.942
$(2,1,1)$	+ 0.466	+ 0.688	− 0.688	− 0.894	+ 0.910	+ 0.988
$(3,1,1)$	+ 0.522	− 0.657	+ 0.705	− 0.851	+ 0.985	+ 1.053
$(4,1,1)$	+ 0.561	− 0.603	+ 0.734	− 0.851	+ 1.032	+ 1.164
$(5,1,1)$	− 0.541	+ 0.569	+ 0.746	− 0.904	+ 1.078	+ 1.317
$(6,1,1)$	− 0.488	+ 0.516	+ 0.809	− 0.997	+ 1.123	+ 1.49
$F(7,1,1)$	3 0.453	3 0.453	1 0.908	3 1.110	3 1.110	3 1.635
$(2,2,1)$	+ 0.499	− 0.647	+ 0.686	+ 0.935	− 0.976	+ 1.004
$(3,2,1)$	0.508	0.628	0.718	0.921	1.019	1.104
$(4,2,1)$	0.514	0.623	0.727	0.910	1.064	1.232
$(5,2,1)$	0.522	0.626	0.688	0.911	1.113	1.40
$(6,2,1)$	+ 0.514	− 0.573	+ 0.714	+ 0.955	− 1.132	− 1.539
$(3,3,1)$	+ 0.484	− 0.599	+ 0.808	+ 0.971	+ 1.009	+ 1.203
$(4,3,1)$	0.473	0.596	0.827	0.964	1.060	1.291
$(5,3,1)$	+ 0.491	+ 0.623	− 0.752	+ 0.928	− 1.122	− 1.378
$D(4,4,1)$	1 0.461	4 0.582	3 0.914	1 0.986	2 1.026	3 1.312
$\Lambda(2,2,2)$	1 0.559	3 0.629	3 0.629	3 0.970	3 0.970	1 1.113
$(3,2,2)$	+ 0.556	− 0.616	+ 0.674	− 0.955	+ 1.015	+ 1.224
$(4,2,2)$	+ 0.544	− 0.609	+ 0.720	− 0.946	+ 1.044	+ 1.347
$(5,2,2)$	+ 0.567	− 0.600	+ 0.680	− 0.967	+ 1.056	+ 1.51
$F(6,2,2)$	3 0.586	3 0.586	1 0.629	3 1.032	3 1.032	1 1.672
$(3,3,2)$	+ 0.553	− 0.596	+ 0.722	+ 0.987	− 1.014	+ 1.335
$(4,3,2)$	0.531	0.599	0.762	0.987	1.037	1.43
$(5,3,2)$	+ 0.539	+ 0.619	− 0.722	+ 0.980	− 1.049	− 1.524
$D(4,4,2)$	1 0.530	4 0.587	3 0.809	1 1.004	2 1.030	3 1.45
$\Lambda(3,3,3)$	3 0.605	3 0.605	1 0.681	3 1.016	3 1.016	1 1.45
$(4,3,3)$	+ 0.575	− 0.633	+ 0.710	− 1.015	+ 1.031	+ 1.549
$F(5,3,3)$	1 0.554	3 0.676	3 0.676	1 1.020	3 1.020	1 1.652
$D(4,4,3)$	4 0.606	1 0.610	3 0.717	1 1.025	2 1.033	3 1.596
$P(4,4,4)$	4 0.647	4 0.647	4 0.647	3 1.033	3 1.033	4 1.725

limited number of points in the Brillouin zone at which calculations have been carried out, this density-of-states would be necessarily crude. In order to obtain a more meaningful density of states, a simple interpolation scheme has been devised. This scheme approximates the nth-band eigenvalue for an energy-band state whose wave vector lies within a given cubic subzone by a weighted average of the nth-band APW eigenvalues at the cube corners. This method is such that along a cube edge, the interpolation is linear, on a cube face, it is planar, and at the cube center, the weighting factors are equal.

This interpolation scheme is admittedly poor along symmetry directions and in symmetry planes because it does not allow states with different symmetry to cross. However, as the mesh is reduced, a large proportion of wave vectors fall at general points in the Brillouin zone where such crossings are forbidden. Therefore, the results of such an interpolation scheme are expected to reproduce the gross features of the actual density of

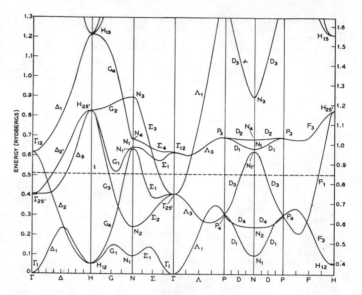

FIG. 3. Energy bands $E_1(\mathbf{k})$ along symmetry directions in the Brillouin zone for tungsten. The energy scale to the right corresponds to that of Table II. To the left, the zero of energy coincides with $E(\Gamma_1)$.

states. However, some of the peaks and singularities in the actual density of states may be broadened or washed out completely in the interpolation procedure.

The results of the density-of-states calculations for W_1 and W_2 are shown in Figs. 5 and 6, respectively. These figures result from calculations involving 221, 184 points in the Brillouin zone. Decreasing the total number of points to 65, 536 causes little change in the results. From Figs. 5 and 6, the Fermi energies for W_1

and W_2 are 0.850 and 1.155 Ry, respectively, as indicated by the dashed horizontal lines of Figs. 3 and 4, respectively.

Using the energy-band results tabulated in Table II, the nonrelativistic Fermi surfaces for W_1 and W_2 have been calculated in the (100) and (110) planes, and these are shown in Figs. 7(b) and 7(c), respectively. For comparison, the corresponding Fermi surface which results from Wood's iron calculations is drawn [7(a)], assuming

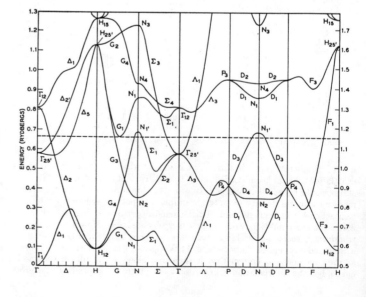

FIG. 4. Energy bands $E_2(\mathbf{k})$ along symmetry directions in the Brillouin zone for tungsten.

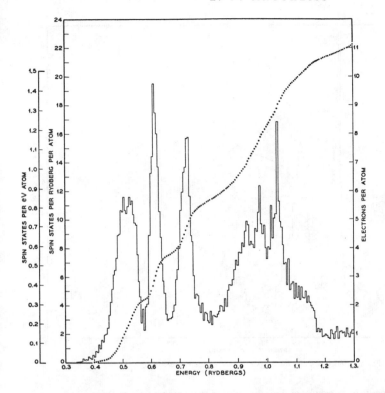

FIG. 5. Density-of-states curve for tungsten based on the W_1 results. The units to the left are states of one spin per eV atom and states of one spin/Ry atom. The dotted line is the integrated density of states; the corresponding units to the right are electrons per atom.

six occupied electronic states per atom. In computing the Fermi surfaces in Figs. 7(a), 7(b), and 7(c), graphical interpolation has been used along symmetry and non-symmetry lines in the (100) and (110) planes to map out the Fermi surfaces as precisely as possible.

Convergence studies indicate that the APW eigenvalues for tungsten converge at approximately the same rate that Wood found in iron.[15] Sufficient APW basis functions have been included in the present calculations for tungsten to ensure convergence to 0.001 or 0.002 Ry at symmetry points, along symmetry lines, and in symmetry planes in the Brillouin zone. For convenience, the number of basis functions has been restricted for calculations at general points in the Brillouin zone such that these eigenvalues converge to approximately 0.004 Ry.

IV. SPIN-ORBIT COUPLING

The size-effect results of Walsh and Grimes indicate that the electron "jack" and hole "octahedron" are separated by a gap along $\langle 100 \rangle$ which is equal to approximately 5% the ΓH distance. This gap has been attributed to spin-orbit splitting of the Δ_5 state at the Fermi energy in tungsten.[18] By means of a simplified tight-binding calculation involving the present W_1

energy bands, it has been possible to estimate the $5d$ spin-orbit coupling parameter in metallic tungsten to be approximately 0.03 Ry (0.4 eV). A similar approach has been used by Friedel et al. to study spin-orbit effects in the face-centered cubic transition metals.[26]

The effects of spin-orbit coupling on the W_1 energy bands along Δ are shown in Fig. 8. In Fig. 8(a), the nonrelativistic results of Fig. 3 are replotted, using the double-group notation to label the various states.[27] From Fig. 8(a), it is clear that four energy bands cross the Fermi energy, three with Δ_7 and one with Δ_6 symmetry. The upper and lower Δ_6 states would also cross the Fermi energy if they were not repelled by s-d mixing.

It is possible to obtain a semiquantitative estimate of these spin-orbit effects by assuming tight-binding $5d$ wave functions for the $\Delta_{2'}$, Δ_5, and Δ_2 states. If it is further assumed that these $5d$ wave functions have the same radial function $P_{5d}(r)$, then the spin-orbit effects can be described in terms of a single spin-orbit parameter ξ_{5d}. Along $\langle 001 \rangle$, the $\Delta_{2'}$, Δ_5, and Δ_2 tight-binding wave functions can be characterized by the polynomials $xy(\Delta_{2'})$, xz, $yz(\Delta_5)$, and $(x^2-y^2)(\Delta_2)$, respec-

[26] J. Friedel, P. Lenglart, and G. Leman, J. Phys. Chem. Solids 25, 781 (1964).
[27] R. J. Elliott, Phys. Rev. 96, 280 (1954).

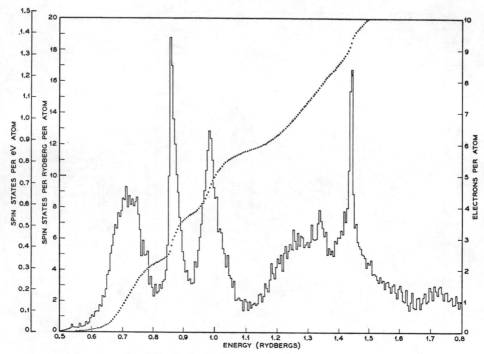

FIG. 6. Density of states for tungsten based on the W₂ results.

tively. Using the coupling coefficients tabulated by Koster *et al.*[28] to form functions which transform irreducibly under the double-group, it is straightforward to calculate diagonal and off-diagonal matrix elements of the spin-orbit operator $H_{so} = \xi(r)\mathbf{l}\cdot\mathbf{s}$ among these functions. Neglecting off-diagonal matrix elements, it is found that

$$E(\Delta_7) = E(\Delta_5) + \tfrac{1}{2}\xi_{5d},$$
$$E(\Delta_6) = E(\Delta_5) - \tfrac{1}{2}\xi_{5d}. \qquad (1)$$

The corresponding calculation at Γ (or H) yields the result

$$E(\Gamma_{7^+}) = E(\Gamma_{25'}) + \xi_{5d},$$
$$E(\Gamma_{8^+}) = E(\Gamma_{25'}) - \tfrac{1}{2}\xi_{5d}. \qquad (2)$$

The Hamiltonian matrix for the Δ_7 states has the following form when $\xi_{5d}\neq 0$:

$$\begin{vmatrix} E(\Delta_{2'}) & (\sqrt{2}/2)\xi_{5d} & -\xi_{5d} \\ (\sqrt{2}/2)\xi_{5d} & E(\Delta_5) + \tfrac{1}{2}\xi_{5d} & (\sqrt{2}/2)\xi_{5d} \\ -\xi_{5d} & (\sqrt{2}/2)\xi_{5d} & E(\Delta_2) \end{vmatrix}. \qquad (3)$$

By means of a unitary transformation, this matrix can

---

[28] G. F. Koster, J. O. Dimmick, R. G. Wheeler, and H. Statz, *Properties of the Thirty-Two Point Groups* (MIT Press, Cambridge, Massachusetts, 1963).

be reduced to its proper form at Γ (or H):

$$\begin{vmatrix} E(\Gamma_{25'}) + \xi_{5d} & 0 & 0 \\ 0 & E(\Gamma_{25'}) - \tfrac{1}{2}\xi_{5d} & (\sqrt{6}/2)\xi_{5d} \\ 0 & (\sqrt{6}/2)\xi_{5d} & E(\Gamma_{12}) \end{vmatrix}. \qquad (4)$$

The first row and column represent the Γ_{7^+} state, while the remaining two rows and columns correspond to Γ_{8^+} states. The corresponding matrix for the Δ_6 states is complicated by s-d mixing. Since the Δ_6 states do not cross, it is reasonable to assume that the effects due to off-diagonal spin-orbit matrix elements connecting the central Δ_6 state with the upper and lower ones cancel approximately and can be neglected.

The three-by-three secular determinant for the Δ_7 states has been solved as a function of ξ_{5d}. It has been found that the gap Δk between the central Δ_6 and Δ_7 states at the Fermi energy is 5% the $\overline{\Gamma H}$ distance when ξ_{5d} is approximately 0.03 Ry. The results are shown in Fig. 8(b).

The upper Δ_7 state barely crosses the Fermi energy when $\xi_{5d}\simeq 0.03$ Ry. This state produces the "lenses" within the "necks" of the electron "jack." Spin-orbit coupling reduces the size of these "lenses," separates these "lenses" from the "necks" in the (100) and (110) planes, and could cause the "lenses" to disappear

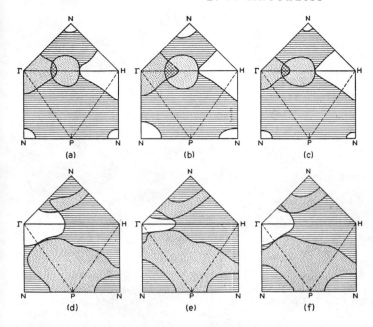

FIG. 7. Central (100) and (110) cross sections of the chromium-(a, b, c)- and vanadium-(d, e, f)-group Fermi surfaces, calculated using energy bands for iron (a, d), W_1(b, e), and W_2(c, f), respectively.

entirely in tungsten. However, spin-orbit coupling is not expected to have any other important consequences in tungsten as far as the topology of the Fermi surface is concerned.

V. FERMI SURFACE IN VANADIUM-GROUP METALS

The fact that the three model Fermi surfaces in Figs. 7(a), 7(b), and 7(c) are qualitatively similar confirms Lomer's suggestion that the basic Fermi-surface topology for the chromium or group-VI transition metals is relatively insensitive to small changes in the band structure.[14] In the case of the group-V transition metals, the situation is somewhat more delicate since the Fermi energy is expected to fall near the energy-band state with $\Gamma_{25'}$ symmetry, $E(\Gamma_{25'})$. Small changes in the band structure could lead to vastly different Fermi surfaces. Experimental data for the group-V transition metals is limited, due to the lack of pure single crystals.

Nevertheless, it seems worthwhile to discuss the Fermi surface for group-V transition metals which results from the present nonrelativistic energy-band calculations for tungsten, especially since it is remarkably similar to the corresponding Fermi surface which is obtained from Wood's iron calculations.[15] Assuming a rigid-band model, the Fermi energies for the vanadium-group metals (as predicted from the present tungsten and previous iron calculations) lie slightly below $E(\Gamma_{25'})$. The corresponding Fermi surfaces

are shown in Figs. 7(d), 7(e), and 7(f). These represent central sections of the (100) and (110) planes in the body-centered cubic Brillouin zone.

The topology of this Fermi surface is evident from the three-dimensional drawing in Fig. 9. The inner and

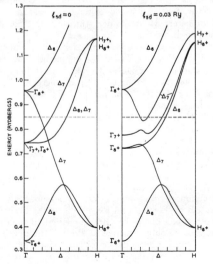

FIG. 8. Results of a simplified spin-orbit calculation along Δ for tungsten with $\xi_{5d}=0$ and 0.03 Ry.

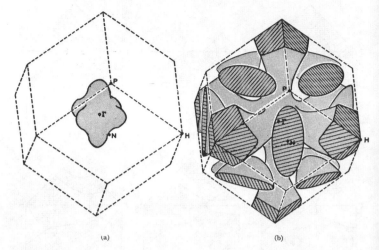

FIG. 9. Proposed Fermi surface for the vanadium-group transition metals.

(a)

(b)

outer hole sheets are indicated in Figs. 9(a) and 9(b), respectively. The outer sheet consists of hole tubes along the ⟨100⟩ axes plus large ellipsoids at N. The iron results predict that these ellipsoids at N are joined by necks along $\bar{\Gamma}\bar{N}$ to the outer hole surface. Otherwise, the three calculations predict qualitatively similar results.

From Figs. 7(d), 7(e), and 7(f) there are points of accidental degeneracy in the (100) and (110) planes where the inner closed hole sheet at Γ contacts the outer, multiply connected hole surface. These degeneracies will be removed by spin-orbit coupling. However, they could lead to magnetic breakdown in vanadium or niobium, where the spin-orbit coupling parameter is smaller.

In the previous section, it was shown that spin-orbit coupling reduces the sixfold $\Gamma_{25'}$ degeneracy, and splits this state into a doubly (Γ_{7+}) and a fourfold (Γ_{8+}) degenerate state. From Eq. (2), the energy of the Γ_{8+} state $E(\Gamma_{8+}) = E(\Gamma_{25'}) - \frac{1}{2}\xi_{5d}$ if the off-diagonal matrix element connecting the two Γ_{8+} states is neglected. Therefore, spin-orbit splitting of the $\Gamma_{25'}$ state, which is presumably of the order of 0.03 Ry for the $5d$ transition metals, could push Γ_{8+} below the Fermi energy in tantalum. In terms of Figs. 7(d), 7(e), and 7(f), this would extend the dotted region into Γ, producing a Fermi surface which consists of closed hole surfaces about N and H in the Brillouin zone.

Preliminary magnetoresistance measurements on tantalum by Fawcett and Reed indicate the likelihood of open orbits along the ⟨100⟩ directions, though this conclusion is only tentative at the present time.[29] In terms of the present model Fermi surface for the group-V transition metals, these results imply that Γ_{8+} remains

above the Fermi energy in tantalum, and the Fermi-surface topology is qualitatively similar to that shown in Figs. 7(d), 7(e), 7(f), 9(a), and 9(b) with the accidental degeneracies removed by spin-orbit coupling. In addition, recent high-field Hall-effect measurements in normal niobium by Reed, Fawcett, and Kim[30] show that the density of carriers equals one hole per atom, a result which is also consistent with this model.

VI. DISCUSSION OF THE RESULTS

The nonrelativistic energy bands for tungsten are very similar to those found previously using the APW method for the body-centered cubic $3d$ transition metals,[15,20] aside from a substantial increase in the d bandwidth. This increased bandwidth can be attributed to increased overlap of the $5d$ functions. Comparing the Hartree-Fock-Slater atomic $3d$ and $5d$ wave functions for chromium and tungsten, respectively,[22] we find that the $5d$ radial functions are more extended than the relatively compact $3d$ functions. In order to determine the relative bandwidths for the $3d$, $4d$, and $5d$ group-VI transition metals, limited APW calculations have been performed for (nonmagnetic) chromium and molybdenum, assuming $(d)^5(s)^1$ atomic configurations and using the methods described in Sec. II to calculate the corresponding potentials. Taking the energy difference $\Delta_d \equiv E(H_{25'}) - E(H_{12})$ as a measure of the d bandwidth, Δ_d values of 0.51, 0.68, 0.77, and 1.04 Ry are obtained for Cr($3d$), Mo($4d$), W_1($5d$), and W_2($5d$), respectively. The large difference between the W_1 and W_2 $5d$ bandwidths indicates the extent to which this parameter depends on the potential.

The neglect of relativistic effects in the present energy-

[29] E. Fawcett and W. A. Reed (private communication).

[30] W. A. Reed, E. Fawcett, and Y. B. Kim (to be published).

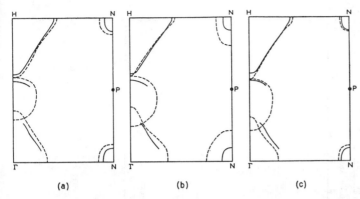

FIG. 10. Central (110) section of the tungsten Fermi surface, comparing the experimental dimensions (solid lines) with those calculated from the iron (a), W_1 (b), and W_2 (c) energy bands (dashed lines).

(a)   (b)   (c)

band calculations for tungsten represents a serious deficiency. Herman and Skillman have indicated the importance of mass-velocity and Darwin corrections in the heavier atoms.[22] Herman *et al.* have shown that these corrections for the outermost s and p electrons can be very large in tetrahedrally bonded semiconductors.[31] Clearly, these same corrections represent an important factor in determining the correct s-d energy separation in metallic tungsten as well. Owing to the *ad hoc* nature of the potentials which have been used in the present calculations for tungsten, the uncertainty in the nonrelativistic s-d energy separation is comparable in magnitude with these relativistic corrections. In view of this situation, it is reasonable to neglect these relativistic corrections. However, it is necessary to keep in mind that any detailed agreement between theory and experiment could be fortuitous, owing to cancellation of errors.

It would be interesting to apply the Slater-Koster tight-binding interpolation scheme[32] to tungsten since the simplified treatment of spin-orbit coupling that is described in Sec. IV could then be applied at more general points in the Brillouin zone. Our attempts to apply this method to the tungsten energy bands indicate that a large number of parameters would be required in order to obtain an accurate fit. For example, if five tight-binding parameters are chosen to fit the state with Δ_5 symmetry at Γ, H, and three evenly spaced points along Δ in the W_1 calculations, the tight-binding results at the remaining points along Δ differ from the APW results by as much as 0.01 Ry. This implies that either a large number of tight-binding parameters are required to fit the tungsten $5d$ bands or the shape of the Δ_5 band is affected by $6p$-$5d$ interactions. The latter alternative would complicate the simplified treatment of spin-orbit coupling that is presented in Sec. IV and vitiate our estimate of the spin-orbit parameter ξ_{5d}.

Comparisons between the theoretically and experimentally determined Fermi surfaces in tungsten do not test critically the accuracy of the present calculations. This is clear from Figs. 7(a), 7(b), and 7(c), where the nonrelativistic Fermi surface is found to be rather insensitive to the d bandwidth. There are some features of the Fermi surface which provide indirect information about the $5d$ bandwidth and the s-d energy separation in tungsten. However, accurate relativistic calculations, including spin-orbit coupling, would be required in order to extract this information reliably.

The most useful experimental information about the larger pieces of Fermi surface in tungsten have been obtained by Walsh and Grimes, using the size-effect technique.[12] Their results, which map out the linear dimensions of portions of the electron "jack" and the entire hole "octahedron" in a (110) plane in tungsten, are indicated by the solid lines in Fig. 10. These size-effect results are in excellent agreement with the recent magnetoacoustic data of Jones and Rayne.[6] The ellipsoids at N are also drawn in with solid lines in Fig. 10, using the dimensions obtained by Sparlin from his de Haas–van Alphen results.[17] The dashed lines in Fig. 10(a) represent the Fermi surface for chromium-group metals that is obtained from Wood's iron calculations.[15] The corresponding dashed lines in Figs. 10(b) and 10(c) are the Fermi surfaces obtained from the present W_1 and W_2 calculations, respectively.

The agreement between the measured and calculated Fermi surface dimensions in the (110) plane is fairly good. As described in Sec. IV, the fact that the electron "jack" and hole "octahedra" fail to touch along Δ is readily explained in terms of spin-orbit coupling. Spin-orbit coupling also causes the "lenses" inside the "necks" of the electron "jack" (which are omitted from Fig. 10) to be reduced in size and perhaps removed entirely in tungsten.

The dimensions of the hole ellipsoids at N are determined by the energy difference between $E(N_{1'})$ and the Fermi energy. Since $N_{1'}$ is primarily a $6p$ state, this energy difference depends on the energy separation

[31] F. Herman, C. D. Kuglin, K. F. Cuff, and R. L. Kortum, Phys. Rev. Letters 11, 541 (1963).
[32] J. C. Slater and G. F. Koster, Phys. Rev. 94, 1498 (1954).

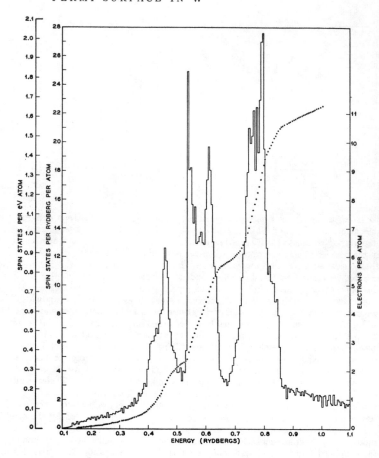

Fig. 11. Density of states
for iron based on Wood's
energy-band results.

between the s-p and d bands. In the W_1 calculation, $E(N_{1'})$ is approximately 0.13 Ry above the Fermi energy and the dimensions of these ellipsoids are large. In the W_2 calculation, this energy difference has been reduced to 0.025 Ry with a corresponding reduction in the ellipsoid dimensions. Sparlin has deduced that the major axis of these ellipsoids is along $\langle 100 \rangle$, with the minor axes along $\langle 110 \rangle$.[17] This result is consistent with the present calculations, which also predict that the larger and smaller of the minor axes are in the $\bar{\Gamma}\bar{N}$ and $\bar{H}\bar{N}$ directions, respectively.

Assuming parabolic bands and using experimentally determined cyclotron masses, Sparlin has estimated that $E(N_{1'})$ is approximately 0.28 eV (0.02 Ry) above the Fermi energy in tungsten. Using either the W_1 or W_2 energy-band results, a surface of constant energy which is 0.02 Ry below $E(N_{1'})$ predicts axes for the general ellipsoids which are within a few percent of the values obtained by Sparlin.

According to Fig. 7, the dimensions and shape of the hole "octahedron" at H are relatively insensitive to the details of the band structure. This is not true for the electron "jack" at Γ. Changes in the s-d energy separation and the d bandwidth affect the relative sizes of the octahedral body and the balls which make up this "jack." It is found that the position of the "neck" along Δ is approximately proportional to the d bandwidth. The size-effect results suggest that a plane through a "neck" intersects the Δ axis at a distance from Γ which is 27% of the $\bar{\Gamma}\bar{H}$ distance. In terms of the present nonrelativistic results, this implies that actual $5d$ bandwidth in tungsten is closer to that predicted by the W_1 rather than the W_2 calculations.

An accurate calculation of the cyclotron masses for orbits on the larger pieces of Fermi surface in tungsten is difficult due to the small number of points in the Brillouin zone at which energy-band results have been obtained. Although graphical interpolation is adequate for estimating Fermi-surface dimensions and areas in a given plane, the rate of change of area is more difficult to estimate using these techniques.

An approximate calculation of the cyclotron mass has been made for the extremal orbit around the hole "octahedron" at H with the magnetic field in a $\langle 100 \rangle$ direction. The calculated values for m_c/m_0 are found to be 0.93 and 0.82 for W_1 and W_2, respectively, with an estimated error of about 10%. These masses have been measured by Walsh[33] and Sparlin,[17] who find values of 1.02 and 1.06–1.11, respectively. By comparison, Wood's energy bands for iron predict $m_c/m_0 \simeq 1.63$. Whether the discrepancies between the calculated and experimental values for this cyclotron mass are due to the neglect of relativistic effects, overestimation of the $5d$ bandwidth, or electron-phonon effects is still uncertain.

The similarity between the density of states for W_1 (Fig. 5) and W_2 (Fig. 6) suggests that the gross features of the density-of-states curves for body-centered cubic transition metals are only slightly affected by appreciable changes in the d bandwidth. This similarity is further reflected by the density-of-states curve for iron which is shown in Fig. 11. This density of states has been calculated using the interpolation procedure that is described in Sec. III and Wood's energy-band results. This density of states for iron is similar to one obtained by Wohlfarth and Cornwell,[34] which also was based on Wood's results. However, Wohlfarth and Cornwell fitted these results using the tight-binding interpolation scheme. Using thirty parameters to represent the $4s$, $4p$, and $3d$ bands, Wohlfarth and Cornwell have calculated a density of states which exhibits many sharp peaks. Most of this fine structure in the density of states has been presumably lost in the present calculation as a result of the relatively crude interpolation procedures that have been used.

Assuming a rigid-band density-of-states model for the body-centered cubic transition metals, the combined results of Figs. 5, 6, and 11 suggest that there are three peaks in the density of states below the Fermi energy for the group-VI transition metals. Above the Fermi

energy, there is a relatively broad peak, with a fairly sharp spike near the top of the d band. Measurements of the specific-heat coefficients γ for the $3d$, $4d$, and $5d$ transition metals and alloys by Cheng et al.,[35] Morin and Maita,[36] and Bucher et al.,[37] respectively, indicate the presence of the first peak in the density of states below the group-VI Fermi energy. Outside this range, structure changes prevent any detailed comparisons with experiment.

In the case of tungsten, a recent measurement of γ by Maita, using a sample with a resistivity ratio of 20 000, has been reported by Geballe.[38] Maita finds $\gamma = 2.0 \times 10^{-4}$ cal/mole^{-1} deg^{-2}, which corresponds to a density of states at the Fermi energy $N(0) = 0.18$ states of one spin/eV atom. This result is in fair agreement with the values of approximately 0.28 and 0.16 states of one spin/eV atom that are obtained from the present W_1 and W_2 calculations, respectively.

In conclusion, the fact that these nonrelativistic energy-band results for tungsten are in good qualitative agreement with experiment leads to the hope that approximate energy bands and Fermi surfaces for other $5d$ transition metals can be calculated nonrelativistically. However, preliminary calculations for hexagonal rhenium indicate a rather complicated Fermi surface which could be severely modified by spin-orbit and other relativistic corrections.

Note added in proof. The results of relativistic energy-band calculations for tungsten, [T. L. Loucks, Phys. Rev. Letters **14**, 693 (1965)], are in good qualitative agreement with the present results.

ACKNOWLEDGMENTS

The author is grateful to W. M. Walsh, Jr. and J. H. Condon for helpful discussions regarding the experimental results and their interpretation. He is indebted to J. H. Wood for providing the APW programs that have been used in this investigation.

[33] W. M. Walsh, Jr. (private communication).
[34] E. P. Wohlfarth and J. F. Cornwell, Phys. Rev. Letters **7**, 342 (1961).

[35] C. H. Cheng, C. T. Wei, and P. A. Beck, Phys. Rev. **120**, 426 (1960).
[36] F. J. Morin and J. P. Maita, Phys. Rev. **129**, 1115 (1963).
[37] E. Bucher, F. Heiniger, and J. Muller, Proceedings of the Ninth International Conference on Low Temperature Physics, Columbus, 1964 (to be published).
[38] T. H. Geballe, Rev. Mod. Phys. **36**, 134 (1964).

PHYSICAL REVIEW   VOLUME 143, NUMBER 2   MARCH 1966

Relativistic Electronic Structure in Crystals. II. Fermi Surface of Tungsten*

T. L. Loucks

Institute for Atomic Research and Department of Physics, Iowa State University, Ames, Iowa
(Received 10 September 1965)

The relativistic augmented-plane-wave method developed in the first paper of this series has been applied to tungsten. Relativistic effects on the energy bands and the Fermi surface are presented. The angular dependence of de Haas–van Alphen frequencies, as well as other experimental results, are determined from the theoretical Fermi surface. A comparison with experimental results supports the general conclusion that relativistic effects reduce the size of the Fermi surface of tungsten.

INTRODUCTION

IN the first paper of this series[1] (hereafter referred to as THEORY) the derivation was given of a relativistic method for calculating the electronic structure of crystals. This method can be considered a relativistic generalization of the augmented plane wave (APW) method of Slater.[2] For this reason it will be referred to as the RAPW method. The basis function consists of an expansion of 4-component central field orbitals of the Dirac Hamiltonian inside the APW spheres and a Dirac plane wave outside. The choice of the expansion coefficients was discussed in THEORY and the following expression for the matrix elements was developed:

$$M\binom{N\,M}{n\,m} = (k_N{}^2 - E)\Omega_{nN}\delta_{mM}$$

$$+ 4\pi R^2 \sum_{\kappa} D_{\kappa}\binom{N\,M}{n\,m} j_l(k_n R)$$

$$\times \{ j_l(k_N R)c f_{\kappa}(R,E)/g_{\kappa}(R,E) - j_{l'}(k_N R)k_N S_{\kappa} \}, \quad (1)$$

where

$$\Omega_{nN} = \Omega\delta_{nN} - 4\pi R^2 j_1(|\mathbf{k}_N - \mathbf{k}_n| R)/|\mathbf{k}_N - \mathbf{k}_n|. \quad (2)$$

In this equation $\mathbf{k}_n = \mathbf{k} + \mathbf{K}_n$ where $\mathbf{k}$ is the electron wave vector and $\mathbf{K}_n$ is a reciprocal lattice vector. E is the characteristic energy in the secular equation. The unit cell volume is Ω, and R is the radius of the APW spheres. The κ summation is over positive and negative integers (not zero). The following rules specify l and l':

$$\begin{aligned} l = \kappa \quad &\text{and} \quad l' = \kappa - 1, \quad (\kappa > 0), \\ l = -\kappa - 1 \quad &\text{and} \quad l' = -\kappa, \quad (\kappa < 0). \end{aligned} \quad (3)$$

Spherical Bessel functions of order l are written $j_l(x)$. S_{κ} is the sign of κ. The geometric coefficients are given by

$$D_{\kappa}\binom{N+}{n+} = |\kappa| P_l(\hat{N}\cdot\hat{n}) - iS_{\kappa}(\hat{N}\times\hat{n})_z P_l'(\hat{N}\cdot\hat{n}), \quad (4)$$

$$D_{\kappa}\binom{N-}{n+} = -S_{\kappa}P_l'(\hat{N}\cdot\hat{n})\{(\hat{N}\times\hat{n})_y + i(\hat{N}\times\hat{n})_x\}, \quad (5)$$

where $P_l(x)$ is the Legendre polynomial of order l, and the prime indicates differentiation with respect to argument x. Equation (4) is for parallel spins and Eq. (5) for antiparallel spins. The orbitals $c f_{\kappa}$ and g_{κ} in Eq. (1) are regular solutions (at the origin) of the following coupled first-order differential equations[3]:

$$\frac{d(cf)}{dr} = \frac{(\kappa - 1)}{r}cf - (E - V)g, \quad (6)$$

$$\frac{dg}{dr} = \left(\frac{E - V}{c^2} + 1\right)cf - \frac{(\kappa + 1)}{r}g. \quad (7)$$

The potential enters the matrix element only as the ratio of these orbitals evaluated at the APW sphere radius.

In the most recent application of the RAPW method the energy bands in lead were determined.[4] These results were found to be in close agreement with energy bands based on a model given by Anderson and Gold.[5] This model, which included spin-orbit effects, was based on the comparison of their extensive de Haas–van Alphen data with the results from a four-parameter model based on the pseudopotential formalism. The parameters were adjusted to give the best (in a least-squares sense) agreement between the model and the experimental results. The energy bands calculated from first principles using the RAPW method were in very good agreement with those predicted by this model, especially near the Fermi energy.

The RAPW method was originally developed to study the splitting of energy bands in tungsten.[6] In this application only the symmetry axis ΓH was considered. These results are shown in Fig. 1. The splitting indicated on this figure by the separation bc was found to be in close agreement with the results obtained from the size-effect measurements of Walsh and Grimes.[7]

The calculations for tungsten have now been extended throughout the Brillouin zone in order to determine the relativistic Fermi surface. Extremal cross-sectional

---

* Work was performed at the Ames Laboratory of the U. S. Atomic Energy Commission. Contribution No. 1783.
[1] T. L. Loucks, Phys. Rev. 139, A1333 (1965).
[2] J. C. Slater, Phys. Rev. 51, 846 (1937).

[3] In atomic units with $e^2 = 2$, $m = \frac{1}{2}$, and $h = 2\pi$, the speed of light c is 274.
[4] T. L. Loucks, Phys. Rev. Letters 14, 1072 (1965).
[5] A. R. Anderson and A. V. Gold, Phys. Rev. 139, A1459 (1965).
[6] T. L. Loucks, Phys. Rev. Letters 14, 693 (1965).
[7] W. M. Walsh and C. C. Grimes, Phys. Rev. Letters 13, 523 (1964).

areas of the Fermi surface have been measured, and the theoretically predicted de Haas–van Alphen frequencies are presented for magnetic field directions in the (011) plane. These and other results are compared with various experimental results, and it is concluded that relativistic effects reduce the size of the Fermi surface.

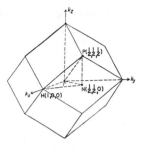

FIG. 2. Brillouin zone for the body-centered cubic lattice.

RESULTS

A complete discussion of the procedure used in constructing the muffin-tin potential has been given in a paper[8] on the nonrelativistic Fermi surfaces of Cr, Mo, and W (hereafter referred to as NON-REL). The same APW sphere radius and lattice constant given in NON-REL were used for the present calculations. The potential for the relativistic calculation was constructed using the relativistic atomic calculations of Liberman, Waber, and Cromer.[9] The procedure for performing RAPW calculations was outlined in THEORY. For this particular calculation a basis set of 39 RAPW's was used. For each of these a spin-up and spin-down component was included yielding a matrix of order 78. The κ summation for each of these matrix elements was truncated at $\kappa = \pm 10$.

1. Fermi Surface of Tungsten

The Brillouin zone for the body-centered cubic lattice is shown in Fig. 2. Cross sections of the Fermi surface of tungsten as given in NON-REL are reproduced in Fig. 3. The nonrelativistic surface consists of four different pieces. There is a large electron surface centered at Γ which resembles a child's jack. A hole surface centered at H has the shape of an octahedron with slightly rounded edges. It has about the same

volume as the electron jack. Smaller pieces consist of six equivalent electron "lenses" inside the "necks" of the electron jack. The neck is the restriction between the knobs and the octahedral body of the jack. In addition there are six equivalent hole ellipsoids located at N.

Cross sections of the relativistic Fermi surface are shown in Fig. 4. Both the electron "lenses" and the holes at N have disappeared. The electron jack and the hole octahedron no longer touch along the ΓH axis. They are separated by the distance bc shown in Fig. 1. The jack has been reduced in size and the necks have been smoothed out by the spin-orbit interaction.

2. de Haas–van Alphen Frequencies

A scale model of the electron jack was made using the cross sections of Fig. 4 and one additional slice located halfway between the planes ΓPH and ΓNH. A photograph of the model is shown in Fig. 5. Because of the extensive computing required to evaluate these cross sections, it was decided to use this scale model to determine extremal areas rather than to compute them numerically. To accomplish this another model like the one in Fig. 5 was constructed out of brass, and the regions between the ribs were filled with plaster. This was then sanded and filed until the edges of the brass fins were exposed and the surface was smooth. This model was mounted with a particular orientation and the cross-sectional areas of horizontal slices through the surface were measured. A typical set of results is shown in Fig. 6 for the magnetic field oriented 65° from the (001) direction in the (011) plane. The extremal areas

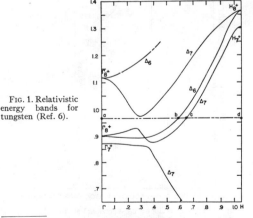

FIG. 1. Relativistic energy bands for tungsten (Ref. 6).

[8] T. L. Loucks, Phys. Rev. **139**, A1181 (1965).
[9] D. Liberman, J. T. Waber, and Don T. Cromer, Phys. Rev. **137**, A27 (1965).

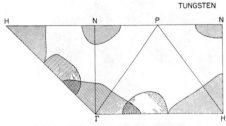

TUNGSTEN

FIG. 3. Nonrelativistic Fermi surface of tungsten (Ref. 8).

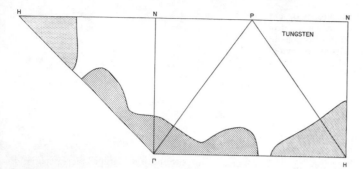

FIG. 4. Relativistic Fermi surface
of tungsten.

were converted to de Haas–van Alphen frequencies using the Onsager relation. The results for magnetic field orientations in the (011) plane are given in Fig. 7.

This method of determining the extremal cross-sectional areas is probably not accurate to more than $\pm 5\%$. It was decided, however, that the advantages of direct experience with an almost-to-scale model were more important than having precise theoretical values. It is clear from the complexity of Fig. 6 that it would not be easy to predict extremal areas simply by a casual glance at the cross sections given in Fig. 4.

3. Assorted Other Results

The Fermi energy E_F was determined by the requirement of equal hole and electron volumes. The value is given in Table I along with the result from NON-REL. It was only necessary to determine the constant-energy surfaces for two values of the energy before the hole and electron volumes were found to be nearly equal (Fig. 8). The slopes of these volume curves can be used to calculate the density of electronic states at the Fermi energy $G(E_F)$ (factor of 2 included for spin degeneracy). This is given in Table I with the low-temperature

electronic specific heat coefficient γ. As a final result the k vectors of the Fermi surface are presented in Table II.

DISCUSSION OF RESULTS

There are several relativistic effects on the Fermi surface of tungsten as determined from this theoretical calculation. The first is that the electron jack and hole octahedron are separated along the ΓH axis by the spin-orbit splitting of degenerate bands. The calculated splitting is in good agreement with the experimental results.[6] Spin-orbit splitting of degenerate bands also

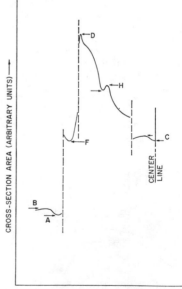

FIG. 6. Typical results for cross-sectional area of electron jack at different positions along a particular axis. Orientation of axis shown is 65° from the (001) direction in the (011) plane. Letters indicate extremal areas and correspond to de Haas–van Alphen frequencies in Fig. 7.

FIG. 5. Model of electron jack constructed from cross sections in Fig. 4.

TABLE I. Some results of APW and RAWP calculations.

	RAPW	APW[a]	Experimental[b]
Tungsten			
E_F (Ry)	0.760	0.548	...
$G(E_F)$ (electrons/a.u. Ry)	0.0387	0.0673	...
γ (10^{-4} cal/mole deg²)	1.72	2.98	3.1
Molybdenum			
E_F (Ry)	...	0.542	...
$G(E_F)$ (electrons/a.u.³ Ry)	...	0.0695	...
γ (10^{-4} cal/mole deg²)	...	3.04	4.8

[a] Reference 8. [b] Reference 14.

causes the disappearance of the electron lenses inside the necks of the jack. Of course, it is possible that an improved potential (there was no attempt made toward self-consistency) or an expanded basis set would alter the bands and Fermi energy as shown in Fig. 1. A small change could produce very small electron lenses inside the necks of the jack. Even so, it is clear that they would be greatly reduced in size as compared with the nonrelativistic result.

Another theoretical result is the disappearance of the ellipsoidal holes at N. This was not the result of spin-orbit splitting, but instead was due to relativistic contributions to the effective potential. These effects are perhaps more familiar as the so-called mass-velocity and Darwin terms which result from successive applications of the Foldy-Wouthuysen transformation to the Dirac Hamiltonian. These first-order terms are not visibly displayed in our more general treatment, but effects of this kind are certainly present. Any energy levels which are very sensitive to the potential will therefore be shifted. The result in the present calculation is the disappearance of the holes at N. A similar result was predicted for chromium in NON-REL. In that instance the change in the potential was the result of less effective screening of the nuclear charge near the origin by the core electrons in chromium as compared to molybdenum and tungsten. It was, however, the same sensitive energy levels near the symmetry point N which were involved in both cases.

Actually there is experimental evidence which indicates that the holes at N have not disappeared com-

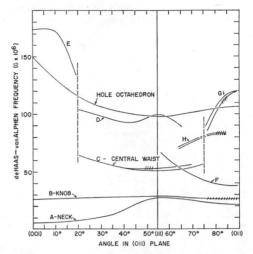

FIG. 7. de Haas–van Alphen frequencies predicted from relativistic Fermi surface of tungsten for magnetic field orientations in the (011) plane. Slashes indicate regions where beats are possible.

pletely but are greatly reduced in size. Sparlin[10] has measured de Haas–van Alphen frequencies with the appropriate angular dependence for the holes at N. These frequencies are in the range of 6.0 to 9.4 G. They are much smaller than the range 16.5 to 32.3 G as predicted in NON-REL.

The primary relativistic effect on the electron jack is to reduce it in size and smooth out the neck region. The reduction in size of the knobs and necks is supported by the experimental results of Sparlin[10], Brandt and Rayne,[11] and Girvan.[12] The results of Sparlin are shown in Fig. 9 for comparison with the theoretical neck and knob orbits. The neck orbit predicted in NON-REL for the (100) direction was too large by nearly a factor of 2. These results are compared in Table III. We see that the relativistic shrinking of the knobs and neck is supported by the experimental

TABLE II. k vectors of Fermi surface (atomic units⁻¹).

	Direction	APW	RAPW	Size-effect experiment[a]
Hole octahedron	(001)	0.45	0.41	0.41
	(011)	0.33	0.31	0.32
	(111)	0.28	0.26	0.27
Electron jack	(001)	0.61	0.57	0.59
	(011)	0.26	0.21	...
	(111)	0.23	0.19	0.22

[a] Walsh and Grimes, Ref. 7.

FIG. 8. Volume contained by electron jack and hole octahedron for two energies near the Fermi energy.

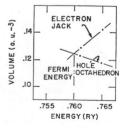

[10] D. M. Sparlin, thesis, Northwestern University, 1964 (unpublished).
[11] G. B. Brandt and J. A. Rayne, Phys. Rev. 132, 1945 (1963).
[12] R. F. Girvan, M. S. thesis, Iowa State University, 1964 (unpublished).

TABLE III. Tungsten de Haas–van Alphen frequencies (10^6 G).

	Direction and orbit	Theory		Experiment	
		APW	RAPW	Sparlin[a]	Girvan[b]
Hole octahedron	(001)	168	149	150	152
	(011)	130	107	111	116
	(111)	108	98	104	104
Electron jack	(001) 4-Ball	227	172	...	...
	(001) Neck	11.3	5.6	6.1	...
	(001) Knob	33.6	24.0	22.7	23.4

[a] Reference 10.　　　　　[b] Reference 12.

results. It is apparent from Table II that the hole octahedron is also reduced in size. However, the reduction is a relatively small percent of the nonrelativistic size. Although the reduction tends to bring the theoretical results into closer agreement with experimental results, it is evident from Figs. 7 and 9 that the relativistic hole octahedron yields de Haas–van Alphen frequencies about 5% smaller than the experimental results of Sparlin.[10] A similar comparison can be found with the size effect experiments of Walsh and Grimes.[7] As shown in Table II, the k vectors of the hole octahedron as calculated relativistically and nonrelativistically tend to bracket the experimental results, the relativistic results being smaller. However, the differences are small in either case. Comparison of the electron jack dimensions with size-effect measurements is also given in Table II.

de Haas–van Alphen data for the electron jack in tungsten are apparently not easy to obtain. We see from Fig. 7 that the larger frequencies expected from the jack are of the same order of magnitude as those

from the hole octahedron. Because the extrema are very narrow for most of the jack orbits (Fig. 6), the signals from the hole octahedron would probably be much stronger and dominate the experimental results for the higher frequencies. The strongest signals from the jack should, however, come from the central waist orbits near the (111) direction because the extrema are flatter than for the other orbits. These frequencies are also lower than the ones from the hole octahedron and should not be as difficult to separate experimentally. Girvan[12] has measured these waist orbits, and the results are shown in Fig. 9. The angular dependence of our results (curve C in Fig. 7) is in close agreement with Girvan, but the theoretical waist is somewhat smaller than experimentally observed. The experimental results reported do not indicate the splitting into two frequencies near the (111) direction. Apparently the noncentral knob and body orbit (curve F) and the noncentral waist orbit (curve H) have not been experimentally observed.

It is interesting to examine the shapes of the extremal areas for different angles along the curves E, D, and G of Fig. 7. For angles between 20° and 75° we consider curve D instead of C because portions of these orbits remain on the knobs. A typical extremal cross-section for curve E is shown in Fig. 10. It is sometimes referred to as the "4-ball" orbit. Also shown are typical extremal cross-sections corresponding to various angles along curve D. Starting at 30° a with "mouse," we arrive at the (111) direction with the "cloverleaf" orbit. A typical "2-ball" orbit for curve G is also shown in Fig. 10.

By now it is evident that relativistic effects have generally decreased the size of the Fermi surface. For most of the experimental results the relativistic surface is in better agreement than the one given in NON-REL, which was shown to be almost identical with the Fermi surface of molybdenum (see also Table I). Since these nonrelativistic theoretical surfaces are the same, and relativistic effects should be almost negligible in Mo, a comparison for these two metals of physical properties depending on the Fermi surface should indicate the extent of the relativistic effects. For instance the surface area of the Fermi surface, as determined by anomalous skin effect measurements, should be smaller for W than

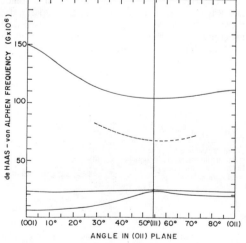

FIG. 9. Experimental de Haas–van Alphen frequencies: solid lines are results of Sparlin (Ref. 10) and dashed line is from Girvan (Ref. 12).

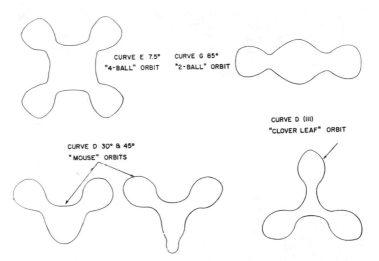

CURVE E 7.5°
"4-BALL" ORBIT

CURVE G 85°
"2-BALL" ORBIT

CURVE D (III)
"CLOVER LEAF" ORBIT

CURVE D 30° & 45°
"MOUSE" ORBITS

FIG. 10. Typical extremal cross-sections of electron jack corresponding to curves E, D, and G of Fig. 8.

Mo. Fawcett and Griffiths[13] have indeed measured 1.74 atomic units (a.u.) for the surface area of Mo and 1.66 a.u. for W. We have not accurately measured the surface area of the relativistic Fermi surface, but it is estimated to be about 7/10 of the nonrelativistic value 6.7 a.u. This difference is considerably more than is experimentally observed. However, not only the ratio of the Mo and W values differs from experiment, but also the individual magnitudes. As discussed in NON-REL, the anisotropy of the Fermi surface apparently makes it difficult to interpret the anomalous skin effect data for these metals.

Properties which depend on the density of states at the Fermi energy should, according to the results given for W in Table I, be very sensitive to relativistic effects. The apparent agreement in W between the APW results and experiment[14] is felt to be fortuitous. One obtains a more significant comparison if ratios of the quantities are examined. For instance, in Mo the ratio of γ (expt) to γ (APW) is 1.6. Since relativistic effects are not large in Mo, this would be about the same ratio if γ (RAPW) were used instead of γ (APW). However, for W the ratio γ (expt) to γ (APW) is only 1.0, whereas with γ (RAPW) we find 1.8. We thus find about the same enhancement in Mo and W (apparently due to the electron-phonon interaction) only if relativistic effects are considered for W.

From this we can conclude that the lower experimental value for W is due to relativistic effects. Shimizu, Takahashi, and Katsuki[15] also report the magnetic susceptibility (which is proportional to the density of state at the Fermi energy) for Mo and W. Their values have a ratio of about 1.5, which is further evidence that the density of states at the Fermi energy is decreased by relativistic effects.

We notice in Table I that the Fermi energy as measured from the bottom of the band is greater for the relativistic calculation. This results from the energy of the lower momentum states having been decreased by the relativistic contributions to the effective potential. In NON-REL we found the bandwidths of Mo and W to be nearly the same. It would be interesting to find experimental evidence to support this expected increase of the bandwidth of W compared to Mo.

Note added in proof. Further results on the electronic structure of W have been given by L. F. Mattheiss, Phys. Rev. **139**, A1893 (1965). His calculations were done using the nonrelativistic APW method. It is interesting that we agree on the nonrelativistic value of γ (Table I), but that the change attributed here to relativistic effects can equally well be accounted for by a 30% reduction of the exchange contribution to the potential. Such a reduction is certainly justified for states near the Fermi energy (see discussion by J. C. Slater, MIT Quarterly Progress Report No. 58, SSMTG (unpublished). Since both effects vary the *s-d* energy separation it is difficult to separate them. However,

[13] E. Fawcett and D. Griffiths, J. Phys. Chem. Solids **23**, 1631 (1962).
[14] *American Institute of Physics Handbook*, edited by D. E. Gray *et al.* (McGraw-Hill Book Company, Inc., New York, 1963), 2nd ed., pp. 4–61.

[15] M. Shimizu, T. Takahashi, and A. Katsuki, J. Phys. Soc. Japan **17**, 1740 (1962).

changes in the exchange potential should also affect the results for Mo and we have seen (Ref. 8) that this is not necessary to get agreement with experiment. This, coupled with the fact that Mo and W differ in several experiments, leads us to attribute these differences mainly to relativistic effects.

ACKNOWLEDGMENTS

Measurement of extremal areas of the electron jack was very carefully done by John Hinrichsen as part of his activities under the Summer Undergraduate Trainee Program at the Ames Laboratory.

EPILOGUE

It is not possible, of course, to include in this volume reprints of all the articles dealing with the APW method and its many applications. We are able, however, to include at least one recent example of each type of calculation most frequently performed; most of the historically significant articles dealing with the theoretical aspects of the APW method are also included. These articles should serve as a guide to the many additional applications which appear in the literature and have been listed in the references.

Since the original manuscript was completed, several importnat applications of the APW method have been published and additional calculations now in progress have come to the author's attention. The remainder of this section is devoted to a discussion of this recent work.

Self-consistent APW calculations are currently being performed at Sandia by E. D. Jones and A. C. Switendick for the III-V face centered cubic compounds (Sc or Y with N, P, As or Se, for instance). Relativistic APW calculations for Ir and Pt have been completed by A. R. Mackintosh at the Technical University, Lyngby, Denmark.

Relativistic APW calculations for some of the lighter actinides are being performed by J. T. Waber, et al, at Los Alamos. E. C. Snow and J. T. Waber have calculated self-consistent energy bands for metallic copper. E. C. Snow has also completed a self-consistent APW calculation for aluminum. J. T. Waber and A. C. Switendick earlier reported APW calculations for metallic cerium (Proceedings of the 5th Rare Earth Research Conference, 1966, Iowa State University, Ames), and further work (self-consistent relativistic calculations) is currently in progress for this metal by J. T. Waber, D. Liberman and D. T. Cromer.

Energy bands for ferromagnetic Ni and EuS have been completed by J. W. D. Connolly, S. J. Cho, J. B. Conklin, Jr., and J. C. Slater at the University of Florida, Gainesville. J. C. Slater has also summarized the past progress of his Solid-State and Molecular Theory Group at MIT in a recent Quarterly Progress Report (No. 61, July 15,

1955). Further work by this group includes preliminary results on
the spin density of iron by P. DeCicco and A. Kitz, and a theoretical
study of the energy band problem for a deformed lattice by J. Kenney.

A very interesting application of the relativistic APW method to
rhenium has recently been published by L. F. Mattheiss (Phys. Rev.
151, 450 (1966)). He is currently performing calculations for compounds with the perovskite structure.

Other recent publications include the following:

J. H. Terrell, "Band Structure of Beryllium by the APW Method",
    Phys. Rev. 149, 526 (1966),

R. Keown, "Energy Bands in Diamond", Phys. Rev. 150, 568 (1966),

Keith H. Johnson, "Relationship between the APW and KKR Methods of
    Band Theory", Phys. Rev. 150, 429 (1966).
    (A similar article is to be published by G. J. Morgan, Zenith
    Radio Corporation, Middlesex, England.)

Articles to be published in The Physical Review cover the following topics:

Theoretical x-ray scattering factors (F. J. Arlinghaus),

Self-consistent energy bands and cohesive energy of KCl (P. D. DeCicco),

Fermi surface of thorium (S. C. Keeton and T. L. Loucks).

Further APW calculations being performed at Iowa State University, Ames include the following:

Relationship between antiferromagnetism and rare earth Fermi surfaces (S. C. Keeton and T. L. Loucks), Fermi surface calculations
for Eu and some very heavy transplutonium elements using the relativistic APW method (S. C. Keeton and T. L. Loucks), Fermi surface
calculations for the double hexagonal close-packed metals La, Pr, Nd,
Am and Cm (L. Hodges and T. L. Loucks), Energy band calculations
for $NaWO_3$ and ReO_3 (B. C. Gerstein, L. Thomas and T. L. Loucks).

For completeness we mention some earlier work which has only
recently come to our attention. H. Bross and H. Stöhr have developed
a modified form of the APW method (Phys. Letters 8, 25 (1964)), and
it has been applied to copper by H. Bross and H. G. Junginger (Phys.
Letters 8, 240 (1964)). The method is much more complicated than
the ordinary APW method, but has the advantage that the trial functions are not discontinuous across the sphere boundaries.